# THE THEORY OF RESONANCE
## *AND ITS APPLICATION TO*
## ORGANIC CHEMISTRY

# THE THEORY OF RESONANCE
## *AND ITS APPLICATION TO*
## ORGANIC CHEMISTRY

BY GEORGE WILLARD WHELAND
*Associate Professor of Chemistry*
*University of Chicago*

*Fifth Printing*

*NEW YORK* · JOHN WILEY AND SONS, INC.
*LONDON* · CHAPMAN AND HALL, LIMITED

PRINTED IN THE UNITED STATES OF AMERICA

# PREFACE

The theory of resonance is the most important addition to chemical structural theory that has been made since the concept of the shared-electron bond was introduced by G. N. Lewis. Its general acceptance has doubtless been delayed to some extent, however, by the fact that, although the literature dealing with it has been voluminous, no comprehensive survey of the subject has existed. This book is intended to provide such a survey. It has grown out of a course of lectures which I have presented during the last several years to the advanced undergraduate and beginning graduate students at the University of Chicago. It has been written with the idea that its readers would have at least a sound knowledge of elementary organic chemistry, considerable familiarity with the electronic theory of valence, and some acquaintance with physical chemistry.

A comprehensive discussion of resonance offers difficulties. On the one hand, this theory has been found to have its most interesting applications, and to be of greatest value, in the field of organic chemistry. For that reason, it should preferably be presented in terms with which the organic chemists are familiar. On the other hand, its basis lies in the mathematical depths of quantum mechanics. For that reason, it can be presented precisely and completely only in highly mathematical language. Some sort of working compromise must therefore be reached. Since my own interest in the subject of resonance has been from the organic chemical viewpoint, it is inevitable that the final result should be heavily weighted in favor of the more qualitative and descriptive approach. Experience has shown, however, that often more difficulties are created than are avoided if the attempt is made to ignore entirely the underlying physical basis of the theory. Indeed, many of the present common misinterpretations of the theory seem to be directly attributable to the fact that practically all the discussions of it that have been published in the past (including, it must be admitted, some written by myself) have too drastically oversimplified the treatment. Consequently, a rather detailed, but non-technical and actually non-mathematical, discussion of the essential fundamental principles is given in Chapter 1, and particularly in Sections 1·5 and 1·6. No effort has been spared to make this discussion completely rigorous, even at the risk of

sometimes going into boring detail in regard to apparently trivial
matters. Since the subject is unfortunately a very complex one, it
cannot be adequately treated without a careful examination of a number
of special cases, only a few of which may turn out to be interesting
chemically.

I wish at this time to express my appreciation to Professor Linus
Pauling, from whom I received my first and greatest inspiration to go
deeply into the theory of resonance. This book is to be considered dedi-
cated to him, in partial acknowledgment of my great indebtedness to
him, even though the wartime restrictions on the use of paper have made
impossible the inclusion of the customary dedication page.

I wish also to acknowledge the valuable assistance rendered me by the
John Simon Guggenheim Memorial Foundation, which gave me the
opportunity to develop some of the viewpoints and to gather some of the
material used in this book; by Professors C. K. Ingold, J. E. Lennard-
Jones, R. Robinson, and N. V. Sidgwick, who granted me the inestimable
benefit of helpful discussions; by Professors H. C. Brown, R. S.
Mulliken, F. H. Westheimer, and T. F. Young, and Doctors F. R. Mayo
and V. Schomaker, who aided me by critically examining part or all of
the manuscript; by Professors W. G. Brown and M. S. Kharasch, who
permitted me to use an unpublished table of heats of combustion that
they had compiled; and by Doctor D. F. Peppard, who helped me in
reading proof.

Since it is hardly conceivable that this book could be completely free
either of misprints or of errors in theory, interpretation, and fact, I
would welcome any suggestions and corrections that the readers may
care to make.

GEORGE WILLARD WHELAND

# CONTENTS

v

# Chapter 1

## THE THEORY OF RESONANCE

**1·1  The Structural Theory.**  Ever since the middle of the nineteenth century, the progress of chemistry, and especially of organic chemistry, has been closely associated with the development of the structural theory.  One can, in fact, hardly question that this theory, more than any other single factor, must be given the credit for the remarkable advances that have occurred in the science during the last hundred years.  However, in spite of its outstanding success in correlating and systematizing the vast body of facts with which it deals, its history has been marked from the very beginning by a series of attempts to revise and to amplify it in such a way that its field of usefulness might be extended still further.

A number of these attempts have met with complete acceptance, and now form an integral part of the theory.  One thinks at once, in this connection, of the stereochemical ideas developed by van't Hoff and by Le Bel, of the concept of coordination developed by Werner, and of the electronic theory of valence developed by Kossel and by Lewis.  To these must now apparently be added the theory of resonance, a description of which is the object of the present book.

Many of the features of the theory of resonance had already been anticipated by the organic chemists in their search for a more comprehensive structural theory.  Early in the second half of the last century, it was found that for some substances, of which benzene was perhaps the most striking example, *no* completely satisfactory structures of the conventional type could be devised at all.  The idea then slowly emerged that perhaps these substances must be described not in terms of one single structure but of two or even more structures simultaneously. At the outset, this idea was probably not essentially different from that denoted now by the word " tautomerism," as, for example, in Kekulé's theory[1] of " oscillation " in benzene.  In time, however, a distinction came to be drawn.  A vague suggestion of this new point of view is perhaps to be found as early as 1887 in the well-known centric structure of benzene.[2]  Neither Armstrong nor Baeyer was very explicit about

---

[1] A. Kekulé, *Ann.*, **162**, 77 (1872).

[2] H. E. Armstrong, *Phil. Mag.*, [5] **23**, 73 (1887);  *J. Chem. Soc.*, **51**, 258 (1887). A. Baeyer, *Ann.*, **245**, 103 (1888).

the exact significance of the centric bonds in this structure, but the idea was elaborated further by Claus[3] (on the basis of his own, essentially equivalent, diagonal structure) so that it became surprisingly similar in some regards to that accepted now. A rather more definite suggestion appeared a few years later in Thiele's theory of partial valence,[4] which was applicable not only to aromatic ring systems but also to open-chain unsaturated molecules.

**1·2   The Theories of Intermediate Stages, Mesomerism, and Resonance.** It was not until after 1920, however, that the ideas to be discussed in this and the succeeding chapters began to take precise form. The first important advances were made by two different groups of organic chemists, who came simultaneously and quite independently to very much the same final conclusions. On the one hand, Arndt and his co-workers in Germany brought forward the theory of intermediate stages (Zwischenstufen),[5] and, on the other hand, various English chemists, of whom only Robinson and Ingold need be mentioned explicitly here, brought forward the theory of mesomerism.[6] The significant feature which these theories had in common was that *they considered it possible for the true state of a molecule to be not identical with that represented by any single classical valence-bond structure, but to be intermediate between those represented by two or more different valence-bond structures.*

Since it is important that this new concept not be confused with tautomerism, let us discuss an example in some detail. We shall consider a molecule which is in an intermediate stage, or is mesomeric, between two structures. For definiteness, we can think of the substance in question as benzene. If this substance exists as a tautomeric mixture of molecules with the Kekulé structures I and II, then some of the molecules have structure I whereas the others have structure II, or, if the equilibrium is supposed to be mobile, any one molecule spends part of its time in structure I and the rest in structure II. On the other hand, if

[3] A. Claus, *J. prakt. Chem.*, **37**, 455 (1888).

[4] J. Thiele, *Ann.*, **306**, 87 (1899).

[5] F. Arndt, E. Scholz, and P. Nachtwey, *Ber.*, **57**, 1903 (1924); F. Arndt, *Ber.*, **63**, 2963 (1930). Recently the adherents of this school have adopted the terminology of the English school. For a comprehensive survey of the subject, see B. Eistert, *Tautomerie und Mesomerie*, Ferdinand Enke, Stuttgart, 1938.

[6] Since the theory in its present form is the result of a long and slow development, it seems desirable to give references here only to comparatively recent review articles. Of these may be mentioned especially: R. Robinson, *Two Lectures on an " Outline of an Electrochemical (Electronic) Theory of the Course of Organic Reactions,"* The Institute of Chemistry of Great Britain and Ireland, London, 1932; *J. Soc. Dyers Colourists, Jubilee Issue,* 65 (1934). C: K. Ingold, *J. Chem. Soc.*, 1120 (1933); *Chem. Rev.*, **15**, 225 (1934). The use of the word " mesomerism " is comparatively recent, having been proposed originally by Ingold in the former of the two papers mentioned above.

the substance is correctly described instead in terms of the theories of intermediate stages or mesomerism, the situation is quite different: All the molecules have the same structure; this structure, which does

I                                    II

not change with the time, is not identical with either I or II, but it is intermediate between them.

Throughout this book, structures will be designated by Roman numerals. The first structure *in each section* will be assigned the number I.

The significance of the above distinction between tautomerism and the newer concepts can be made clearer with the aid of an analogy. A mule is a hybrid between a horse and a donkey. This does not mean that some mules are horses and the rest are donkeys, nor does it mean that a given mule is a horse part of the time and a donkey the rest of the time. Instead, it means that a mule is a new kind of animal, neither horse nor donkey, but intermediate between the two and partaking to some extent of the character of each. Similarly, the theories of intermediate stages and of mesomerism picture the benzene molecule as having a *hybrid* structure, not identical with either of the Kekulé structures, but intermediate between them.

In order to obtain a mental picture of such a hybrid structure, let us center our attention upon some particular bond, say the one between the two carbon atoms on the right sides of the structures I and II above. If benzene consists of a tautomeric mixture of molecules with the Kekulé structures, this bond is a double bond part of the time (structure I) and a single bond the rest of the time (structure II). On the other hand, if the substance is in an intermediate stage, or is mesomeric, between the Kekulé structures, the bond does not change with the time. Moreover, it is neither a double nor a single bond, but it is instead a new type of bond, not envisaged by the classical structural theory. We might call it a " one-and-a-half bond " (however, see Section 4·4) or possibly a " benzene bond." We can obtain a more definite picture by making use of the fact that the average density of electronic charge in the region between two carbon atoms is greater if the atoms are joined by a double bond than it is if they are joined by a single bond   Consequently, we can visualize the bond in benzene as one in which the density of charge is greater than would correspond to a single bond, but less than would correspond to a double bond.

The following difficulty arises in the minds of many people when they first encounter a discussion of the structure of benzene from the present point of view. The structures I and II are completely equivalent since either can be transformed into the other by merely a rotation of 60° in the plane of the paper. What then is the difference between these structures, and what is the meaning of the statement that the true structure of benzene is neither the one nor the other but something intermediate? Moreover, since the carbon atoms are in principle indistinguishable (unless they are of different isotopes), how can we say that a *given pair* of them are joined by a double bond in I and by a single bond in II? A partial answer to these questions has already been implied in the preceding paragraph; the statement that benzene is a hybrid of I and II means that the carbon-carbon bonds are not alternately single and double, as would be true if the molecule had either structure alone, but all are instead of the same, intermediate type. A deeper insight into the problem can be obtained from a more careful examination. Although the various carbon atoms are not distinguishable, the positions in space which they are capable of occupying *are* distinguishable. Consequently, we could define the difference between structures I and II by the statement that the " two easternmost atoms " are joined by a double bond in I and by a single bond in II. This statement has a definite meaning, even though the " two easternmost atoms " cannot be more precisely specified as being identical with, say, atoms 1 and 2, or 3 and 6, or the like. This interpretation is most logical if the molecule is considered to be held in a fixed orientation, as in a crystal lattice, but it is not actually restricted to any such special situation. A further way of evading the present difficulty is by considering a particular case in which two adjacent carbon atoms are distinguished from the remaining four either by being of a different isotope or by carrying different substituents. Then the difference between structures I and II is quite apparent, but the situation has been made too highly specialized to be completely illuminating.

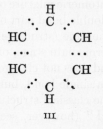

III

A further question which occasionally arises is the following. If altogether eighteen electrons are employed in benzene to produce the six completely equivalent carbon-carbon bonds, then would it not be satisfactory and highly convenient to describe the bonds as three-electron bonds and to write the structure of the molecule simply as III? There are two different reasons why this proposed alternative is inferior to the method of description adopted in the preceding paragraphs. In the first place, the term " three-electron bond " has already been defined to mean something quite different from the type of bond in benzene (see Section 2·5); and, in the second place, no corresponding description can be devised for the apparently very similar bonds in naphthalene and other condensed aromatic ring systems. Consequently, the use of the structure III for benzene would be not only confusing but also incapable of generalization to other closely related situations.

With the development of the quantum mechanics, it soon became apparent that the theories of intermediate stages and of mesomerism were not merely arbitrary hypotheses, as they had appeared to be when first advanced, but were two equivalent chemical expressions of what is known as quantum-mechanical resonance. This latter, more precise concept, which was reached first in 1926 by Heisenberg[7] in quite another connection, is a simple mathematical consequence of the fundamental equations of quantum mechanics, and its essential correctness has been established beyond question. Its application to chemical problems was initiated largely by Pauling and his collaborators.[8] This newer quantum-mechanical approach not only provides a sound theoretical basis for the earlier and less precise ideas outlined above but also supplements them in several important regards by introducing into them certain refinements or extensions which could have been reached in other ways only with greater difficulty. It leads, for example, to an understanding of the conditions under which a molecule can, or cannot, be expected to exist in an intermediate stage or mesomeric state, and, even more important, it accounts for the observed greater stability of those molecules of which mesomerism or resonance occurs. The first of these additional features of the more detailed theory will be discussed at some length in Section 1·4, and the second will be referred to at frequent intervals throughout the book, and especially in Chapters 2 and 3.

**1·3 Nomenclature.** As we have seen, the theory of intermediate stages, or of mesomerism, or, as we shall say hereafter, of resonance, is an outgrowth of several earlier and less precise theories. Perhaps largely on this account, the language used to describe it is unusually varied, and no single, uniform system of nomenclature has as yet been adopted for it. Thus, the fact that, in benzene, resonance occurs between the two Kekulé structures I and II of the preceding section can be expressed by the statements that the substance has a hybrid structure, that it is a resonance hybrid, that it is in an intermediate stage or mesomeric state, or that it resonates between the structures in question.

---

[7] W. Heisenberg, *Z. Physik*, **38**, 411 (1926).

[8] See L. Pauling, *The Nature of the Chemical Bond*, Cornell University Press, Ithaca, N. Y., 1st ed., 1939, 2nd ed., 1940, and numerous further references given there.

The structures themselves may also be said to resonate with each other, or to contribute to the state of the molecule.   There is little to choose among these various equivalent modes of expression, and all can be used interchangeably.

Some authors speak of resonance between two, or among more than two, *forms*.   This terminology is confusing, however, because the word "forms" commonly implies the actual existence of distinct substances which could (in principle, even if not always in practice) be separated from each other. Thus, we speak, for example, of the keto and enol *forms* of acetoacetic ester, the *d*- and *l-forms* of lactic acid, the rhombic and monoclinic *forms* of sulfur, and so on.   The *structures* among which resonance occurs, however, are usually only intellectual constructions, which nevertheless are useful aids in the under-standing of the true state of the molecule in question.   This problem of the physical reality of the resonating structures is discussed in greater detail in Sections 1·5 and 1·6.

No unique symbols for the graphical representation of resonating molecules have as yet received unanimous acceptance.   The most widely adopted procedure at present is a completely general, but rather cumber-some, one, which consists in writing down either all the structures in-volved or else a sufficient number of representative examples.   The fact that resonance occurs among them is then indicated either by an explicit statement to that effect in the text or by the use of double-headed ar-rows,[9] as in

The symbol $\leftrightarrow$ must, of course, be carefully distinguished from the simi-lar one, $\rightleftarrows$, which is commonly employed to show the existence of a chemical equilibrium.   A further, more compact, system of representa-tion, which was devised by the English school of organic chemists,[6] will be described in Section 8·4.

**1·4   The Conditions for Resonance.**   As was mentioned above, the quantum-mechanical approach leads to an understanding of the condi-tions that must be satisfied in order that resonance may occur.   Al-though the following rules may perhaps seem arbitrary, since the reasons for them are not self-evident, it must be borne in mind that they, like the existence of resonance itself, are simple corollaries of the basic equa-tions of quantum mechanics.   In the present section, these rules will

[9] C. R. Bury, *J. Am. Chem. Soc.*, **57**, 2115 (1935).   B. Eistert, *Angew. Chem.*, 9, 33 (1936).

be stated not quite rigorously, but in their simplest and most generally useful forms; in part D of Section 1·5, certain refinements in them will be discussed, which are required for complete rigor, but which almost never need to be considered explicitly in any practical application of the theory.

1. *Resonance can occur only between structures that correspond to the same, or to very nearly the same, relative positions of all the atomic nuclei.* Some such restriction as this is obviously necessary, since otherwise the phenomenon of isomerism would be impossible.   If the two structures

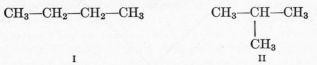

I and II, for example, were able to resonate with each other, they could not represent two distinct and different substances, as they in fact do, but they would have to represent only a single substance with a structure of intermediate type.   This last possibility, however, is precluded by the fact that the two structures in question correspond to widely different positions of the nuclei, so that the occurrence of resonance is rendered impossible by this condition 1.

The situation encountered generally in those molecules in which resonance does occur can be illustrated by a discussion of benzene.   For this substance, the two Kekulé structures III and IV can be written.

These do not correspond to exactly the same nuclear configuration because the length of a carbon-carbon single bond is normally about 1.54 A, whereas that of a carbon-carbon double bond is normally about 1.34 A.   The symbol A is an abbreviation for the *angstrom unit*, which is equal to $10^{-8}$ cm.   (See Chapter 4.)   However, atoms in molecules do not occupy definitely fixed positions; even at the absolute zero of temperature they are instead constantly executing vibrations about their positions of minimum potential energy with amplitudes of the order of magnitude of 0.1 A.   The above-cited lengths of single and double bonds refer only to the distances between these positions of minimum energy.   Consequently, the two Kekulé structures do overlap in a sense, and so we need not be surprised if we find that resonance between them actually does occur.

A more detailed analysis of this first rule can be given with the aid of Figures 1·1, 1·2, and 1·3, which show in a schematic manner several possible ways in which the energy $E$ of a given molecule may vary as the atomic positions change in consequence of a transition from some arbitrary structure $R$ to a different structure $S$.

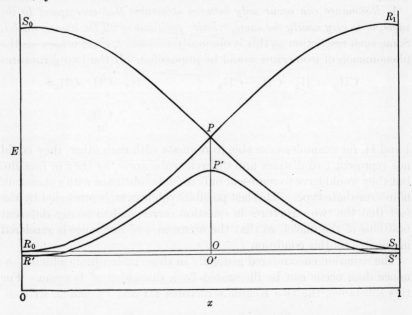

Fig. 1·1. Energies $E$ of two structures $R$ and $S$ and of their resonance hybrid, when the limiting structures differ greatly in nuclear configuration. As the abscissa $x$ varies from 0 to 1, the positions of the atoms change continuously from those characteristic of structure $R$ to those characteristic of structure $S$.

The energy of a molecule is defined as the negative of the amount of energy required to dissociate it, in the gaseous state, into isolated gaseous atoms. The energy of a stable molecule is therefore always a negative quantity. In Figures 1·1, 1·2, and 1·3, the zeros from which the energies are measured would lie some distance above any of the curves. The word "stable," as used here and throughout the remainder of the book, indicates only a low energy and does not necessarily imply a lack of reactivity.

In each figure, the parameter $x$, plotted along the abscissa, is a coordinate which is described sufficiently for our purposes by the statement that it assumes the values 0 and 1 when the relative positions of the atomic nuclei are those corresponding to the structures $R$ and $S$ respectively, and that it assumes intermediate values when the atomic positions are intermediate. The energy of a molecule with structure $R$ is obviously a minimum at $x = 0$, since then by definition the molecule is in its most stable configuration, and it must increase along the curve $R_0PR_1$ as $x$ increases, since in the process the molecule is being distorted from its stable configuration. Conversely, the energy of a molecule

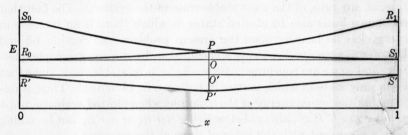

Fig. 1·2. Energies $E$ of two structures $R$ and $S$ and of their resonance hybrid, when the limiting structures differ only slightly in nuclear configuration. The abscissa has the same significance here as in Fig. 1·1.

with the structure $S$ has a high value (indicating instability) at $x = 0$, and must decrease along the curve $S_0PS_1$ to a minimum (indicating stability) at $x = 1$. For simplicity in exposition, the energies of structure $R$ at $x = 0$ and of structure $S$ at $x = 1$ have been assumed equal, and likewise the energies of structure $R$ at $x = 1$ and of structure $S$ at

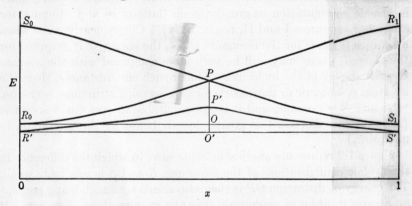

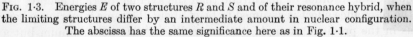

Fig. 1·3. Energies $E$ of two structures $R$ and $S$ and of their resonance hybrid, when the limiting structures differ by an intermediate amount in nuclear configuration. The abscissa has the same significance here as in Fig. 1·1.

$x = 0$ have also been assumed equal; these assumptions are not essential to the following discussion, however, and the extension to the general case should be obvious.

When the possibility of resonance between the structures $R$ and $S$ is taken into account, another factor arises. As has already been mentioned and as will be discussed later in greater detail (see, for example, Section 1·5 and Chapters 2 and 3), an important effect of resonance is to make a molecule in which it occurs more stable (that is, of lower energy) than any one of the individual structures involved. This is true, at any rate, of the most stable state of the system. The fact that resonance leads also to excited states in which there is an increase in energy has no bearing upon the present problem (see Section 1·5 and Chapter 6); we are discussing a chemical and not a spectroscopic question, and so we are concerned only with the most stable state, since that is the only state in which matter in bulk can be obtained. Thus, it follows that the actual energy of the molecule, when plotted against $x$, must give a curve $R'P'S'$, always below either $R_0PR_1$ or $S_0PS_1$, but becoming nearly coincident with the lower of these at the extremes.

Figure 1·1 represents a case in which the structures $R$ and $S$ differ greatly in the relative positions of the atomic nuclei, so that a large distortion is required to change one configuration into the other. If resonance did not occur, the minimum energy necessary for the transition to occur would be represented in the figure by the distance $OP$; when the resonance is taken into account, this energy is reduced to the smaller value $O'P'$. The distance $OP$, however, could easily correspond to an energy of 100 kcal per mole or more if the structures $R$ and $S$ differ in atomic configuration as greatly as do those of $n$- and $i$-butane, for example (structures I and II, respectively). Consequently, even when allowance is made for the resonance effect, the energy $O'P'$ required for the rearrangement may still be very large compared with the average thermal energy of the molecules. Under such circumstances, then, the isolation of isomeric or tautomeric forms possessing structures very close to $R$ and $S$ is possible, and it is not profitable to speak of resonance. (This point is discussed at greater length below in the paragraph in fine print.)

Figure 1·2 represents another extreme case, in which the difference in the atomic configurations of the structures $R$ and $S$ is relatively small. The energy of distortion $OP$ is then also relatively small, being perhaps no greater in order of magnitude than the average thermal energy. If the resonance effect is assumed to be of about the same importance here as in the previous example, the curve $R'P'S'$ has no maximum but a minimum instead at some value of $x$ intermediate between 0 and 1. Under such circumstances, the molecule will take up a configuration corresponding to this minimum. Isolation of isomeric or tautomeric forms possessing structures close to $R$ and $S$ will then be impossible; there will instead exist only a single substance, possessing a structure intermediate between $R$ and $S$. This is the situation which one ordi-

type, since this is just the regard in which the ionic and covalent structures differ most strikingly.  A rough, qualitative understanding of the origin of dipole moments can, in fact, be reached from this point of view, as will be shown in Section 5·2.  In a molecule like $H_2$, however, which is formed from two atoms of the same kind, the ionic character has no such effect upon the charge distribution.  This is because the two ionic structures, XVI and XVII, being equivalent, make the same contribution, and their effects just cancel out.

$$H^+ \quad H^- \qquad\qquad H^- \quad H^+$$
$$\text{XVI} \qquad\qquad\qquad \text{XVII}$$

A second effect of the resonance between the ionic and covalent structures is to increase the strength of the bond; for any actual bond must be more stable, on account of the resonance, than it would have been if it were purely ionic or purely covalent.   (See Section 3·6.)

It would be exceedingly awkward in writing and speaking if explicit recognition had always to be made of all the ionic and covalent contributions to each bond.  For the sake of convenience, therefore, we shall hereafter adopt the convention of writing each bond as either purely ionic or purely covalent (unless, of course, a more detailed analysis happens to be necessary for the particular subject under discussion).  Thus, we shall speak of sodium chloride, hydrogen, and nitrogen, and even of hydrogen fluoride, *as if* they possess unique structures of one extreme type or the other.   The reader is then, of course, to understand that the symbol used should be interpreted as representing the kind of bond which is actually present in the molecule in question or (in examples like the Kekulé structure of benzene) which would be present in a hypothetical molecule having the structure written.

There is one type of bond, however, in which it is customary to show somewhat more explicitly the ionic and covalent characters.  We shall, for example, write the structure of an amine oxide as XVIII or XIX. The bond between the nitrogen and the oxygen atoms here is, in effect,

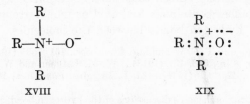

XVIII    XIX

a double one, consisting of an essentially ionic plus an essentially covalent bond.   (The covalent contribution to the former and the ionic contribution to the latter can be left implicit.)   Such bonds, which have been called semipolar double bonds, dative bonds, and coordinate covalencies by various authors, are encountered fairly frequently in both organic and inorganic compounds.   Since their occurrence is always apparent from the structure, however, we shall have little occasion in the future to call especial attention to them, other than by representing them in one of the above equivalent manners.

**2·8   The Hydrogen Bond.**   An essentially different type of bond from any of the foregoing is the so-called hydrogen bond or hydrogen bridge, in which a hydrogen atom serves to hold two other atoms together.   The possibility of such a union seems to have been first clearly suggested by Moore and Winmill,[16] who used it to account for the low base strengths of ammonia and the primary, secondary, and tertiary amines as compared with the quaternary ammonium hydroxides.   Their explanation was that fairly stable undissociated molecules of the type I or II could be formed as long as there was at least one hydrogen atom

$$R_3N\text{---}H\text{ - - }OH \qquad R_3N\text{ - - }H\text{---}OH \qquad (R = H \text{ or alkyl})$$
$$\quad\text{I} \qquad\qquad\qquad\quad \text{II}$$

attached to the nitrogen in the ammonium ion.   The significance of the apparently divalent hydrogen atom and the distinction between the different symbols used to represent its two " bonds " is discussed later in this section.

This idea of a hydrogen bond has been widely extended in subsequent years,[17] and it has received complete confirmation from studies of association, solubility, spectra, and other physical and chemical properties.[18] It would carry us too far afield here to go into all the experimental evidence bearing upon this point; we shall instead content ourselves with a brief description of the bond itself and with a discussion of the theories which have been proposed to explain its existence.   As we shall see, resonance is probably not a major factor in the hydrogen bond; it is often considered to be, however, and for that reason a critical survey of the problem seems desirable here.

It is now generally agreed that the association of hydrogen fluoride and of substances containing hydroxyl or amino groups is due to the formation of hydrogen bonds between the molecules.   The structures

---

[16] T. S. Moore and T. F. Winmill, *J. Chem. Soc.*, **101**, 1635 (1912).

[17] P. Pfeiffer, *Ann.*, **398**, 137 (1913).   W. M. Latimer and W. H. Rodebush, *J. Am. Chem. Soc.*, **42**, 1419 (1920).   M. L. Huggins, *Phys. Rev.*, **18**, 333 (1921); **19**, 346 (1922).

[18] For recent comprehensive discussions of the hydrogen bond, see M. L. Huggins, *J. Org. Chem.*, **1**, 407 (1936); E. N. Lassettre, *Chem. Rev.*, **20**, 259 (1937); W. H. Rodebush and A. M. Buswell, *J. Phys. Chem.*, **43**, 219 (1939); L. Pauling, *The Nature of the Chemical Bond*, Cornell University Press, Ithaca, N. Y., 1st ed., 1939, 2nd ed., 1940, Chapter IX.

III, IV, and V can accordingly be written for the dimeric forms of

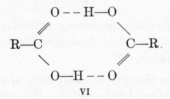

|  |  |
|:-:|:-:|
| III | IV          V |

hydrogen fluoride, water, and ammonia, respectively. With these substances, the association can clearly proceed further, and polymers of any desired complexity can be produced. With a carboxylic acid, on the other hand, the association apparently stops with the formation of the dimer,[19] which has the structure VI. The molecules joined by the

$$O--H—O$$
$$R—C \qquad\qquad C—R$$
$$O—H--O$$

VI

hydrogen bond need not be of the same kind; ammonia in aqueous solution, for example, probably exists at least partially in the form of undissociated ammonium hydroxide, as was mentioned above, and similar situations doubtless occur in other mixtures of suitable substances.

Intramolecular hydrogen bonds also are well known. They exist especially in substances like *o*-nitrophenol, VII, and the enol form of acetylacetone, VIII, in which unsaturated six-membered rings can be formed, although they do occur under other circumstances as well.

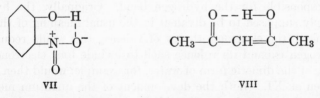

VII                                VIII

The tendencies toward intra- and intermolecular hydrogen bonds sometimes compete with each other, as is shown, for example, by the fact that *o*-nitrophenol is not associated, whereas its *meta* and *para* isomers are.

For reasons which will become apparent later, the strength of a hydrogen bond is greatest in general when the atoms linked by it are most

[19] However, see F. H. MacDougall, *J. Am. Chem. Soc.*, **63**, 3420 (1941).

electronegative. Only with fluorine, oxygen, and nitrogen, in fact, do such bonds occur at all frequently, although they are occasionally encountered with other elements. Hydrogen cyanide, for example, is highly associated, and hydrogen bonds of the type IX are doubtless involved. The ability of the carbon atom here to enter into a hydrogen bond is presumably due to the fact that the carbon-nitrogen bond receives relatively large contributions from such partially ionic structures

$$H—C\equiv N\ \text{-}\ \text{-}\ H—C\equiv N$$
IX

as X and so on. These produce a net positive charge upon the carbon

$$H\overset{+}{C}\equiv\overset{-}{N}$$
X

atom and so increase its electronegativity. Similar considerations apply in other substances also in which hydrogen bonds are formed with the less electronegative elements.[20]

The apparent paradox that the electro*negativity* of an atom is increased by a *positive* charge is explained by the fact that the word " electronegativity," as used in this book, refers to the ability to attract electrons and not explicitly to the state of charge. No reference is intended to " electronegativity " in the sense in which the term is used by Kharasch and his co-workers.[21]

Even under the most favorable circumstances, hydrogen bonds are always much weaker than the ionic and covalent bonds considered previously. Their energies of dissociation, in fact, are usually about 5, and never more than about 10 kcal per mole, as compared with the 25–100 kcal per mole characteristic of the other types.[18]

There is as yet no complete unanimity in regard to the nature of the forces responsible for the hydrogen bond. Originally, the hydrogen was simply supposed to be divalent in the usual meaning of the word. According to the electronic theory of valence, this would require that the hydrogen expand its valence shell to include four electrons. The structure of the dimeric form of water, for example, would then have to be written as XI. With the development of the quantum mechanics and with a better understanding of the nature of valence, however, it soon became apparent that such a structure was at any rate highly improbable. A large amount of energy would, in fact, have to be sup-

[20] See, for example, G. F. Zellhoefer, M. J. Copley, and C. S. Marvel, *J. Am. Chem. Soc.*, **60**, 1337 (1938).

[21] M. S. Kharasch and A. L. Flenner, *J. Am. Chem. Soc.*, **54**, 674 (1932). M. S. Kharasch and O. Reinmuth, *J. Chem. Education*, **5**, 404 (1928); **8**, 1703 (1931). M. S. Kharasch, O. Reinmuth, and F. R. Mayo, *ibid.*, **11**, 82 (1934); **13**, 7 (1936).

plied if the hydrogen atom were forced to accommodate four electrons, and this would make the system quite unstable.

$$\underset{XI}{\overset{\displaystyle H \qquad\quad H}{H : \overset{..}{\underset{..}{O}} : H : \overset{..}{\underset{..}{O}} :}}$$

A reasonable, and probably adequate, explanation of the hydrogen bond is to be found in a consideration of the electrostatic interactions between the atoms or groups that are linked by it. From this point of view, the above example of the dimeric form of water would be described as follows: It is known that the average distribution of electric charge in the water molecule is quite unsymmetrical and that, in particular, the hydrogen and oxygen atoms have fairly large net positive and negative charges, respectively. This is, of course, a result of the partial ionic character of the hydrogen-oxygen bonds. (See Section 5·2.) The situation can be described roughly by writing the structure of a single water molecule as XII, in which the symbol $(+)$ represents a positive charge equal in magnitude to about one third that of an electron, and $(--)$ represents a negative charge of twice that magnitude. (These plus and minus signs in parentheses, of course, do not represent formal charges.) The dimeric form of water is then XIII. Although each of

$$\overset{\displaystyle H^{(+)}}{\underset{\displaystyle XII}{\overset{\displaystyle |}{{}^{(+)}H{-}O^{(--)}}}}$$

the molecules is electrically neutral as a whole, the two are clearly

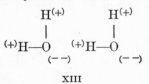

XIII

attracted to each other when their relative positions are as illustrated in this structure. This is because the attractions between the oppositely charged regions outweigh, on account of their smaller separations, the repulsions between the like charged regions.

Such an explanation is in accord with the fact that hydrogen bonds are observed only between strongly electronegative atoms, since only then are the net charges on the atoms large. It may seem strange, however, that this type of linkage occurs only when hydrogen is present. In acetone, for example, the net charges on the carbon and oxygen atoms are apparently larger than those present in water and, consequently, a dimeric molecule, XIV, with "carbon bonds" or "oxygen bonds" might be anticipated.    (The symbols (+) and (−) represent charges of

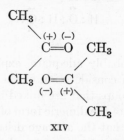

XIV

greater magnitude here than in the corresponding structure for water.) Actually, the substance is not measurably associated, although the fact that its boiling point is higher than that of a hydrocarbon of comparable molecular weight does show that this electrostatic interaction produces some attraction between the molecules.    The explanation is perhaps steric; the oppositely charged portions of the two acetone molecules may not be able to get close enough together for the attraction between them to be very great.    It is doubtless significant that the hydrogen atom, which *can* come in close enough to a negative center, is not only extremely small but also is univalent, so that any steric interference is at a minimum.

An alternative interpretation of the hydrogen bond involves the idea of resonance.    Returning to the example of the dimeric form of water, we see that we can write for this the two structures, XV and XVI, in each of which the usual valence rules are obeyed.    If these correspond to the same relative positions of all the nuclei, resonance between them

will occur.    Since the resulting stabilization of the system would then be greatest when the oxygen atoms are close together, the necessary condition for the existence of a valence bond is satisfied.    An effect of this type may be involved, but there are reasons to suspect that it is of considerably less importance than the electrostatic interactions considered above.

The situation is complicated by the fact that the position of the hydrogen atom which forms the link is not known with certainty.    One possibility is that it is equidistant from the two atoms joined by it.    Then the two structures in question would correspond to the same nuclear configuration, and resonance should be important.   Under these conditions, however, a difficulty arises which can be most easily illustrated by a comparison of the relative stabilities of the dimeric forms of water and of formic acid.   For the first of these, the above structures, XV and XVI, between which resonance is presumed to occur, are not equivalent, and the former is much more stable than the latter; for the second, on the other hand, the corresponding structures, XVII and XVIII, are equivalent and so equally stable.   Experience has shown that the stabilization due to resonance is always tremendously greater when the

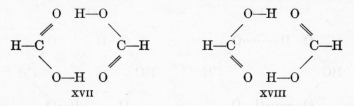

structures involved are of the same stability than when they differ considerably in that regard.   Dimeric formic acid ought, therefore, to have a much greater energy of dissociation than dimeric water.   Actually, however, the energy of dissociation per hydrogen bond is only about 50 per cent higher for formic acid than for water (7 and 4.5 kcal per mole, respectively).[18]

The other possibility for the position of the hydrogen atom which forms the link is that it is closer to one of the two atoms joined by it than it is to the other.   If there are two possible positions for the proton, there are then four structures altogether which have to be considered for each substance.   For dimeric water these are XIX–XXII, and for

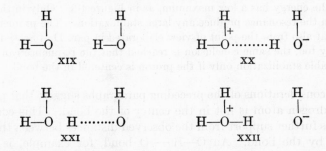

dimeric formic acid they are XXIII–XXVI.   An attempt has been made here to indicate the actual geometrical arrangements as closely as possible, and the dotted lines, as usual, represent formal bonds.   In those structures in which the hydrogen atom is linked by a formal bond to the more distant oxygen, it is, of course, not bonded in any way to the closer one. If we apply the rule that resonance can occur only between structures with the same relative positions of the atomic nuclei, we see that, for either water or formic acid, resonance is possible only between the first and second or between the third and fourth structures;

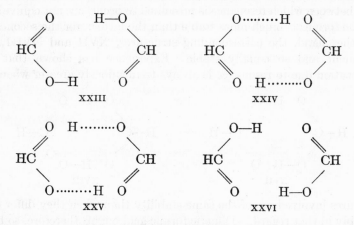

the two resonance hybrids which result for each substance are then in something like tautomeric equilibrium with each other. Moreover, the resonance which does occur is always between non-equivalent structures, so that the stabilization resulting from it might be expected to be small for both water and formic acid — probably smaller than that resulting from the electrostatic interaction.

The question at issue here can be described with the aid of Figures 1·2 and 1·3. If the proton is equidistant from the two atoms joined by it, the energy has a minimum, as in Figure 1·2; if the proton is nearer one atom than the other, the energy has a low maximum, as in Figure 1·3. Only in the former case can the resonance produce any large stabilization. The problem can be looked at also from the point of view elaborated in part D of Section 1·5; in this way too, the same conclusion is reached that the resonance can produce appreciable stabilization only if the proton is centered in the bond.

The considerations of the preceding paragraphs suggest that probably the hydrogen atom is not in the center of the bond. This conclusion receives further support from the observed distances between the atoms linked by the bond. An O—H – – O bond, for example, is usually found to be about 2.5–2.8 A in length,[18] which is considerably more than twice the ordinary oxygen-hydrogen distance of 0.96 A. (See Section 4·3.) If the hydrogen is in the center, then the oxygen-hydrogen bond in each structure must have been greatly stretched. A different method of attacking the problem has been given by Pauling,[22] who has shown that the observed entropy of ice requires that each proton be closer to one oxygen than to any other. Spectroscopic data also have been interpreted[23] as leading to the same conclusion in regard to the hydrogen bonds between the oxygen atoms both here and in several other substances. The situation is still not completely clear, however, and further work is required before the question can be considered solved. The possibility cannot be ruled out that the hydrogen may be centered in some bonds and not in others.

No complete uniformity exists as yet in regard to the graphical representation of the hydrogen bond. Throughout this book, we shall continue the method used in the preceding pages, which consists in writing one full and one broken line between the hydrogen atom and the two atoms linked by it. Whenever a reasonable guess can be made as to the approximate position of the proton (on the assumption that it is not centrally located) the full line will be drawn to the nearer neighbor; in any event, the full line can be considered to represent an essentially covalent bond, and the broken line to represent an electrostatic interaction. The broken line, of course, must be carefully distinguished from the dotted line that is used to represent a formal bond.

The belief that the hydrogen atom is not centered in a hydrogen bond receives considerable further support from an electron-diffraction investigation of the dimeric forms of formic, acetic, and trifluoroacetic acids, and of deuterium acetate.[24] In these substances, the two carbon-oxygen bonds formed by any given carbon atom have been found to differ markedly in length. This fact would be very difficult to explain if resonance occurred between equivalent structures like XVII and XVIII, but it would be an immediate consequence of resonance between non-equivalent structures like XXIII and XXIV.

[22] L. Pauling, *J. Am. Chem. Soc.*, **57**, 2680 (1935).
[23] See, for example, P. C. Cross, J. Burnham, and P. A. Leighton, *J. Am. Chem. Soc.*, **59**, 1134 (1937). R. C. Herman and R. Hofstadter, *Phys. Rev.*, **53**, 940 (1938); *J. Chem. Phys.*, **6**, 534 (1938).
[24] J. Karle and L. O. Brockway, *J. Am. Chem. Soc.*, **66**, 574 (1944).

# Chapter 3

## RESONANCE ENERGY

**3·1 Introductory Remarks.** Resonance always has the effect of increasing the stability, or, in other words, of decreasing the energy, of any molecule in which it occurs. (Attention should perhaps be called to the fact that the energy of any molecule, being negative in sign, is *increased* in absolute magnitude by being *decreased* in value. See the paragraphs in fine print at the end of this section.) The *resonance energy*, which is defined as the quantity obtained by subtracting the actual energy of the molecule in question from that of the most stable contributing structure, is therefore always positive. This new principle is probably the most important addition to chemical theory that has been made within the last twenty years. We have already seen in Chapter 2 how it accounts, in a qualitative way, for the existence of covalent bonds and so, in a certain sense, for the existence of chemistry itself. We shall now consider its application to the less fundamental, but more familiar problem of resonance among ordinary valence-bond structures. We shall be concerned, for example, with the resonance between the two Kekulé structures of benzene, but we shall have little further occasion to make explicit mention of the resonance which produces the bonds themselves, or which gives them their partial ionic character. (It is worthy of note that the word " mesomerism " is commonly applied only to resonance of the present restricted type and is not used to describe the relation between the " structures " discussed in Chapter 2.)

The initial statement of the preceding paragraph is somewhat too broad, inasmuch as the resonance leads also to states of higher energy, as was pointed out in Section 1·5. However, these latter *excited* states are of only spectroscopic interest and so do not ordinarily need to be considered explicitly in the discussion of any chemical problem. For that reason, we shall ignore them in this, and in most of the succeeding, chapters. (However, see Chapter 6.)

There are two distinct points of view that can be adopted in the discussion of resonance energy, and also of the other molecular properties to be taken up in the following chapters. In the first place, the empirical data can be used to show the absence or the occurrence of resonance, as the case may be, and hence to shed light upon the structures of the substances in question. And in the second place, the absence or the occurrence of resonance can be deduced from general considerations and then used to " explain " the empirical data. We shall adopt both of these points of view, as the particular occasions demand, and we shall make no effort to develop a single consistent approach.

It is desirable to have information regarding the magnitudes of the resonance energies in as large a number of substances as possible. The ways in which such information can be derived from thermochemical data will be described in the following sections.

The relations among the various energy quantities are shown schematically in Figure 3·1, in which the heights of the horizontal lines represent the energies of the appropriate structures or systems. For definiteness, we shall consider that we are dealing with a substance which resonates between only two structures, $R$ and $S$, of which the latter is the more stable. The highest line of the figure corresponds to the isolated gaseous atoms, and so, in accordance with the convention introduced in Section 1·4, it defines the zero of energy from which all the other (necessarily negative) energies are measured. The resonance energy is given by the distance $BC$ (or $AC - AB$) between the lines corresponding to the more stable structure $S$ and the resonance hybrid. The energy which is needed for the dissociation of the substance into atoms is therefore increased by the resonance, since $AC$ is greater than $AB$.

The lines labeled $X$ and $Y$ are drawn to represent two extreme possible values of the energies of the elements in their *standard states* (i.e., diamond or

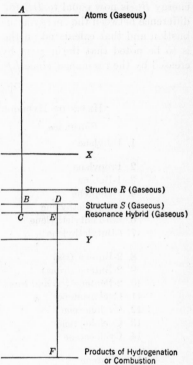

FIG. 3·1. Diagram illustrating the relationship between the resonance energy $BC = DE$, and the experimentally accessible thermal data. The heights of the various horizontal lines above some arbitrary base-line correspond to the energies of the appropriate structures or systems.

graphite, molecular hydrogen, molecular oxygen, and so on). Clearly, the energy required to dissociate the compound into the elements in these standard states could be either positive or negative, and its magnitude could be either increased or decreased by the resonance, since either line $X$ or line $Y$, respectively, might apply to the particular substance under consideration. (Clearly also, still a further situation would arise if the energy of the elements in their standard states were intermediate between the energies of the more stable structure $S$ and the resonance hybrid.)

The lowest line of Figure 3·1 is of interest in connection with the evaluation of resonance energies from heats of hydrogenation or combustion. (See Sections 3·2 and 3·3, respectively.) This line corresponds to the energy of the products of the hydrogenation or combustion, as the case may be, *minus* the energy of the hydrogen or oxygen consumed in the reaction. The resonance energy $BC$ is now equal to $DE$ (or $DF - EF$), which in turn is equal to the difference between the energy actually liberated in the hydrogenation or combustion and that calculated on the basis of the more stable structure $S$. It is to be noted that the heat of hydrogenation or combustion is always decreased by the resonance, since $EF$ is necessarily less than $DF$.

TABLE 3·1

HEATS OF HYDROGENATION OF MONOÖLEFINES

| Substance | Heat of Hydrogenation[a] |
|---|---|
| 1. Ethylene | 32.8 kcal per mole |
| 2. Propylene | 30.1 |
| 3. 1-Butene | 30.3 |
| 4. 1-Heptene | 30.1 |
| 5. *i*-Propylethylene | 30.3 |
| 6. *neo*-Pentylethylene | 29.5 |
| 7. *t*-Butylethylene | 30.3 |
| 8. 2-Butene (*cis*) | 28.6 |
| 9. 2-Butene (*trans*) | 27.6 |
| 10. 2-Pentene (*cis* and *trans* mixture) | 28.0 |
| 11. Cyclopentene | 26.9 |
| 12. Cyclohexene | 28.6 |
| 13. Cycloheptene | 26.5 |
| 14. Cycloöctene | 23.5 |
| 15. *i*-Butene | 28.4 |
| 16. *unsym.* Methylethylethylene | 28.5 |
| 17. *unsym.* Methyl-*i*-propylethylene | 28.0 |
| 18. 2,4,4-Trimethyl-1-pentene | 27.2 |
| 19. Trimethylethylene | 26.9 |
| 20. 2,4,4-Trimethyl-2-pentene | 28.4 |
| 21. Tetramethylethylene | 26.6 |

[a] The quantities listed are the amounts of heat liberated when the hydrogenations are carried out at 1 atmosphere pressure and 82° C. The data listed here are taken from the work of Kistiakowsky and co-workers. See reference 1.

## 3·2 Resonance Energies from Heats of Hydrogenation.

The most accurate thermochemical data available for the determination of resonance energies are the heats of hydrogenation of certain unsaturated compounds. In Table 3·1 are listed the results of measurements made by Kistiakowsky and his co-workers[1] upon a number of monoölefines. The quantities listed are the amounts of heat liberated at a constant pressure of 1 atmosphere and at a temperature of 82° C in the reactions

$$X \text{ (gas)} + H_2 \text{ (gas)} \rightarrow XH_2 \text{ (gas)}$$

where X is the unsaturated, and $XH_2$ is the saturated compound. It is to be noted that the data apply to reactions in which all the substances are gaseous; this fact is important since it makes unnecessary any corrections for the large interactions that operate between the molecules in the solid and liquid phases. It is seen that the values given in the table are dependent upon the number of substituents on the unsaturated atoms, but that they are fairly constant for all the molecules of any given degree of substitution. (An explanation of this variation is given in Section 3·7. For the present, however, we shall regard it merely as an empirical fact.) Some irregularities are observed, mostly in cases of *cis-trans* isomerism or of ring formation, but these are generally smaller than the differences accompanying changes in the number of substituents. This uniformity makes it possible for one to predict the heat of hydrogenation of any olefine to usually within about 1 kcal per mole.

In Table 3·2 similar data are given for hydrocarbons containing two or more double bonds per molecule. We might anticipate that, as a first approximation, the total heats of hydrogenation would be the sums of the heats characteristic of the individual bonds. As long as these latter are not conjugated with each other, this is actually what is observed. For example, the heat of hydrogenation of 1,5-hexadiene is 60.5 kcal per mole, which is almost exactly twice the value found generally for substances with the structure $RCH{=}CH_2$. With limonene, the agreement is not quite so good, but is still fair; the observed value of 54.1 kcal per mole is only 0.8 kcal per mole less than the sum of the values for the monoölefines with the most closely analogous double bonds, *unsym.* methyl-*i*-propylethylene and trimethylethylene.

When the double bonds are conjugated with each other, the situation is different, and the observed heats of hydrogenation are lower than the predicted. With 1,3-butadiene, for example, the observed value of 57.1 kcal per mole is less by 3.5 kcal per mole than twice the value for 1-butene. Since the same product, *n*-butane, is obtained in both reactions, the only possible explanation of the data is that 1,3-butadiene is more stable by 3.5 kcal per mole than would have been anticipated by

---

[1] See R. B. Williams, *J. Am. Chem. Soc.*, **64**, 1395 (1942) for the most recent paper of this series and for references to the preceding papers.

## TABLE 3·2

HEATS OF HYDROGENATION OF HYDROCARBONS WITH MORE THAN
ONE DOUBLE BOND

| Substance | Heat of Hydrogenation[a] Calcd | Obs | Reference Substances[b] | Resonance Energy |
|---|---|---|---|---|
| 1,4-Pentadiene | 60.6 kcal | 60.8 kcal | 3 | — |
| 1,5-Hexadiene | 60.6 | 60.5 | 3 | — |
| 1,4-Dihydronaphthalene[c] | 28.6 | 27.6 | 12 | — |
| Limonene | 54.9 | 54.1 | 17, 19 | — |
| | | | | |
| 1,3-Butadiene | 60.6 | 57.1 | 3 | 3.5 kcal |
| 1,3-Cyclopentadiene | 53.8 | 50.9 | 11 | 2.9 |
| 1,3-Pentadiene | 58.3 | 54.1 | 3, 10 | 4.2 |
| 1,3-Cyclohexadiene | 57.2 | 55.4 | 12 | 1.8 |
| 2,3-Dimethyl-1,3-butadiene | 56.8 | 53.9 | 15 | 2.9 |
| 1,3,5-Cycloheptatriene | 79.5 | 72.8 | 13 | 6.7 |
| 1,3-Cycloheptadiene | 53.0 | 51.3 | 13 | 1.7 |
| α-Phellandrene | 55.5 | 53.4 | 12, 19 | 2.1 |
| α-Terpinene | 53.8 | 50.7 | 19 | 3.1 |
| | | | | |
| Benzene | 85.8 | 49.8 | 12 | 36.0 |
| Ethylbenzene | 84.1 | 48.9 | 12, 19 | 35.2 |
| o-Xylene | 82.4 | 47.3 | 12, 19 | 35.1 |
| Hydrindene | 82.4 | 45.8 | 12, 19 | 36.6 |
| Mesitylene | 80.7 | 47.6 | 19 | 33.1 |
| | | | | |
| Styrene | 114.4 | 77.5 | 3, 12, 19 | 36.9 |
| Indene | 109.3 | 69.9 | 11, 12, 19 | 39.4 |
| 1,2-Dihydronaphthalene[c] | 28.6 | 24.6 | 12 | 4.0 |
| 1,2-Diphenylethylene (cis)[c] | 28.6 | 26.3 | 8 | 2.3 |
| 1,2-Diphenylethylene (trans)[c] | 27.6 | 20.6 | 9 | 7.0 |
| 1,4-Diphenyl-1,3-butadiene[c] | 55.2 | 44.5 | 9 | 10.7 |

[a] See note a, Table 3·1.

[b] The entries in this column refer to the numbers assigned to the various hydrocarbons in Table 3·1.

[c] This substance was investigated in solution, but its heat of hydrogenation was corrected to the gas phase in order to be made directly comparable with the others in this table and in Table 3·1. The calculated and observed heats are for the hydrogenation of only the bond, or bonds, not in intact benzene rings. The resonance energy given in the last column is therefore only the excess over that in these benzene rings.

comparison with 1-butene. The other conjugated dienes also show anomalous stabilities of about the same magnitude, so that the phenomenon appears to be quite general. Moreover, with cycloheptatriene, the only non-aromatic, fully conjugated triene for which data are available, the effect is greater, the extra stability here amounting to 6.7 kcal per mole.

The fact that conjugated systems exhibit a special stability in comparison with unconjugated systems of analogous structure has long been recognized and indeed formed one of the chief supports of Thiele's theory of partial valence.[2]  However, it was not until the development of the theory of resonance that a completely logical and convincing explanation was found.  Thus, for butadiene, we can write not only the usual structure I but also the less stable one II, with a formal bond between the terminal carbon atoms.  (Cf. Section 1·4.)  Resonance occurs between

$$CH_2 = CH - CH = CH_2 \qquad \overset{\cdots\cdots\cdots\cdots\cdots}{CH_2 - CH = CH - CH_2}$$

I                 II

these, and the resulting resonance energy stabilizes the molecule.  It is evident then that in this substance the resonance energy is equal to about 3.5 kcal per mole, its observed extra stability.  With cycloheptatriene, the fact that the resonance energy is still greater can be accounted for in the following manner.  There are altogether five structures, III–VII, which need to be considered.  The relationship between III and IV, or between III and V, is essentially the same as that between I and II for butadiene.  If the resonance were restricted to III and IV,

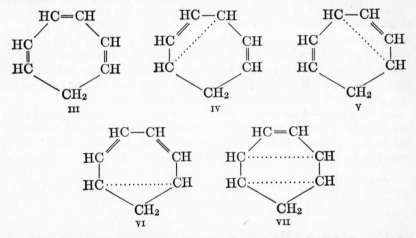

or to III and V, the resonance energy of the triene should therefore be about the same as that of a diene.  The resonance cannot be thus restricted, however, and so the effect of the remaining structures must be to increase the resonance energy.

Two further points require some elaboration in connection with the above discussion of the resonance energy of cycloheptatriene.  In the first place, there are still many further structures which can be written for this substance in addition to III–VII.  Some of these are of the type of structure VIII with

[2] J. Thiele, *Ann.*, **306**, 87 (1899).

crossing bonds (either formal or effective).  Such structures add nothing new, however, since they can be shown[3] to be themselves resonance hybrids of the

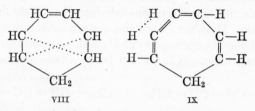

VIII                              IX

structures without crossing bonds.  (In particular, structure VIII is a resonance hybrid to which III and VII contribute equally.)  They can therefore be ignored.  Other structures of the type of IX are also possible.  These will be neglected since their contributions are particularly unimportant.  Resonance with them would be an example of second-order hyperconjugation.  (Cf. Section 3·7.)  In the second place, the statement that the resonance energy of the triene must be greater than that of a diene because of the additional structures for the former substance must not be taken as expressing the common, but fallacious, view that, of two molecules, the one with the larger number of resonating structures must have the greater resonance energy.  The point at issue here is that the triene has structures analogous to *all those of the diene, and some other ones in addition.*  On the other hand, octatetraene,  $CH_2=CH-CH=CH-CH=CH-CH=CH_2$, doubtless has a smaller resonance energy than benzene, although the former has altogether fourteen structures of the above type without crossing bonds and the latter has only five; this is because octatetraene has only one, whereas benzene has two, particularly stable structures without formal bonds.

It may seem that resonance should occur also in an unconjugated diene like 1,4-pentadiene, for which the two structures, X and XI, can be written.  For such a substance, however, the less stable structure, XI, has *two* formal bonds, so that it has *two* fewer effective bonds than X.  It is therefore par-

$$CH_2=CH-CH_2-CH=CH_2 \qquad \dot{C}H_2-CH-CH_2-CH-\dot{C}H_2$$

X                                    XI

ticularly unstable, and the resulting resonance energy is negligibly small.  It can be shown also that in this molecule, and in other ones of similar type, the "coupling" between the structures is of such nature as to lead to especially small resonance energies.  (For the significance of "coupling," see the mechanical analogy described in Section 1·5.)  It is not possible here to go further into this rather technical point.

For each of the simple conjugated systems considered up to the present, there has been a single structure of greater stability than any of the others.  As a result, the resonance has been of only minor impor-

[3] G. Rumer, *Nachr. Ges. Wiss. Göttingen, Math. physik. Klasse*, 337 (1932).

tance — that is, the actual structures of the molecules have differed only slightly from the most stable structures, and the resonance energies have been small.  In fact, the resonance energies have been so small that one might feel justified in questioning their reality.  This is especially true since, in determining their values, we have had to make estimates of what the heats of hydrogenation of the substances in question would have been if no resonance had occurred.  Any errors in these estimates are, of course, contained in the values found for the resonance energies. It is fortunate, therefore, that data are available also for a number of aromatic hydrocarbons;  these have such large resonance energies that small uncertainties in regard to their exact magnitudes are inconsequential.  The observed heats of hydrogenation of these substances are also given in Table 3.2.  It will be noted that benzene and its simple alkyl derivatives all have resonance energies in the neighborhood of 35 kcal per mole.  This is about ten to fifteen times as great as the resonance energies of the simple conjugated dienes and about five times as great as that of cycloheptatriene.

The reason for these tremendously greater resonance energies in the aromatic hydrocarbons can be seen from a consideration of benzene This substance resonates between the two equivalent Kekulé structures XII and XIII.  Since these have the same energy content, the reso-

nance between them must be very important — that is, the actual structure of the molecules cannot be very close to either of the Kekulé structures, and the resonance energy must be large.  The three Dewar structures, XIV, XV, and XVI, also make small contributions, but, since they are relatively unstable, they are much less important than the Kekulé structures.  They can, therefore, be ignored in a qualitative

discussion like the present one, and we shall refer to them very little hereafter.  Approximate calculations of the sort discussed in Section 3.5 have shown that they are responsible for only about 20 per cent of the total resonance energy.[4]

[4] L. Pauling and G. W. Wheland, *J. Chem. Phys.*, **1**, 362 (1933).

With some of the other aromatic hydrocarbons, such as *o*-xylene, for example, the Kekulé structures between which resonance occurs are not quite equivalent, on account of the presence of substituents. Even under such circumstances, however, the structures differ so little in stability that, for all practical purposes, they may be considered equivalent. This conclusion is borne out by the above-mentioned approximate constancy of the resonance energy in benzene and its alkyl derivatives.

In those molecules in which the benzene rings are conjugated with olefinic double bonds, the resonance energies are still greater. This is to be expected because resonance can occur not only among the Kekulé and Dewar structures but also with such additional ones as XVII. All these have at least one formal bond and so make only small contributions either to the states of the molecules or to the resonance energies.

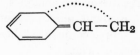

XVII

It is interesting that the additional stabilization resulting from the conjugation of a double bond with a benzene ring is of the same order of magnitude as that resulting from the conjugation of two double bonds with each other. This is not unreasonable in view of the similarity between the types of resonance involved. It is interesting also that when the conjugated system becomes fairly long, as in diphenylbutadiene, the resulting resonance energy becomes of appreciable magnitude. This again is not unreasonable because, as was explained above in connection with cycloheptatriene, the possibilities for resonance increase with the length of the conjugated system. Finally, attention may be called to the striking difference in resonance energies of *cis* and *trans* stilbene; the lowered stability of the *cis* compound is probably due to its considerable amount of steric strain and to its non-planar configuration. (Cf. Section 4·2.)

Data similar to the foregoing are given in Table 3·3 for a number of olefines containing oxygen. Since the heat of hydrogenation of allyl alcohol is close to that of propylene, it appears that the mere presence of oxygen in the neighborhood of the olefinic double bond produces no significant effect. Comparison is apparently permissible, therefore, with the hydrocarbons discussed above. The fact that the heat of hydrogenation of crotonaldehyde is less than that of *trans* 2-butene, for example, can be taken as evidence that a carbon-carbon double bond can be conjugated with an aldehydic carbonyl group as well as with a second ethylenic linkage. The situation is different, however, with

## TABLE 3·3

HEATS OF HYDROGENATION OF SUBSTANCES CONTAINING OXYGEN

| Substance | Heat of Hydrogenation[a] Calcd | Obs | Reference Substances[b] | Resonance Energy |
|---|---|---|---|---|
| Allyl alcohol | 30.1 kcal | 31.5 kcal | 2 | — |
| Crotonaldehyde | 27.6 | 25.2 | 9 | 2.4 kcal |
| Methyl methacrylate | 28.4 | 28.6 | 15 | — |
| Ethyl maleate | 28.6 | 34.0 | 8 | — |
| Ethyl fumarate | 27.6 | 29.8 | 9 | — |
| Methyl cinnamate (*cis*)[c] | 28.6 | 28.7 | 8 | — |
| Methyl cinnamate (*trans*)[c] | 27.6 | 24.7 | 9 | 2.9 |
| Divinyl ether | 60.6 | 57.2 | 3 | 3.4 |
| Ethyl vinyl ether | 30.3 | 26.7 | 3 | 3.6 |
| 2-Ethoxypropene | 28.4 | 25.1 | 15 | 3.3 |
| 2-Methoxy-2-butene | 26.9 | 24.8 | 19 | 2.1 |
| Vinyl acetate | 30.3 | 31.1 | 3 | — |
| Furan | 53.8 | 36.6 | 11 | 17.2 |

[a] See note *a*, Table 3·1.
[b] See note *b*, Table 3·2.
[c] See note *c*, Table 3·2.

methyl methacrylate, which has practically the same heat of hydrogenation as *i*-butene; this shows that only a negligibly small resonance energy results from conjugation involving the carbonyl part of a carbomethoxy group. In *cis* methyl cinnamate and in ethyl fumarate and maleate, the significance of the data is obscured by the steric strains and by the large electrostatic interactions. In *trans* methyl cinnamate, on the other hand, the strains and the electrostatic interactions are smaller, and the conjugation of the ethylenic double bond with the benzene ring apparently leads to a resonance energy of the usual magnitude.

A somewhat different type of resonance is illustrated by divinyl ether. The observed heat of hydrogenation here is 57.2 kcal per mole, which is less than twice the value for the analogous 1-butene. The difference of 3.4 kcal per mole may be due to the resonance among the structures XVIII, XIX, and XX. The effect is so small, however, that it cannot be accepted without some reserve, since there is no assurance

$$H_2C=CH-O-CH=CH_2 \qquad\qquad H_2\overset{..}{C}-CH=\overset{..}{\overset{+}{O}}-CH=CH_2$$
$$\text{XVIII} \qquad\qquad\qquad\qquad\qquad \text{XIX}$$

$$H_2C=CH-\overset{+}{O}=CH-\overset{..}{C}H_2$$
$$\text{XX}$$

that, even in the absence of resonance, the heat of hydrogenation of divinyl ether would be exactly twice that of 1-butene.   It is surprising, moreover, that the resonance energy of ethyl vinyl ether seems to be slightly greater than that of divinyl ether; it would have been expected to be smaller since only a single structure analogous to XIX and XX can be written for this substance.   In vinyl acetate, on the other hand, an apparently similar type of structure seems to result in no resonance energy at all, the observed heat of hydrogenation being, in fact, higher than that calculated.   The possibility cannot be excluded that in all these substances the actual resonance energies are negligibly small, and that the observed effects are due to some other factors which are not understood at present.

In view of the above uncertainties, it is fortunate that in furan a rather similar type of resonance produces a stabilization that is large enough to be beyond question.   For this substance, the heat of hydrogenation is only 36.6 kcal per mole, as compared with 53.8 kcal for two moles of cyclopentene.   The difference of 17.2 kcal apparently requires that resonance among the structures XXI–XXVI be involved.   The

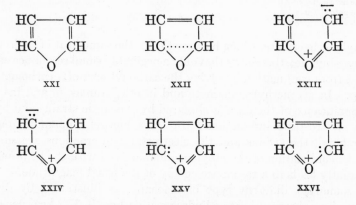

first two of these structures, XXI and XXII, are of the type characteristic of any conjugated diene; resonance between them alone should therefore produce only a small resonance energy, as in cyclopentadiene. The structures XXIII and XXIV are analogous to XIX and XX; their contribution to the resonance energy is also presumably rather small, as in divinyl ether.   The structures XXV and XXVI, however, have no close analogs in either cyclopentadiene or divinyl ether, and, moreover, are relatively stable since the formal charges have not been widely separated; they are therefore probably responsible for a large part of the comparatively great resonance energy of furan.

**3·3   Resonance Energies from Heats of Combustion.**   Although the heats of hydrogenation provide the most accurate available data for the

determination of resonance energies, they are not so extensive as might
be desired.  Recourse must therefore be had to other types of thermochemical data if the treatment is to be extended further.  For this purpose, the heats of combustion are particularly useful since they have
been measured for a very large number of substances.  They suffer from
the disadvantage, however, of being subject to relatively large experimental errors.  The reason for this can be seen from the following example.  The heat of combustion of benzene is 788 kcal per mole, so
that an error of 0.1 per cent would amount to 0.79 kcal per mole.  Its
heat of hydrogenation, on the other hand, is only 49.8 kcal per mole, so
that a similar error of 0.1 per cent would amount to only 0.05 kcal per
mole.  The same percentage error thus leads to about sixteen times as
great an absolute error in the heat of combustion as in the heat of hydrogenation.  This difficulty, which is encountered quite generally, is
especially serious since relatively few thermochemical measurements can
be relied upon to within 0.1 per cent, and since many of the values in the
literature may be in error by as much as 1 per cent or more.  It is
evident then that the heats of combustion will be most useful in connection with the aromatic compounds, for which the resonance energies are
large, and quite unreliable for the simple conjugated systems like
butadiene, for which the resonance energies are smaller than the uncertainties in the data.

In order to use the measured heats of combustion for the determination of resonance energies, we must have a method of estimating what the
heats of combustion would have been in the absence of resonance.  For
this purpose, we shall employ the well-known empirical rule that the
heat of combustion, $\Lambda$, of any given substance can be expressed as the
sum of contributions, $\lambda(A-B)$, from the various bonds, $A-B$, which
are present in the molecule.  This rule owes its importance to the fact
that the value of the contribution made by each type of bond is approximately constant from substance to substance, or, at any rate, varies in
an approximately predictable manner.  Different authors[5] have assigned
different sets of values to the various $\lambda(A-B)$'s.  Although these are
sometimes not in very good detailed agreement with each other, any one
set, if used consistently, can usually be expected to permit the calcula-

[5] J. Thomsen, *Thermochemistry*, Longmans Green Company, London, 1908 (Trans-
lated by K. A. Burke).  W. Swietoslawski, *J. Am. Chem. Soc.*, **42**, 1312 (1920).
M. S. Kharasch, *Bur. Standards J. Research*, **2**, 359 (1929).  Attention should be
called also to L. Pauling, *The Nature of the Chemical Bond*, Cornell University Press,
Ithaca, N. Y., 1st ed., 1939, pp. 53, 123; 2nd ed., 1940, pp. 53, 131.  O. K. Rice,
*Electronic Structure and Chemical Binding*, McGraw-Hill Book Company, New
York, 1940, p. 190.  In these last two references are given tables of bond energies,
from which heats of combustion can be calculated.  Cf. Section 3·4.

tion of heats of combustion to within perhaps 1–2 per cent. Such calculations apply, of course, only to those substances to which unique structures can be assigned, since the occurrence of resonance among several structures is always accompanied by a decrease in energy content and hence also in the measured heat of combustion.

The most complete, self-consistent set of $\lambda(A—B)$'s that is available at the present time seems to be one derived from, and therefore equivalent to, Pauling's bond energies.[5] The values from this set that are important for the following discussion are listed in Table 3·4. It is

TABLE 3·4

CONTRIBUTIONS OF THE VARIOUS TYPES OF BOND TO THE HEAT OF COMBUSTION[a]

|   |   | C | N | O | S | Cl | Br | I |
|---|---|---|---|---|---|---|---|---|
| H |   | 53.3 | 30.6 | $5.25^b$ | 67.0 | — | — | — |
| C | single bond | 50.8 | 34.5 | 14.25 | 68.8 | 5.0 | 23.75 | 34.8 |
|   | double bond | 118.8 | 72.1 | $\begin{cases} 26.5^c \\ 19.5^d \\ 16.5^e \end{cases}$ | 143.6 | — | — | — |
|   | triple bond | 205.2 | 105.2 | — | — | — | — | — |

[a] The quantities listed are the contributions in kilocalories per mole made to the heats of combustion (see equation 1) by the bonds, of the types noted, between the elements given at the left of the rows and those given at the tops of the columns. The values have been derived from, and are equivalent to, Pauling's bond energies. Cf. reference 5 and Section 3·4.

[b] The "heat of combustion" of 10.5 kcal per mole calculated for water with this value is, of course, actually the heat of vaporization. See equation 1.

[c] This value applies to formaldehyde only.

[d] This value applies to other aldehydes.

[e] This value applies to ketones.

especially to be noted that these $\lambda$'s are restricted to molecules in which each atom exhibits its normal valence — that is to say, four for carbon, three for nitrogen, two for oxygen and sulfur, and one for hydrogen and the halogens — and to structures which contain no formal bonds. The heats of combustion to which these $\lambda$'s refer are the values of $\Lambda$ which appear in the equations

$$C_aH_bO_cN_dS_eCl_fBr_gI_h \text{ (gas)} + [a + (b - f)/4 + e - c/2]O_2 \text{ (gas)} \rightarrow$$

$$aCO_2 \text{ (gas)} + (b - f)/2H_2O \text{ (liq)} + d/2N_2 \text{ (gas)} + eSO_2 \text{ (gas)} \quad (1)$$

$$+ fHCl \text{ (gas)} + g/2Br_2 \text{ (vapor)} + h/2I_2 \text{ (sol)} + \Lambda \text{ kcal}$$

The substance of interest, $C_aH_bO_cN_dS_eCl_fBr_gI_h$, is always to be taken as gaseous. Data referring to other states can be used with the aid of the relation

$$\Lambda = \Lambda_x + \mu_x \tag{2}$$

where $\Lambda_x$ and $\mu_x$ are the heats of combustion and vaporization, respectively, of the substance in the state $x$ (solid or liquid). As with the heats of hydrogenation, this emphasis upon the gaseous state is for the purpose of avoiding the complications that arise from the large intermolecular interactions which are always present in solids and liquids. The remaining substances (oxygen, carbon dioxide, water, etc.) are taken arbitrarily in whatever states may be convenient experimentally. The fact that some of these (for example, water) may not be gaseous is of no moment, since the making of the necessary corrections would change both the " observed " heats of combustion and the values of the $\lambda(A—B)$'s in such a way that the agreement would not be affected. The combustions are assumed to occur at a constant pressure of 1 atmosphere and at a temperature of 18° C.

Data are frequently given in the literature for reactions in which the products of combustion are different from those listed in equation 1, for example, $H_2SO_4$ (dil aq) in place of $SO_2$ (gas) for compounds containing sulfur. Under such circumstances, the $\lambda$'s of Table 3·4, of course, cannot be used unless either they or the " observed " heats of combustion are corrected in a suitable manner.

In Table 3·5 a comparison is made between the observed and calculated heats of combustion for a number of simple, non-resonating substances. These substances have been chosen more or less at random, but in such a way as to cover a fairly large number of different types of compound. (The effort has been made, however, to avoid substances, like carbon tetrachloride, in which the electrostatic interactions between nearby, highly polar groups might be important.) It will be seen that the agreement is usually to within less than 1–2 per cent, and is sometimes quite good, but that the discrepancies are considerably larger than with the heats of hydrogenation. The agreement could doubtless be improved a great deal by the use of further corrections of the sort introduced into Table 3·4 in connection with the carbon-oxygen double bond. Some attempts along this line have been made,[6] but they have usually been restricted to limited fields by the lack of really reliable data. We shall, accordingly, continue to use the values given in Table 3·4 in order to be able to treat as large a number of different substances as possible

[6] For example, see R. S. Mulliken. C. A. Rieke, and W. G. Brown, *J. Am. Chem. Soc.*, **63**, 41 (1941), equation 23.

## TABLE 3·5

### HEATS OF COMBUSTION OF NON-RESONATING SUBSTANCES

| Substance | Heat of Combustion[a] | |
|---|---|---|
| | Calcd[b] | Obs[c] |
| Methane | 213.2 kcal | 212.8 kcal |
| Ethane | 370.6 | 372.8 |
| Propane | 528.0 | 530.6 |
| n-Butane | 685.4 | 688.0 |
| i-Butane | 685.4 | 686.3 |
| n-Pentane | 842.8 | 845.3 |
| i-Pentane | 842.8 | 843.4 |
| neo-Pentane | 842.8 | 840.6 |
| n-$C_pH_{2p+2}$ $(p > 5)$ | $55.8 + 157.4p$ | $60.4 + 157.0p$ |
| Cyclohexane | 944.4 | 943.7 |
| | | |
| Ethylene | 332.0 | 337.1 |
| Propylene | 489.4 | 492.1 |
| 1-Butene | 646.8 | 649.7 |
| 2-Butene (cis) | 646.8 | 647.9 |
| 2-Butene (trans) | 646.8 | 647.0 |
| i-Butene | 646.8 | 646.1 |
| Trimethylethylene | 804.2 | 801.7 |
| | | |
| Acetylene | 311.7 | 310.6 |
| Methylacetylene | 469.1 | 463.0 |
| Dimethylacetylene | 626.5 | 616.2 |
| | | |
| Methyl alcohol | 179.4 | 182.6 |
| Ethyl alcohol | 336.8 | 336.8 |
| n-Propyl alcohol | 494.2 | 493.3 |
| i-Propyl alcohol | 494.2 | 489.5 |
| n-Butyl alcohol | 651.6 | 650.0 |
| i-Butyl alcohol | 651.6 | 649.3 |
| t-Butyl alcohol | 651.6 | 643.3 |
| n-$C_pH_{2p+1}OH$ $(p > 5)$ | $22.0 + 157.4p$ | $21.6 + 157.0p$ |
| | | |
| Dimethyl ether | 348.3 | 347.6 |
| Diethyl ether | 663.1 | 660.3 |
| Diallyl ether | 900.7 | 906.6 |
| | | |
| Formaldehyde | 133.1 | 134.7 |
| Acetaldehyde | 283.5 | 284.7 |
| Acetone | 438.3 | 434.6 |
| Diethylketone | 753.1 | 746.8 |
| Methyl-i-propylketone | 753.1 | 744.9 |
| Di-i-propylketone | 1067.9 | 1059.9[d] |

TABLE 3·5 *(Continued)*

HEATS OF COMBUSTION OF NON-RESONATING SUBSTANCES

| Substance | Heat of Combustion[a] | |
|---|---|---|
| | Calcd[b] | Obs[c] |
| Methylamine | 255.5 kcal | 256.9 kcal |
| Ethylamine | 412.9 | 413.1 |
| *t*-Butylamine | 727.7 | 720[e] |
| Dimethylamine | 419.2 | 418.2 |
| Diethylamine | 734.0 | 730.6 |
| Trimethylamine | 582.9 | 579.5 |
| Triethylamine | 1055.1 | 1042[f] |
| | | |
| Methyl chloride | 164.9 | 164.2 |
| Ethyl chloride | 322.3 | 316.7 |
| Methyl bromide | 183.7 | 184.0 |
| Ethyl bromide | 341.1 | 340.5 |
| Methyl iodide | 194.7 | 200.5 |
| Ethyl iodide | 352.1 | 357.8 |
| | | |
| Methyl mercaptan | 295.7 | 297.6 |
| Ethyl mercaptan | 453.1 | 452.0 |
| Dimethyl sulfide | 457.4 | 455.6 |
| | | |
| Acetonitrile | 315.9 | 310.4 |
| Propionitrile | 473.3 | 464.6 |

[a] Of the gaseous substance.

[b] See Table 3·4.

[c] These observed values are taken from an unpublished table of heats of combustion at 25°, which has been compiled by Professors M. S. Kharasch and W. G. Brown. (See also M. S. Kharasch, reference 5.) The corrections to 18° have not been made because they would be negligibly small for our purposes, and because the necessary data are not available for all the substances. When discordant values are cited by Kharasch and Brown, either an average value or the one reported by J. Thomsen is listed here. For a few substances, corrections to the gaseous state have had to be made by the present author. Except as otherwise noted, this has been done with the aid of the uncorrected heats of vaporization at the boiling point, which are given by Landolt-Börnstein.

[d] The heat of vaporization was assumed to be the same as that given for di-*n*-propylketone in Landolt-Börnstein.

[e] The heat of vaporization was calculated from the boiling point, with a Trouton constant of 23.

[f] The heat of vaporization was calculated from the boiling point, with a Trouton constant of 20.

from a unified point of view, even though this entails the sacrifice of some accuracy at times.

The use of the heats of combustion for the determination of the resonance energies can be illustrated with the example of benzene. Each of the Kekulé structures of this substance contains six carbon-hydrogen bonds, three carbon-carbon single bonds, and three carbon-carbon double bonds. The calculated heat of combustion is therefore

$$\Lambda_{calcd} = (6 \times 53.3) + (3 \times 50.8) + (3 \times 118.8) = 828.6 \text{ kcal}$$

The observed value, however, is only 788 kcal per mole.   The difference of 41 kcal per mole between these values is the resonance energy, since it represents the amount by which the actual molecule is more stable than it would have been if it had possessed either of the two Kekulé structures.   The agreement with the value of 36.0 kcal per mole found from the heat of hydrogenation is probably as good as could have been expected.

The " measured " resonance energies for a number of further substances are listed in Table 3·6.   The observed heats of combustion from which they are derived have been corrected to the gaseous state whenever the reported values have referred to the solid or liquid states. Since the data required for these corrections are not available for most of the substances included in the table, the corrections are necessarily only approximate.   The errors introduced in this way are probably never greater than about 5 kcal per mole, however, and so are often, if not usually, less important than the uncertainties in the measured heats of combustion themselves.   The opportunities for individual judgment, both in making the corrections to the gaseous state and in selecting the original experimental data, are responsible for the fact that the resonance energies given in Table 3·6 often deviate somewhat from the values given by other authors for the same substances.

Several of the individual values of the resonance energy deserve special comment.   With the benzene homologs, for example, there is apparent an increase in the resonance energy with the complexity of the molecule, although no such increase was found in the corresponding values obtained from heats of hydrogenation (Table 3·2).   The explanation of this discrepancy is presumably that all double bonds are considered equivalent in the present treatment, whereas corrections for the degree of substitution were made in the former one.   For example, the observed heat of hydrogenation of mesitylene is actually lower than that of benzene; consequently, its resonance energy would have been found greater, instead of less, if the correction in question had not been made. No similar corrections in the heats of combustion seem to be practicable at present, and so a systematic error in the resonance energies is introduced.

In naphthalene, the resonance energy is nearly twice as great as in benzene.   This fact is in agreement with the view that resonance occurs among the structures I, II, and III, which are analogous to the Kekulé

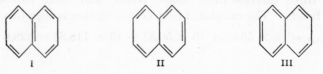

I                          II                          III

## TABLE 3·6

### HEATS OF COMBUSTION OF RESONATING MOLECULES[a]

| Substance and Physical State[b] | Calcd for Gas[c] | Obs[d] | Corr to Gas[e] | Resonance Energy |
|---|---|---|---|---|
| Benzene (l) | 829 | 780 | 788 | 41 |
| Toluene (l) | 986 | 935 | 945 | 41 |
| Ethylbenzene (l) | 1143 | 1090 | 1100 | 43 |
| o-Xylene (l) | 1143 | 1091 | 1099 | 44 |
| Mesitylene (l) | 1301 | 1243 | 1251 | 50 |
| Hexamethylbenzene (s) | 1773 | 1704 | 1722 | 51 |
| Diphenylmethane (s) | 1759 | 1651 | 1666 | 93 |
| | | | | |
| Naphthalene (s) | 1325 | 1230 | 1248 | 77 |
| β-Methylnaphthalene (s) | 1483 | 1384 | 1397 | 86 |
| Anthracene (s) | 1822 | 1685 | 1706 | 116 |
| Phenanthrene (s) | 1822 | 1675 | 1692 | 130 |
| Pyrene (s) | 2042 | 1873 | 1890 | 152 |
| Chrysene (s) | 2318 | 2134 | 2155 | 163 |
| | | | | |
| Biphenyl (s) | 1601 | 1494 | 1510 | 91 |
| Fluorene (s) | 1703 | 1585 | 1602 | 101 |
| α,α'-Binaphthyl (s) | 2595 | 2396 | 2418 | 177 |
| 1,3,5-Triphenylbenzene (s) | 3147 | 2925 | 2947 | 200 |
| | | | | |
| Styrene (l) | 1105 | 1046 | 1054 | 51 |
| Stilbene (*trans*) (s) | 1878 | 1759 | 1777 | 101 |
| Phenylacetylene (l) | 1085 | 1024 | 1033 | 52 |
| Diphenylacetylene (l) | 1857 | 1732 | 1744 | 113 |
| | | | | |
| Phenol (s) | 795 | 730 | 745 | 50 |
| Anisole (l) | 964 | 903 | 912 | 52 |
| Resorcinol (s) | 761 | 681 | 704 | 57 |
| Aniline (l) | 871 | 810 | 820 | 51 |
| m-Toluidine (l) | 1028 | 965 | 975 | 53 |
| Methylaniline (l) | 1035 | 974 | 986 | 49 |
| Ethylaniline (l) | 1192 | 1121 | 1132 | 60 |
| Dimethylaniline (l) | 1198 | 1140 | 1151 | 47 |
| | | | | |
| Benzaldehyde (l) | 899 | 843 | 852 | 47 |
| Acetophenone (s) | 1053 | 986 | 999 | 54 |
| Benzophenone (s) | 1669 | 1553 | 1576 | 93 |
| Benzoquinone (s) | 687 | 656 | 671 | 16 |
| | | | | |
| Formic acid (l) | 92 | 63 | 74[f] | 18 |
| Acetic acid (l) | 247 | 208 | 222[f] | 25 |
| Propionic acid (l) | 404 | 365 | 380[f] | 24 |
| i-Butyric acid (l) | 562 | 517 | 535[f] | 27 |
| Phenylacetic acid (s) | 1020 | 929 | 954[f] | 66 |
| Benzoic acid (s) | 862 | 771 | 795[f] | 67 |

## TABLE 3·6 (*Continued*)

### HEATS OF COMBUSTION OF RESONATING MOLECULES[a]

| Substance and Physical State[b] | Heat of Combustion | | | Resonance Energy |
|---|---|---|---|---|
| | Calcd for Gas[c] | Obs[d] | Corr to Gas[e] | |
| Acetic anhydride (l) | 483 | 430[g] | 442 | 41 |
| Propionic anhydride (l) | 798 | 747 | 759 | 39 |
| Succinic anhydride (s) | 427 | 370 | 387 | 40 |
| | | | | |
| Methyl formate (g) | 261 | 244 | 244 | 17 |
| Methyl acetate (g) | 416 | 398 | 398 | 18 |
| Methyl propionate (g) | 573 | 552 | 552 | 21 |
| Methyl benzoate (l) | 1031 | 944 | 954 | 77 |
| Ethyl formate (g) | 419 | 398 | 398 | 21 |
| Ethyl acetate (g) | 573 | 548 | 548 | 25 |
| Ethyl propionate (g) | 730 | 706 | 706 | 24 |
| Ethyl benzoate (l) | 1188 | 1099 | 1109 | 79 |
| Methyl carbonate (l) | 393 | 342 | 350 | 43 |
| Ethyl carbonate (l) | 708 | 646 | 655 | 53 |
| | | | | |
| Formamide (l) | 168 | 136 | 148 | 20 |
| Acetamide (s) | 323 | 282 | 298 | 25 |
| Benzamide (s) | 938 | 846 | 864 | 74 |
| Formanilide (s) | 948 | 859 | 877 | 71 |
| Urea (s) | 208 | 151 | 167 | 41 |
| Urethane (s) | 458 | 396 | 413 | 45 |
| | | | | |
| Furan (l) | 530 | 499 | 506 | 24 |
| Thiophene (l) | 639 | 603[h] | 610 | 29 |
| Pyrrole (l) | 601 | 568 | 577 | 24 |
| Indole (s) | 1098 | 1020 | 1035 | 63 |
| α-Methylindole (l) | 1255 | 1168 | 1180 | 75 |
| Carbazole (s) | 1594 | 1475 | 1497 | 97 |
| | | | | |
| Pyridine (l) | 712 | 659 | 669 | 43 |
| | | 665 | 675 | 37 |
| α-Methylpyridine (l) | 870 | 812 | 822 | 48 |
| Quinoline (l) | 1209 | 1123 | 1134 | 75 |
| | | | | |
| Cyanogen (g) | 261 | 261 | 261 | — |
| | | 251 | 251 | 10 |
| o-Tolunitrile (l) | 1089 | 1030 | 1041 | 48 |
| Phenylpropiolic nitrile (l) | 1187 | 1117 | 1130 | 57 |
| | | | | |
| Carbon dioxide (g) | 33 | 0 | 0 | 33 |
| Carbon oxysulfide (g) | 160 | 131 | 131 | 29 |
| Carbon disulfide (g) | 287 | 258 | 258 | 29 |
| Methyl isocyanate (l) | 283 | 269 | 276 | 7 |
| Ethyl isocyanate (l) | 440 | 425 | 432 | 8 |

TABLE 3·6 (*Continued*)

*a* All energy quantities are expressed in kilocalories per mole.

*b* The meanings of the letters in parentheses are: g, gas; l, liquid; s, solid.

*c* See Table 3·4.

*d* These values have been taken from the compilations of Kharasch and Brown and of Kharasch. (See Table 3·5, note *c*.)

*e* Corrections to the gas phase have been made with the use of data from Landolt-Börnstein, or else have been estimated by the writer.

*f* The values for the carboxylic acids have been corrected not only to the gas phase but also to the monomeric form.

*g* The value for acetic anhydride was obtained by combining that for acetic acid with the heat of hydrolysis of acetic anhydride. See J. B. Conn, G. B. Kistiakowsky, R. M. Roberts, and E. A. Smith, *J. Am. Chem. Soc.*, **64**, 1747 (1942).

*h* This value for thiophene has been corrected for the fact that the sulfur-containing product of combustion was not $SO_2$ (gas) but $H_2SO_4$ (aq).

structures of benzene. The relation between the first two of these (or between the first and the third) is, in fact, the same as that between the Kekulé structures, so that resonance among all three must result in a resonance energy greater than in benzene. (See the discussion of cycloheptatriene in Section 3·2.) A number of further, less stable structures, such as IV, V, and VI, can still be written. Like the Dewar structures of benzene, to which they are analogous, these are relatively

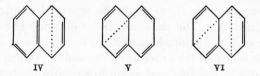

IV   V   VI

unstable, however, and so make relatively small contributions. They can, accordingly, be neglected for most practical purposes.

The resonance energies of the remaining condensed aromatic hydrocarbons, such as anthracene, phenanthrene, and so on, are still larger, being roughly proportional to the number of aromatic rings. This fact can be related again to the increased possibilities for resonance in the more complex molecules.

In biphenyl, the resonance energy seems to be slightly greater than twice that of benzene, and the effect is still greater in the analogously constituted fluorene. A reasonable explanation can be given on the basis of resonance not only among the various Kekulé and Dewar structures of each ring separately, but also with such further structures as VII.

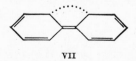

VII

(It is unexpected, however, that the resonance energy of the unconjugated diphenylmethane should apparently be as great as that of biphenyl.) The situations are similar in the other substances in which benzene rings are conjugated with each other (as in 1,3,5-triphenyl-benzene) or with double or triple bonds (as in stilbene or diphenyl-acetylene, respectively). The increased stabilities resulting from the conjugation in all these molecules are small, however, and the large uncertainties in the treatment make their exact values uncertain.

In phenol, the resonance energy appears to be slightly greater than would have been expected from merely the resonance in the benzene ring. For this substance, the structures VIII, IX, and X can be written in addition to the customary Kekulé structures. (Cf. structures XVIII, XIX, and XX of the preceding section for divinyl ether.) The possi-

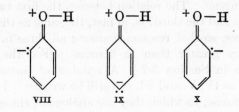

bility of resonance with these might be expected to produce a small further stabilization. The data are not sufficient, however, to shed much light upon the magnitude of the effect. In anisole and resorcinol, as well as in aniline and the other aromatic amines, resonance with analogous structures is possible and again apparently leads to a small increase in resonance energy.

That conjugation between a carbonyl group and a phenyl group or an olefinic double bond can lead to stabilization is suggested by the values of the resonance energies for benzaldehyde, the aromatic ketones, and quinone. The effect is too small, however, to be certainly established (except in quinone). It is interesting and significant that the *total* resonance energy of the non-aromatic quinone is definitely smaller than that of any of the aromatic substances.

The carboxylic acids apparently possess rather large resonance energies, which can be accounted for as resulting from resonance between the structures XI and XII. With these compounds, the measured heats of combustion must be corrected not only to the gaseous state but also

to the monomeric forms. This is because the gaseous substances exist largely as dimers, at any rate at low temperatures. (See Section 2·8.) Consequently, the "observed" heats of combustion are of especially dubious reliability. Moreover, even the *calculated* heats of combustion as well are uncertain because they have been obtained with the use of the aldehydic value of $\lambda(C=O)$ for formic acid, and of the ketonic value for the other acids. This procedure is extremely questionable in view of the large variations in $\lambda(C=O)$ that are observed to occur with changes in structure. For both these reasons, the resonance energies given for the acids can be accepted only with considerable reserve. In particular, the definite trend toward higher values as the molecular weight increases suggests that some systematic error is present. (The especially high value for benzoic acid is due partly, of course, to the presence of the benzene ring in addition to the carboxyl group.)

In the acid anhydrides, the esters, and the amides, resonance of the same type as in the acids themselves is possible. The values of the resonance energies of these substances are again dependent upon the use of the aldehydic or ketonic values of $\lambda(C=O)$ and so are again of questionable reliability. It is probably significant, however, that the resonance energies appear to increase as the possibilities for resonance increase. Thus, in the acid anhydrides, resonance can occur among the *three* structures, XIII, XIV, and XV, and so the resonance energy should be expected to be larger than in an acid. Moreover, in the alkyl car-

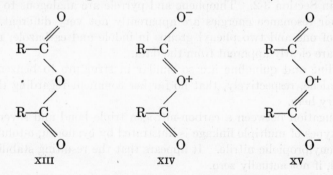

bonates, there are again three structures, XVI, XVII, and XVIII, for the resonance, and the resulting stabilization is again increased. Urea

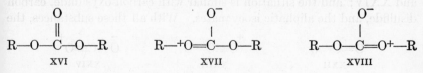

and urethane are analogous to the alkyl carbonates.

Although the values of the resonance energies of the carboxylic acids and derivatives cannot be relied upon to any great extent, there are nevertheless reasons for believing that they may be rather large. One way of reaching this conclusion is the following. It was found in the preceding section that apparently no additional stabilization results from conjugation of an ethylenic double bond with the carbonyl part of the carbalkoxy group in methyl methacrylate. A possible explanation of this is that the conjugation is relatively ineffective here because it interferes with a much more important resonance within the carbomethoxy group itself. In other words, the resonance between the structures XIX and XX may perhaps lead to so great a stabilization that the comparatively unstable structure XXI can have only a slight additional

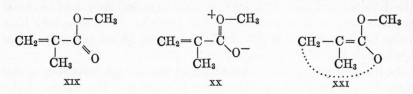

effect. A consideration of the analogous situation in vinyl acetate leads also to a similar conclusion. A further, and more conclusive, argument supporting the large resonance energy in the carbalkoxy group is given in Section 5·6.

The nature of the resonance in furan has already been discussed. The value of 24 kcal per mole found here for the resonance energy of this substance is in fair agreement with that of 17.2 kcal per mole found earlier in Section 3·2. Thiophene and pyrrole are analogous to furan, and their resonance energies are apparently not very different. The effects of one and two phenyl groups in indole and carbazole, respectively, are clearly apparent from the data.

Pyridine and quinoline are so similar in structure to benzene and naphthalene, respectively, that no further comment regarding them is necessary here.

Conjugation between a carbon-nitrogen triple bond and several different types of multiple linkage is illustrated by cyanogen, *o*-tolunitrile, and phenylpropiolic nitrile. It appears that the resulting stabilization is small, if not actually zero.

The apparently large resonance energy of carbon dioxide can be explained on the basis of resonance among the structures, XXII, XXIII, and XXIV; and the situation is similar with carbon oxysulfide, carbon disulfide, and the aliphatic isocyanates. With all these substances, the

$$O{=}C{=}O \qquad \overset{+}{O}{\equiv}C{-}\overset{-}{O} \qquad \overset{-}{O}{-}C{\equiv}\overset{+}{O}$$

XXII          XXIII          XXIV

calculated heats of combustion, and therefore the resonance energies, are uncertain for the same reason as with the carboxylic acids and their derivatives.

It would be interesting to have a resonance energy for carbon monoxide, for which the structures XXV and XXVI can be written. The heat of combustion of this substance cannot be used directly, however,

$$: C = O : \qquad\qquad : C \equiv O :$$

XXV                     XXVI

because the λ's in Table 3·4 are applicable only to molecules in which each element exhibits its normal valence. Consequently, we cannot use these λ's to calculate what the heat of combustion would have been in the absence of resonance. In order to obtain the resonance energy, we must instead have recourse to the bond energies discussed in the following section; in this indirect way, the value of 58 kcal per mole can be derived.[7] It is to be noted, however, that a comparison with the carbonyl groups of aliphatic ketones is even less justifiable here than with the previous substances, so that this value is extremely questionable.

**3·4  Resonance Energies from Bond Energies.**  An alternative, but equivalent, way in which resonance energies can be determined from the heats of combustion is with the aid of the so-called bond energies. We shall illustrate the procedure by discussing in some detail the treatment of a hydrocarbon with the general molecular formula $C_aH_b$. The total energy $E$ of such a substance is defined by the equation

$$C_aH_b \text{ (gas)} \longrightarrow aC \text{ (gas)} + bH \text{ (gas)} + E \text{ kcal} \qquad (1)$$

A reaction of this sort is not suitable for direct investigation, but the value of $E$ can be obtained from a study of the series of simpler reactions:[8]

$$C_aH_b \text{ (gas)} + (a + b/4)O_2 \text{ (gas)} \longrightarrow aCO_2 \text{ (gas)}$$
$$+ b/2H_2O \text{ (liq)} + \Lambda \text{ kcal} \qquad (2)$$

$$aCO_2 \text{ (gas)} \longrightarrow aC \text{ (diamond)} + aO_2 \text{ (gas)} - 94.5a \text{ kcal} \qquad (3)$$

$$aC \text{ (diamond)} \longrightarrow aC \text{ (gas)} - 124.3a \text{ kcal} \qquad (4)$$

$$b/2H_2O \text{ (liq)} \longrightarrow b/2H_2 \text{ (gas)} + b/4O_2 \text{ (gas)} - 34.2b \text{ kcal} \qquad (5)$$

$$b/2H_2 \text{ (gas)} \longrightarrow bH \text{ (gas)} - 51.7b \text{ kcal} \qquad (6)$$

---

[7] L. Pauling, reference 5, 1st ed., 1939, p. 131; 2nd ed., 1940, p. 139.

[8] The thermal data given below are taken from L. Pauling, reference 5, 1st ed., 1939, p. 54; 2nd ed., 1940, p. 54; F. R. Bichowsky and F. D. Rossini, *The Thermochemistry of the Chemical Substances*, Reinhold Publishing Corporation, New York. 1936.

Equation 1 is the sum of the equations 2–6, so that $E$ is given by the relation

$$E = \Lambda - 218.8a - 85.9b \tag{7}$$

According to equation 2, the heat of combustion, $\Lambda$, to be used here is that of the gaseous substance; if data are available only for the substance in some other state, then these must be corrected to the gaseous state. As in the preceding section, the effect of such correction is to replace $\Lambda$ in equation 7 by $\Lambda_x + \mu_x$, where $\Lambda_x$ and $\mu_x$ are the heats of combustion and of vaporization, respectively, of the substance in the state $x$ (solid or liquid).

The reactions 1–6 are considered to occur at a constant pressure of 1 atmosphere and at a temperature of 18° C. Since the *pressure* is held constant, the quantity $E$ as so defined does not strictly represent the *internal energy*, which is the negative of the energy necessary to dissociate the isolated gaseous molecule into isolated gaseous atoms; it represents, rather, the heat content or enthalpy (more customarily designated by the letter $H$) of the molecule. Similarly, the quantities $D(A\!-\!B)$ defined later are not strictly bond *energies*. This incorrect terminology has become firmly established in the literature, however, and for that reason will be adopted here without further apology. In any event, the calculated resonance energies would not be changed significantly if the calculations were based upon the true molecular and bond energies. (However, the quantities referred to in Chapter 2 as bond energies were the true bond energies.)

It can be shown (see the following paragraph) that the total energy, $E$, of a molecule is an additive property of its bonds to exactly the same extent that the heat of combustion $\Lambda$ (or $\Lambda_x + \mu_x$) is. This means that each type of bond, $A\!-\!B$, can be assigned a bond energy, $D(A\!-\!B)$, in such a way that the total energy, $E$, is minus the sum of the energies of the various bonds. The minus sign is introduced here because, although the energy, $E$, is always negative for a stable molecule, the bond energies, $D(A\!-\!B)$, are customarily taken as positive quantities.

The relation between the bond energies, $D(A\!-\!B)$, and the contributions, $\lambda(A\!-\!B)$, to the heats of combustion can be found in the following manner. Let us first consider the molecule of methane, $CH_4$. In this, there are just four carbon-hydrogen bonds. Consequently, within the limits of accuracy of the present treatment, the heat of combustion is

$$\Lambda_{\text{methane}} = 4\lambda(C\!-\!H)$$

and the energy is

$$E_{\text{methane}} = -4D(C\!-\!H)$$

Equation 7 then gives

$$-4D(\text{C—H}) = 4\lambda(\text{C—H}) - (218.8 + 4 \times 85.9) \text{ kcal}$$

or

$$D(\text{C—H}) = 140.6 \text{ kcal} - \lambda(\text{C—H}) = 87.3 \text{ kcal}$$

The value of $\lambda(\text{C—H})$ used in the last of the above equations is taken from Table 3·4. In a similar manner for ethane, $\text{C}_2\text{H}_6$,

$$E_{\text{ethane}} = -D(\text{C—C}) - 6D(\text{C—H})$$

$$= \Lambda_{\text{ethane}} - (2 \times 218.8 + 6 \times 85.9) \text{ kcal}$$

$$= \lambda(\text{C—C}) + 6\lambda(\text{C—H}) - 952.8 \text{ kcal}$$

or

$$D(\text{C—C}) = 58.6 \text{ kcal}$$

The extension to carbon-carbon double and triple bonds should be obvious.

When elements other than carbon and hydrogen are present, the treatment proceeds along similar lines but becomes rather more complicated. For example, if a substance has the formula $\text{C}_a\text{H}_b\text{O}_c\text{N}_d\text{S}_e\text{Cl}_f\text{Br}_g\text{I}_h$, its energy $E$ is defined by the equation 1′,

$$\text{C}_a\text{H}_b\text{O}_c\text{N}_d\text{S}_e\text{Cl}_f\text{Br}_g\text{I}_h \text{ (gas)} \longrightarrow a\text{C (gas)} + b\text{H (gas)} + c\text{O (gas)}$$
$$+ d\text{N (gas)} + e\text{S (gas)} + f\text{Cl (gas)} + g\text{Br (gas)} + h\text{I (gas)}$$
$$+ E \text{ kcal} \tag{1′}$$

and its heat of combustion by the equation 2′,

$$\text{C}_a\text{H}_b\text{O}_c\text{N}_d\text{S}_e\text{Cl}_f\text{Br}_g\text{I}_h \text{ (gas)} + [a + (b - f)/4 + e - c/2]\text{O}_2 \text{ (gas)} \longrightarrow$$
$$a\text{CO}_2 \text{ (gas)} + (b - f)/2\text{H}_2\text{O (liq)} + d/2\text{N}_2 \text{ (gas)} + e\text{SO}_2 \text{ (gas)}$$
$$+ f\text{HCl (gas)} + g/2\text{Br}_2 \text{ (vapor)} + h/2\text{I}_2 \text{ (solid)} + \Lambda \text{ kcal} \tag{2′}$$

(See Section 3·3.) The relationship between $E$ and $\Lambda$ can be derived in the same way as before. For this purpose, equation 5 must be multiplied by $(b - f)/b$, so that it becomes 5′ and the further equations[8] 8–15 must be used. Equation 1′ is now the sum of equations 2′, 3, 4, 5′, 6, 8–15,

$$(b - f)/2\text{H}_2\text{O (liq)} \longrightarrow (b - f)/2\text{H}_2 \text{ (gas)} + (b - f)/4\text{O}_2 \text{ (gas)}$$
$$- 34.2 (b - f) \text{ kcal} \tag{5′}$$

$$c/2\text{O}_2 \text{ (gas)} \qquad \longrightarrow c\text{O (gas)} - 59.1c \text{ kcal} \tag{8}$$

$$d/2\text{N}_2 \text{ (gas)} \qquad \longrightarrow d\text{N (gas)} - 85.1d \text{ kcal} \tag{9}$$

$$e\text{SO}_2 \text{ (gas)} \qquad \longrightarrow e\text{S (rhombic)} + e\text{O}_2 \text{ (gas)} - 70.9e \text{ kcal} \tag{10}$$

$$e\text{S (rhombic)} \qquad \longrightarrow e\text{S (gas)} - 66.3e \text{ kcal} \tag{11}$$

$$f\text{HCl (gas)} \qquad \longrightarrow f/2\text{H}_2 \text{ (gas)} + f/2\text{Cl}_2 \text{ (gas)} - 22.1f \text{ kcal} \tag{12}$$

$$f/2Cl_2 \text{ (gas)} \longrightarrow fCl \text{ (gas)} - 28.9f \text{ kcal} \tag{13}$$

$$g/2Br_2 \text{ (vapor)} \longrightarrow gBr \text{ (gas)} - 23.1g \text{ kcal} \tag{14}$$

$$h/2I_2 \text{ (sol)} \longrightarrow hI \text{ (gas)} - 25.6h \text{ kcal} \tag{15}$$

so that

$$E = \Lambda - 218.8a - 85.9b - 59.1c - 85.1d - 137.2e - 16.8f - 23.1g$$
$$- 25.6h \tag{7'}$$

The derivation of the bond energies $D(A\!-\!B)$ from the contributions $\lambda(A\!-\!B)$ to the heat of combustion then proceeds in the manner illustrated above for the carbon-hydrogen and carbon-carbon bonds.

The values of the bond energies $D(A\!-\!B)$ as given by Pauling[5] are listed in Table 3·7. Their use in the determination of resonance energies

### TABLE 3·7

#### BOND ENERGIES[a]

|   |   | C | N | O | S | Cl | Br | I |
|---|---|---|---|---|---|---|---|---|
| H |   | 87.3 | 83.7 | 110.2 | 87.5 | — | — | — |
|   | single bond | 58.6 | 48.6 | 70.0 | 54.5 | 66.5 | 54.0 | 45.5 |
| C | double bond | 100 | 94 | $\begin{cases} 142^b \\ 149^c \\ 152^d \end{cases}$ | 103 | — | — | — |
|   | triple bond | 123 | 144 | — | — | — | — | — |

[a] The bond energies are expressed in kilocalories per mole. Some additional bond energies are given in Table 3·9. (See L. Pauling, reference 5.)

[b] This value applies to formaldehyde only.

[c] This value applies to other aldehydes.

[d] This value applies to ketones.

can be illustrated with the example of benzene. For this substance, the heat of combustion is 788 kcal per mole, so that the energy is

$$E_{\text{obs}} = 788 - (6 \times 218.8) - (6 \times 85.9) = -1040.2 \text{ kcal}$$

The energy calculated from the bond energies is

$$E_{\text{calcd}} = -[(6 \times 87.3) + (3 \times 58.6) + 3 \times 100)] = -999.6 \text{ kcal}$$

The resonance energy is thus $-999.6 - (-1040.2) = 41$ kcal per mole (the final value being rounded off to the nearest kilocalorie). This value of the resonance energy is identical with the one found directly from the heat of combustion, as it must be, of course, in view of the equivalence of the two treatments.

No further discussion of the bond energies need be given here, because no new information is obtainable with their aid, except for a molecule like carbon monoxide, in which at least one of the elements represented displays an anomalous valence.    (See the last paragraph of Section 3·3.) As a matter of fact, the direct use of the heats of combustion is not only more convenient, since it does not require the unnecessary step of calculating the molecular energies, but also avoids a certain more fundamental difficulty as well in connection with the thermochemical data included in equations 3–6, 8–15.    Some of the values given there are of questionable accuracy; the heat of sublimation of diamond (equation 4) in particular may be in error by more than 25 kcal per gram atom in either direction.    The actual values of the bond energies are sometimes therefore quite unreliable.    The usefulness of this present treatment for the determination of resonance energies is not affected in any way, however, because the values found for the resonance energies are actually independent of the data put into the equations mentioned.

A different set of bond energies is given by Rice.[5]   This is less complete than that of Pauling, however, and so is less useful for our purposes.   Rice's and Pauling's values of the $D(A—B)$'s are sometimes rather different from each other; the reason for this is that the two authors based their bond energies upon different numerical data and that, in particular, they used different values for the heat of sublimation of diamond.

**3·5  Theoretical Calculations of Resonance Energies of Hydrocarbons.**   Several methods are available at present for the theoretical calculation of the resonance energies of hydrocarbons.   These are all extremely crude — so crude, in fact, that they might better be regarded merely as empirical methods which are not based upon theory at all, but which nevertheless are suggested by, and can be correlated with, theory.   In spite of their lack of rigor, however, they lead to results which are in general remarkably consistent with each other and with experiment.   This fact forms their only real justification.   None of the methods is an absolute one.   In other words, the quantity which can be calculated is not the actual value of the resonance energy for any given substance, but only the ratio of the resonance energy to that of some other substance chosen as standard.   This is not a serious disadvantage from a practical point of view, however, because, if the resonance energy of any one hydrocarbon is known from experimental data, that of any other can then be calculated.

Of all the methods, there is only one which can be described here. This is an extremely crude one which is almost entirely empirical in nature.   The results obtained with it are fairly accurate, perhaps somewhat more accurate than those obtained by the other, more elaborate methods.   It is based upon the very simple equation

$$\text{Resonance energy} = (AM + BN) \text{ kcal per mole} \qquad (1)$$

where $A$ and $B$ are constant coefficients which are discussed below; $M$ is the number of bonds in the molecule that are represented as single in any one of the resonating structures without formal bonds, but as double in at least one of those structures; and $N$ is the number of bonds that are represented as single in *all* the structures without formal bonds, but as double in at least one of the structures with just one formal bond. For example, in benzene and in mesitylene, $M = 3$ and $N = 0$, and in styrene $M = 3$ and $N = 1$. The relative (as distinguished from absolute) character of the calculations based upon equation 1 enters in the fact that the coefficients $A$ and $B$ must be chosen empirically in such a way that the calculated and observed resonance energies agree as closely as possible for a considerable number of substances. Since there seems to be a small systematic variation in the " observed " resonance energies which are obtained from heats of hydrogenation and from heats of combustion, it would seem advantageous to have slightly different sets of values of $A$ and $B$ for comparison with the data from the two sources. The resonance energies from heats of hydrogenation seem to be reproduced most satisfactorily with $A = 12$ and $B = 3.5$; those from heats of combustion, with $A = 14$ and $B = 6$. A similar variation in the values of the parameters involved seems desirable also in the calculations of resonance energy by the other, more elaborate methods.

In Table 3.8, the observed resonance energies of a number of hydrocarbons are compared with those calculated both by the method described above and also by two further methods that cannot be discussed here.[9] On account of the previously noted small discrepancies between the resonance energies obtained from heats of hydrogenation and of combustion, this table is divided into two parts; the figures above, and below, the dotted line refer to the resonance energies from heats of hydrogenation, and of combustion, respectively. The agreement between calculated and observed values is quite good in general. This fact suggests that the results of similar calculations for other hydrocarbons for which no experimental data are available can be accepted with some confidence. Unfortunately, however, the extension of any of these methods of calculation to molecules other than hydrocarbons cannot be made at the present time.

Some comment is perhaps necessary in regard to the experimental significance of the two different sets of resonance energies that can be calculated

[9] (a) For a general survey of these methods, see G. W. Wheland, *J. Am. Chem. Soc.*, **63**, 2025 (1941) and further references given there. (b) For still further, more elaborate methods of calculation, see J. E. Lennard-Jones, *Proc. Roy. Soc. (London)*, **A158**, 280 (1937); J. E. Lennard-Jones and J. Turkevich, *ibid.*, p. 297; G. W. Wheland, *J. Chem. Phys.*, **3**, 230, 356 (1935).

## TABLE 3·8

CALCULATED RESONANCE ENERGIES OF HYDROCARBONS

| Substance | Resonance Energy[a] | | | |
|---|---|---|---|---|
| | Calcd | | | Obs[e] |
| | I[b] | II[c] | III[d] | |
| Butadiene | 3.5 | 10 | 5 | 3.5 |
| Cycloheptatriene | 7.0 | 15 | 10 | 6.7 |
| Benzene | 36 | 35 | 34 | 36.0 |
| Mesitylene | 36 | 35 | 34 | 33.1 |
| Styrene | 39.5 | 42 | 39 | 36.9 |
| Indene | 39.5 | 42 | 39 | 39.4 |
| 1,4-Diphenyl-1,3-butadiene[f] | 10.5 | — | — | 10.7 |
| · · · · · · · · · · · · · · · · · · · · · · | | | | |
| Benzene | 42 | 42 | 44 | 41 |
| Naphthalene | 84 | 78 | 76 | 77 |
| Anthracene | 126 | — | 107 | 116 |
| Phenanthrene | 126 | — | 113 | 130 |
| Pyrene | 154 | — | 132 | 152 |
| Chrysene | 168 | — | — | 163 |
| Biphenyl | 90 | 90 | 92 | 91 |
| Fluorene | 90 | 90 | 92 | 101 |
| 1,3,5-Triphenylbenzene | 186 | 181 | 190 | 200 |
| Styrene | 48 | 50 | 50 | 51 |
| Stilbene | 96 | 99 | 101 | 101 |

[a] In kilocalories per mole.

[b] The values in this column are obtained from equation 1 of this section, with $A = 12$ and $B = 3·5$ for those above the dotted line, and $A = 14$ and $B = 6$ for those below that line.

[c] The values in this column have been obtained by the valence-bond method, with the integral $J$ set equal to 32 amd 38 kcal per mole, for those above and below the dotted line, respectively. See G. W. Wheland, reference 9(a).

[d] The values in this column have been obtained by the "corrected" molecular orbital method, with the parameter $\beta$ set equal to 32 and 41 kcal per mole for those above and below the dotted line, respectively. See G. W. Wheland, reference 9(a).

[e] The values in this column above, and below, the dotted line are taken from Tables 3·2 and 3·6, respectively.

[f] The observed and calculated resonance energies of this substance refer to only the excess over that in the benzene rings.

by any of the above methods.   The heats of hydrogenation and of combustion should, in principle, lead to identical resonance energies for any given substance, and they would indeed do so if they were based upon equally accurate, and mutually consistent, experimental data.   Since a small discrepancy does exist, however, two questions arise: First, which of the two sets of calculated values is the more reliable; and, second, what useful purpose does the less reliable set serve?   The answer to the first of these questions is that the resonance energies calculated with reference to the heats of hydrogenation are probably the more accurate, because the experimental data which they are designed to fit are the more accurate.   The answer to the second is that the resonance energies calculated with reference to the heats of combustion would be of value in predicting the heats of combustion of new substances for which no experimental values have been reported.

### 3·6 The Effect of Resonance between Ionic and Covalent Structures upon Bond Energies.

In Section 2·7 it was pointed out that the strength of an essentially covalent bond should be increased by resonance with ionic structures. This conclusion cannot be verified directly from the experimental data without some arbitrariness, but the facts are sufficiently suggestive to warrant a brief discussion of them here. The difficulty arises from the fact that no purely ionic or purely covalent bonds are available for comparison. We can overcome this difficulty to some extent, however, by adopting the following procedure, which is due to Pauling.[10] As has already been pointed out, bonds formed between two atoms of the same kind (such as hydrogen-hydrogen or carbon-carbon bonds) are largely covalent. For the hydrogen molecule, for example, approximate numerical calculations[11] have shown that the ionic structures each contribute very little to the actual state of the molecule, and that the resulting resonance energy amounts to only about 5.5 kcal per mole. Such essentially covalent bonds, therefore, provide convenient standards of reference with which the other bonds can be compared. This is because a bond between two dissimilar atoms, $A$ and $B$, must presumably have a somewhat greater ionic character, since one of the ionic structures, $\overset{-}{A} : \overset{+}{B}$ or $\overset{+}{A} : \overset{-}{B}$, must be relatively more stable than either $\overset{-}{A} : \overset{+}{A}$ or $\overset{-}{B} : \overset{+}{B}$. We shall now make the not unreasonable assumption that, except for this variation in ionic character, the energy of a single bond between $A$ and $B$ would be the arithmetic mean of the energies of the single bonds between two atoms $A$ and between two atoms $B$. (No similar treatment seems ever to have been made for multiple bonds.) Since in general the ionic character of the bond $A$—$B$ is greater than that of either $A$—$A$ or $B$—$B$, the actual bond should then be made stronger than the arithmetic mean by this increase in resonance. In other words, if $D(A$—$B)$, $D(A$—$A)$, and $D(B$—$B)$ are the energies of the three bonds, the quantity $\Delta_{AB} = D(A$—$B) - \frac{1}{2}[D(A$—$A) + D(B$—$B)]$ should always be positive. That this is usually true is shown by the data of Table 3·9. The exceptions which do occur do not seem to be very significant, in view of the crudity of the treatment, since, whenever $\Delta$ is negative, it is always small in magnitude. such exceptions are presumably due to at least two different factors.

---

[10] L. Pauling, *J. Am. Chem. Soc.*, **54**, 3570 (1932); reference 5, 1st ed., 1939, pp. 58 ff.; 2nd ed., 1940, pp. 58 ff. For a vigorous criticism of this procedure, see A. Burawoy, *Trans. Faraday Soc.*, **39**, 79 (1943).

[11] S. Weinbaum, *J. Chem. Phys.*, **1**, 593 (1933).

## TABLE 3·9

IONIC CONTRIBUTIONS TO THE ENERGIES OF SINGLE BONDS[a]

|     | H     | C    | N    | O     | S    | Cl    | Br   | I    |
|-----|-------|------|------|-------|------|-------|------|------|
| H   | 103.4 | 87.3 | 83.7 | 110.2 | 87.5 | 102.7 | 87.3 | 71.4 |
|     |       | 81.0 | 63.5 | 69.2  | 83.6 | 80.6  | 74.8 | 69.8 |
|     |       | 6.3  | 20.2 | 41.0  | 3.9  | 22.1  | 12.5 | 1.6  |
| C   |       | 58.6 | 48.6 | 70.0  | 54.5 | 66.5  | 54.0 | 45.5 |
|     |       |      | 41.1 | 46.8  | 61.2 | 58.2  | 52.4 | 47.4 |
|     |       |      | 7.5  | 23.2  | −6.7 | 8.3   | 1.6  | −1.9 |
| N   |       |      | 23.6 |       |      | 38.4  |      |      |
|     |       |      |      |       |      | 40.7  |      |      |
|     |       |      |      |       |      | −2.3  |      |      |
| O   |       |      |      | 34.9  |      | 49.3  |      |      |
|     |       |      |      |       |      | 46.4  |      |      |
|     |       |      |      |       |      | 2.9   |      |      |
| S   |       |      |      |       | 63.8 | 66.1  | 57.2 |      |
|     |       |      |      |       |      | 60.8  | 55.0 |      |
|     |       |      |      |       |      | 5.3   | 2.2  |      |
| Cl  |       |      |      |       |      | 57.8  | 52.7 | 51.0 |
|     |       |      |      |       |      |       | 52.0 | 47.0 |
|     |       |      |      |       |      |       | 0.7  | 4.0  |
| Br  |       |      |      |       |      |       | 46.1 | 42.9 |
|     |       |      |      |       |      |       |      | 41.2 |
|     |       |      |      |       |      |       |      | 1.7  |
| I   |       |      |      |       |      |       |      | 36.2 |

[a] For each type of bond, the observed bond energy in kilocalories per mole is given in the first row; the bond energy calculated by the rule of the arithmetic mean is given in the second row; and the value of Δ is given in the third row. The observed bond energies are taken either from Table 3·7 or from the more complete list given by Pauling.[5,10] A similar table of Δ's is given by Rice, p. 190 of reference 13.

In the first place, there is always considerable uncertainty about the correct value of the energy of any individual bond in a polyatomic molecule, since division of the total energy of the molecule among its various bonds cannot be made without some arbitrariness. For this reason, the "observed" values of the energies of such bonds as the carbon-carbon and the carbon-iodine bonds, which occur only in polyatomic molecules, are not beyond question. In the second place, the use of the arithmetic mean, although not unreasonable, has not been rigorously shown to be correct. As a matter of fact, theoretical considerations[12] have suggested that the *geometric* mean would give a better approximation. Unfortunately, however, it is not practicable to make general use of the geometric mean, because of the fact that many of the "observed" bond energies are subject to errors of unknown magnitude, which result from uncertainties in the data of equations 3–6, 8–15 of Section 3·4. These errors occur in such a way as always to cancel out in calculations based upon the use of the arithmetic mean, but not in calculations based upon the use of the geometric mean. For this reason, it seems necessary to continue the use of the arithmetic mean until all such difficulties have been cleared up.

In addition to being almost always positive, the values of the $\Delta$'s given in Table 3·9 show a further interesting regularity. Although a number of exceptions exist, it seems to be true on the whole that the more the atoms $A$ and $B$ differ in electronegativity, the larger is the magnitude of $\Delta_{AB}$. This is what might have been anticipated, since a large value of $\Delta_{AB}$ is to be related to a large contribution of one of the ionic structures, which in turn is to be related to a large difference in electronegativity between $A$ and $B$. The situation can, in fact, be described in an approximately quantitative manner by assigning to each

TABLE 3·10

ELECTRONEGATIVITIES OF ATOMS

| Atom $(A)$ | Electronegativity $(x_A)$ | |
|:---:|:---:|:---:|
| H | 2.1[a] | 0.00[b] |
| C | 2.5 | 0.47 |
| O | 3.5 | 1.46 |
| N | 3.0 | 1.02 |
| S | 2.5 | 0.30 |
| Cl | 3.0 | 1.09 |
| Br | 2.8 | 0.88 |
| I | 2.5 | 0.47 |

[a] The values in this column are those of Pauling, reference 10.

[b] The values in this column are those of Rice, reference 13. In spite of their quite different appearance, these values are nearly equivalent to those of Pauling, because only the *differences* between electronegativities are significant.

element $A$ a numerical parameter $x_A$, which can be called its *electronegativity*. If this assignment is made as in Table 3·10, the values of $\Delta_{AB}$ are found empirically to be given roughly by the equation[10,13]

$$\Delta_{AB} = 23(x_A - x_B)^2 \text{ kcal per mole}$$

[12] L. Pauling and J. Sherman, *J. Am. Chem. Soc.*, **59**, 1450 (1937).

[13] See also O. K. Rice, *Electronic Structure and Chemical Binding*, McGraw-Hill Book Company, New York, 1940, pp. 195, 196.

**3·7  Resonance Energy due to Hyperconjugation.**  In Section 3·2, attention was called to the fact that the heat of hydrogenation of an olefine is decreased appreciably by the presence of alkyl substituents upon the unsaturated carbon atoms.  This effect has been explained by Mulliken and his co-workers[14] on the basis of a new type of conjugation, for which they have proposed the name " hyperconjugation." Their ideas are difficult to translate exactly into the language of the classical valence theory, but the following discussion will explain the essential principles involved.  A further discussion along more conventional lines is given later in this section.

In propylene, I, the three hydrogen atoms of the methyl group have three valence electrons in all.  In acrylonitrile, II, the nitrogen atom

$$H_3C—CH{=}CH_2 \qquad\qquad N{\equiv}C—CH{=}CH_2$$
$$\text{I} \qquad\qquad\qquad\qquad\qquad \text{II}$$

similarly has three valence electrons.  (The two further electrons of the valence shell that form an unshared pair do not take part in the binding and so can be ignored here.)  This suggests that the structure of propylene might profitably be written as III, in which form it appears analogous to that of acrylonitrile.  The next logical step is to suppose that in propylene resonance occurs between the normal structure III and a less stable one, IV, just as it presumably occurs in acrylonitrile between the normal structure II and the less stable one V.  This

$$H_3{\equiv}C—CH{=}CH_2 \qquad H_3{=}C{=}CH—CH_2 \qquad N{=}C{=}CH—CH_2$$
$$\text{III} \qquad\qquad\qquad \text{IV} \qquad\qquad\qquad \text{V}$$

resonance, which results from the *hyperconjugation* of the methyl group with the double bond, then stabilizes the molecule in the usual manner and so reduces its heat of hydrogenation.  Similarly, in *i*-butene, the hyperconjugation produces still greater stabilization as a result of resonance between the normal structure VI and the two less stable ones VII and VIII.  In general, the stabilization is increased, and the heat of hydrogenation is decreased, as the number of alkyl substituents upon the unsaturated carbon atoms is increased.  Moreover, these alkyl groups need not be methyl, as in propylene and *i*-butene, since

[14] R. S. Mulliken, C. A. Rieke, and W. G. Brown, reference 6.  Essentially the same treatment had been applied earlier to other problems by G. W. Wheland, *J. Chem. Phys.*, **2**, 474 (1934), and by J. W. Baker and W. S. Nathan, *J. Chem. Soc.*, 1844 (1935).  For a recent paper written from the viewpoint of Baker and his school, and for references to the earlier literature, see J. W. Baker and M. L. Hemming, *J. Chem. Soc.*, 191 (1942).

similar hyperconjugation is possible under other conditions as well.

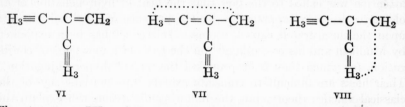

$$H_3 \equiv C - C = CH_2 \qquad H_3 = C = C - CH_2 \qquad H_3 \equiv C - C - CH_2$$
$$\overset{|}{\underset{H_3}{\overset{\|}{C}}} \qquad\qquad \overset{|}{\underset{H_3}{\overset{\|}{C}}} \qquad\qquad \overset{\|}{\underset{H_3}{\overset{\|}{C}}}$$

VI            VII            VIII

The structures IX and X for 1-butene, for example, are analogous to

$$\left(\begin{matrix}H_3C\\H_2\end{matrix}\right) \equiv C - CH = CH_2 \qquad \left(\begin{matrix}H_3C\\H_2\end{matrix}\right) = C = CH - CH_2$$

IX                  X

III and IV, respectively, for propylene, as are also XI and XII for *t*-butylethylene.

$$(CH_3)_3 \equiv C - CH = CH_2 \qquad (CH_3)_3 = C = CH - CH_2$$

XI              XII

A further type of hyperconjugation, which may be called second-order hyperconjugation, can be supposed to result from the interaction of an alkyl group with a second alkyl group instead of with a double bond. For ethane, for example, the structures XIII and XIV are analogous to XV and XVI, respectively, for cyanogen.

$$H_3 \equiv C - C \equiv H_3 \qquad H_3 = C = C = H_3$$

XIII            XIV

$$N \equiv C - C \equiv N \qquad N = C = C = N$$

XV            XVI

The structures III, IV, and so on are of such a radically different type from those with which chemists are familiar that one has difficulty in grasping their significance. For that reason, it is convenient to approach the problem of hyperconjugation from another, more or less equivalent, point of view. In propylene, for example, resonance can occur between the usual structure I and such less stable ones as XVII. In a similar manner, the second-order hyperconjugation in ethane can be related to the possibility of resonance between the usual structure XVIII and such less stable ones as XIX.

$$H_2C = CH - CH_2 \qquad H_2C - CH_2 \qquad H_2C = CH_2$$
$$H \cdots\cdots\cdots \qquad \overset{|}{H} \ \overset{|}{H} \qquad H \cdots H$$

XVII          XVIII          XIX

Ordinary, or first-order, hyperconjugation, such as is present in propylene, appears to produce a resonance energy of about the same order of magnitude as does the conjugation between two double bonds, as in butadiene.  This is shown, for example, by the fact that the difference between the heats of hydrogenation of ethylene and propylene, on the one hand, is about the same as that between the heats of hydrogenation of 1,4-pentadiene and 1,3-butadiene, on the other.  However, the hyperconjugation never achieves an importance comparable with that of the resonance in benzene.  Consequently for most purposes it can be safely neglected, and only occasionally need it be taken explicitly into account.  The second-order hyperconjugation, as in ethane, is probably even less important.  It is difficult to evaluate, however, because it occurs in practically all imaginable substances (except for the very simplest ones like methane), and because, therefore, its effect may be expected to cancel out whenever different substances are compared with each other.[15]  All the discussions in this book are, in the last analysis, based upon such comparisons and, consequently, we shall be justified in ignoring this second-order hyperconjugation hereafter.

[15] Cf. G. W. Wheland and J. T. Pinkston, Jr., *J. Chem. Phys.*, **12**, 69 (1944).

# Chapter 4

## STERIC EFFECTS OF RESONANCE

**4·1 Molecular Symmetry.** One of the first ways in which the Kekulé structure of benzene was found to be inadequate was that it led to incorrect predictions of the numbers of isomeric substitution products $C_6H_nX_{6-n}$. The two structures, I and II, for example, are

definitely different, and yet only a single substance, o-xylene, is known corresponding to them. In order to explain this discrepancy, Kekulé himself postulated[1] that there was an " oscillation " (i.e., a rapid tautomerism) between the two structures, and other authors advanced various other explanations. The final solution of the problem was not found, however, until after the development of the theory of resonance, when it became apparent that o-xylene can possess neither of the structures, I and II, but must be a resonance hybrid with a structure intermediate between them.

This question of isomer number is only a special case of a much more general problem, that of molecular symmetry. From studies of x-ray[2] and electron[3] diffraction, of dipole moments,[4] and of spectra,[5] it is now fairly definitely known that the six carbon atoms in a molecule of benzene are located at the corners of a regular plane hexagon, and that all six carbon-carbon bonds are equivalent to each other. The reason why the Kekulé structure does not give the correct number of isomers is essentially that it does not reproduce the true symmetry of the molecule.

The theory of resonance leads to a logical interpretation of the ob-

[1] A. Kekulé, *Ann.*, **162**, 77 (1872).

[2] L. O. Brockway and J. M. Robertson, *J. Chem. Soc.*, 1324 (1939).

[3] L. Pauling and L. O. Brockway, *J. Chem. Phys.*, **2**, 867 (1934).

[4] J. W. Williams, *Fortschr. Chem., Physik physik. Chem.*, **20**, 257 (1930). C. P. Smyth, *Dielectric Constant and Molecular Structure*, Chemical Catalog Company, New York, 1931, Chapter VI.

[5] C. K. Ingold, *Proc. Roy. Soc. (London)* **A169**, 149 (1938).

served symmetry of benzene and also, as a corollary, of the observed isomer numbers as well. That this is true can be shown in the following way. Let us consider resonance between only the two Kekulé structures III and IV. These are equivalent to each other and, consequently, must make identical contributions to the state of the molecule. No one of the carbon-carbon bonds can then be different in any way from any of the others. From this, we might not be justified in concluding that the ring necessarily lies in a single plane, but most of the other features of the symmetry follow at once. (See the further discussion of the planarity of the molecule in Section 4·2.) The situation is not altered by a consideration of the three Dewar structures,

|   III   |   IV   |   V   |   VI   |   VII   |

V, VI, and VII. These are equivalent to each other and so make identical small contributions. Taken together, therefore, they lead to the same molecular symmetry as do the two Kekulé structures.

With naphthalene, the Erlenmeyer structure VIII has the observed symmetry of the molecule and, as far as the present considerations are concerned, might be the actual structure of the substance. As was pointed out earlier, however, the large resonance energy shows that resonance occurs with the two additional structures IX and X. Al-

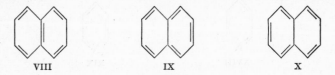

|   VIII   |   IX   |   X   |

though these latter are not equivalent to the former one, VIII, they doubtless make approximately the same contribution that it does. This is because they have the same numbers of the same kinds of bond as it has, and so are of about the same stability. It is necessary, therefore, to make sure that they do not disturb the symmetry of the Erlenmeyer structure. That they do not do so is evident from the fact that, being equivalent to each other, they must be equally important in the resonance. As in benzene, there are a number of further, less stable structures with one or more formal bonds. One of these, XI, has the required symmetry itself, and the others occur in sets of two or of four, such as XII and XIII, or XIV, XV, XVI, and XVII, respectively, in such a way that the original symmetry is not disturbed.

Considerations similar to the foregoing apply to the other condensed aromatic ring systems. For some of these (for example, anthracene), no single structure without formal bonds reproduces the actual sym-

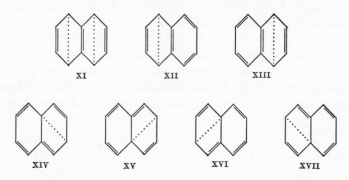

XI　　　　　XII　　　　　XIII

XIV　　　XV　　　XVI　　　XVII

metry of the molecule, whereas for others (for example, phenanthrene) such structures do exist. However, the correct symmetry is always accounted for automatically when the fact is recognized that equivalent structures must make identical contributions.

The problem of molecular symmetry is not limited to the aromatic hydrocarbons. For example, the existence of only a single $\alpha$-methyl-pyridine (or, in other words, the equivalence of the two carbon-nitrogen bonds in pyridine) follows from the equal contributions of the two Kekulé-like structures, XVIII and XIX, in the unsubstituted molecule.

XVIII　　　　　　　XIX

An example of a different type, in which the question of isomer number is not directly involved, is provided by the carbonate ion. From investigations of crystal structure,[6] this is known to lie entirely in one plane, with the oxygen atoms at the corners, and the carbon atom at the center, of an equilateral triangle. Each of the three carbon-oxygen bonds is therefore of the same length as the other two, and so is presumably equivalent to them in all other regards as well; and each of the angles between any two of these bonds is equal to 120°. Such a geometrical arrangement is inconsistent with any one of the three equivalent structures XX, XXI, and XXII alone, but is an immediate

[6] N. Elliott, *J. Am. Chem. Soc.*, **59**, 1380 (1937).

consequence of resonance among them all.   In the same sense in which

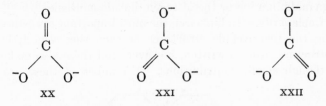

XX                    XXI                   XXII

we speak of one-and-a-half bonds in benzene, we can describe the situation here in terms of one-and-a-third bonds.   In the nitrate ion also, resonance among the three corresponding structures, XXIII, XXIV, and XXV, leads to the same trigonal symmetry, so that again the three

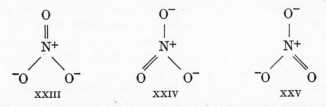

XXIII                 XXIV                  XXV

bonds are equivalent and the three angles are each 120°.   Moreover, the equivalence of the two oxygen atoms in a carboxylate ion,[7] or in a nitro group,[8] is ensured by the resonance between the structures XXVI and XXVII, or XXVIII and XXIX, respectively.   In each of these latter examples, the resonance is between only two equivalent struc-

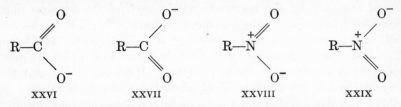

XXVI           XXVII           XXVIII           XXIX

tures, and so the resulting equivalent bonds can be described as one-and-a-half bonds.   (In regard to the suitability of the terms "one-and-a-half bonds" and "one-and-a-third bonds" see Section 4·4.)

   Numerous further examples, similar to the foregoing, could be mentioned, but no attempt will be made here to give an exhaustive survey of the field.   The reader should now be in position to apply the above

[7] L. Pauling and L. O. Brockway, *Proc. Natl. Acad. Sci.*, **20**, 336 (1934).   L. Pauling and J. Sherman, *ibid.*, 340 (1934).   W. H. Zachariasen, *Z. Krist.*, **89**, 442 (1934); *Phys. Rev.*, **53**, 917 (1938).   J. M. Robertson and I. Woodward, *J. Chem. Soc.*, 1817 (1936).

[8] L. O. Brockway, J. Y. Beach, and L. Pauling, *J. Am. Chem. Soc.*, **57**, 2693 (1935). A. J. Stosick, *ibid.*, **61**, 1127 (1939).

principles to any other ions or molecules that may be of interest, such as the guanidinium ion or the nitrogen dioxide molecule.

**4·2  Coplanarity.**  In biphenyl, the most important resonance is that involving the two Kekulé structures of each ring separately. Less stable structures can be written, however, and these also make appreciable, though small, contributions. A number of these are of the

type of I, in which a formal bond is drawn from one ring to the other and in which a double bond connects the two rings. Now, if structure I (or any of the other ones of the same type) were the actual structure of biphenyl, elementary stereochemical considerations would require that all six atoms marked with asterisks lie in the same plane. In reality, such structures are rather unimportant in the resonance, but the possibility remains that their effect upon the properties of the substance may be sufficient to make this particular arrangement of the atoms more stable than any other. If so, then the entire molecule would tend to be planar, inasmuch as the two benzene rings are themselves planar.

An idea of the magnitude of the forces acting to produce coplanarity of the two rings can be obtained by treating the problem from a slightly different point of view. In Section 3·3, we saw that biphenyl is stabilized not only by the resonance within each of the benzene rings separately, but also, to the extent of perhaps a few kilocalories per mole, by the conjugation of the two rings with each other. This latter effect is due to the resonance with structures such as I, which are most stable when the entire molecule is planar. It follows, then, that the conjugation has the greatest effect when the molecule is planar. It follows also that (aside from any steric interactions that may operate) the energy required to twist the molecule about the central carbon-carbon bond cannot be larger than the small additional resonance energy which is due to the conjugation. Rotation should, therefore, be relatively easy even at moderate temperatures, although most molecules may be at, or near, the favored configuration at any given time.

This principle of coplanarity is not restricted to biphenyl but applies generally to any molecule with conjugated double bonds. Butadiene, nitrobenzene, and benzaldehyde, for example, should also tend to lie entirely in one plane. A different type of structure which should lead similarly to coplanarity is illustrated by the carboxyl group. In methyl formate, resonance apparently occurs between the structures II and

III; the effect of the second of these should be to make the carbon atom of the methyl group lie in the plane formed by the four atoms of

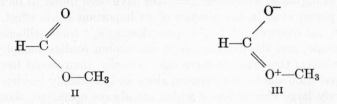

the formate radical. Since the resonance energy of a carbalkoxy group is apparently rather large (Table 3·6) the resistance to deformation out of the plane should be relatively great in esters of this sort.

Since the atoms in a molecule are not at rest but instead are in constant motion with respect to each other, the molecule cannot actually be completely planar except at isolated instants. The above discussion, therefore, applies only to the average positions of the atoms over an extended period of time, rather than to the actual positions at any given time.

The experimental evidence that molecules of the above types tend to be planar in the gaseous and liquid states is fairly satisfactory, but (except for the esters of the carboxylic acids) it is not entirely conclusive. The available data bearing upon this point will be discussed later in some detail. (See Sections 5·5, 5·6, 6·4, 7·4, 7·7, and 8·12.) The existence of coplanarity in the solid phase, on the other hand, has been demonstrated in a number of substances by the determination of their crystal structures. In this way, the molecules of the following substances have been found to lie in a single plane: biphenyl, terphenyl, quaterphenyl, *trans* stilbene, *trans* azobenzene, diphenylacetylene, diphenyldiacetylene, cyanuric triazide, the tricyanmelamine ion, 1,3,5-trinitrobenzene, oxalic acid, and the oxalate ion in various oxalates. (See the table in the Appendix for the references to the original papers dealing with these substances and also to those dealing with the further substances referred to below.) Coplanarity is not universal, however, as a certain number of exceptions do exist. The two benzene rings in any of the optically active biphenyls,[9] for example, are necessarily non-coplanar, since the achievement of coplanarity would result in racemization. These substances do not form significant exceptions to the general rule, however, because the steric interactions between the bulky substituents in the 2, 6, 2′, and 6′ positions are certainly very large. For the same reason, the ob-

[9] See R. L. Shriner, R. Adams, and C. S. Marvel in H. Gilman, *Organic Chemistry,* John Wiley & Sons, New York, 1st ed., 1938, pp. 259 ff.; 2nd ed., 1943, pp. 343 ff.

served lack of coplanarity in solid o-diphenylbenzene[10] and cis azobenzene is only to have been expected.  On the other hand, there are a few examples in which the molecules have been found to be not entirely planar even in the absence of an important steric effect.  This is true, for example, of 1,3,5-triphenylbenzene,[11] trans stilbene, trans azobenzene, and the oxalate ion in ammonium oxalate monohydrate. Exceptions of this type are more rare, however, than would have been anticipated on the basis of chance alone and, especially in view of the relatively large crystal forces which are always operative, should not be regarded too seriously.  The appearance of trans stilbene and trans azobenzene in the lists of both the planar and non-planar molecules is explained by the fact that the crystals of these substances contain two sterically different kinds of molecule.  For each compound, half the molecules are planar and half are not.

In benzene, the resonance between the two Kekulé structures, IV and V, should lead in a similar manner to a completely planar con-

IV                                        V

figuration, as, of course it actually does.  (This completes the derivation of the molecular symmetry of benzene.  See Section 4·1.)  In cyclooctatetraene, resonance between the two Kekulé-like structures, VI and VII, might be expected to give the molecule the shape of a regular plane octagon.  If this were so, however, the C–C–C angles would

VI                                        VII

each have to be 135°, which is considerably larger than their normal value.  It is possible that the strain in the planar configuration might be so great that the ring would pucker, as it certainly does for the same reason in cyclooctane, for example.  If so, the two structures would no longer be equivalent, since one would be highly strained and the other would be strainless, or nearly so.  The resonance energy would then be relatively small.  It is not known which of these two possibilities is correct, but it is evident that, in either case, cycloocta-

[10] C. J. B. Clews and K. Lonsdale, Proc. Roy. Soc. (London), A161, 493 (1937).
[11] K. Lonsdale, Z. Krist., 97, 91 (1937).

tetraene should not exhibit the unusual stability that characterizes benzene. Willstätter and his co-workers[12] have reported that the substance has no aromatic character. Even though their syntheses have recently been questioned,[13] there can be no doubt that the substance is indeed relatively unstable.

**4·3 Interatomic Distances.** There are several experimental methods for the measurement of bond lengths or, in other words, of the distances between atoms joined by valence bonds. It will not be possible here to describe any of these in detail, but a few words regarding the fields of usefulness, and the limitations, of each may be of interest.

The spectroscopic method[14,15] is the most precise of. all, when it can be applied rigorously to a substance in the gaseous state. Under favorable circumstances, it can give a bond length to within a few thousandths of an angstrom unit. Unfortunately, however, it is restricted to extremely simple molecules, and the reliability of the results to which it leads is usually open to some question if the molecule contains more than two or three atoms. For that reason, it is of limited use in the study of organic substances.

The methods based upon the diffraction of x rays by crystals[16] or of electrons by gases[17] are rather less precise than the spectroscopic one. By either of these methods, a bond length can ordinarily be measured to within, at best, a few hundredths of an angstrom unit. The restriction to simple molecules is not so serious here as with the spectroscopic method, so that relatively quite complex organic molecules can often be treated satisfactorily. However, each of the diffraction methods is subject to an awkward difficulty which is not shared by the spectroscopic one, namely, that, except under certain rare circumstances,[18] the complete structure of the crystal or molecule cannot be calculated *directly* from the positions and intensities of the lines, spots, or rings

[12] R. Willstätter and E. Waser, *Ber.*, **44**, 3423 (1911). R. Willstätter and M. Heidelberger, *ibid.*, **46**, 517 (1913).

[13] J. R. Vincent, A. F. Thompson, Jr., and L. I. Smith, *J. Org. Chem.*, **3**, 603 (1939). C. D. Hurd and L. R. Drake, *J. Am. Chem. Soc.*, **61**, 1943 (1939). S. Goldwasser and H. S. Taylor, *ibid.*, **61**, 1260 (1939).

[14] For further discussions of the spectroscopic method, see G. Herzberg, *Molecular Spectra and Molecular Structure, I, Diatomic Molecules* (translated by J. W. T. Spinks), Prentice-Hall, Inc., New York, 1939.

[15] D. M. Dennison, *Rev. Modern Phys.*, **12**, 175 (1940).

[16] For further discussion of the x-ray method, see R. W. G. Wyckoff, *The Structure of Crystals*, Chemical Catalog Company, New York, 1931. See also R. C. Evans, *An Introduction to Crystal Chemistry*, Cambridge University Press, Cambridge, 1939.

[17] For further discussion of the electron-diffraction method, see L. O. Brockway, *Rev. Modern Phys.*, **8**, 231 (1936).

[18] For an example (phthalocyanine) see J. M. Robertson, *J. Chem. Soc.*, **1195** (1936).

appearing on the x-ray or electron-diffraction photographs. Instead, an indirect procedure must be adopted; this consists in finding (usually by trial and error, at any rate in the concluding steps) a structure which leads to a calculated diffraction photograph identical with the observed. Since the structure of the crystal or molecule is often defined by a large number of parameters which can be varied independently of each other, the search for the best set of values may be, and usually is, extremely tedious. As a result, the precision that is permitted by the method itself is not always achieved in practice. (It should perhaps be mentioned that, as soon as a fairly accurate structure has been derived by trial and error, a Fourier analysis of the x-ray, but not of the electron-diffraction, photographs can sometimes lead directly to a final solution.[19] Such a procedure is quite laborious, however, and has not ordinarily been followed in the past.)

In a strict sense, the length of a covalent bond does not have a unique value, because the two atoms that are linked by it are constantly in motion with respect to each other. Consequently, when we speak of a " bond length " or of an " interatomic distance," we have reference not to the actual distance between the atoms themselves, but instead either to the *average* distance of the nuclei, or else to the distance $r_e$ (see Figure 2·2) at which the mutual potential energy is a minimum. These latter two distances are not necessarily exactly equal to each other, but the difference between them is so small that it may be ignored here.

Before the rather extensive data regarding bond lengths can be interpreted in terms of resonance among various structures, a method must be established by which the bond lengths in non-resonating molecules can be predicted. For this purpose, use can be made of the important empirical rule that the length of a pure single, double, or triple covalent bond between a given pair of atoms usually varies only slightly from molecule to molecule. The extent to which this generalization is valid, and the limitations to which it is subject, are illustrated by the data in the third column of Table 4·1. (A much more complete table of bond lengths in molecules of various types is given in the Appendix, since no very comprehensive recent compilation seems to be available elsewhere at present. The reader will find it advantageous to examine this larger list in order to obtain a better idea of the extent and self-consistency of the data.) It is seen that, on the whole, the observed interatomic distances are indeed very nearly constant. The length of the carbon-hydrogen bond, for example, varies only within the

[19] For an example (durene) see J. M. Robertson, *Proc. Roy. Soc. (London)*, **A142**, 658 (1933).

## TABLE 4·1

### LENGTHS OF PURE SINGLE, DOUBLE, AND TRIPLE BONDS

| Type of Bond | Length Calcd[a] | Obs[b] | Substance |
|---|---|---|---|
| C—H | 1.07 | 1.057 | Hydrogen cyanide |
|  | (1.10) | 1.09 | Formaldehyde |
|  |  | 1.09 | Methane |
|  |  | 1.057 | Acetylene |
|  |  | 1.087 | Ethylene |
| N—H | 1.00 | 1.014 | Ammonia |
|  | (1.03) |  |  |
| O—H | 0.96 | 0.958 | Water |
|  | (0.98) |  |  |
| S—H | 1.34 | 1.35 | Hydrogen sulfide |
|  | (1.37) |  |  |
| C—C | 1.54 | 1.542 | Diamond |
|  | (1.54) | 1.55 | Ethane |
|  |  | 1.49 | Methyl cyanide |
|  |  | 1.53 | Cyclopropane |
|  |  | 1.47 | Dimethylacetylene |
|  |  | 1.47 | Diketopiperazine |
|  |  | 1.54 | 2-Butene (cis) |
|  |  | 1.54 | i-Butene |
|  |  | 1.54 | Hexamethylethane[c] |
|  |  | 1.58 | Hexamethylethane[d] |
|  |  | 1.53 | Hexamethylbenzene[e] |
| C—N | 1.47 | 1.46 | Nitromethane |
|  | (1.46) | 1.47 | Methyl azide |
|  |  | 1.39 | Glycine |
|  |  | 1.54 | Trimethylamine oxide |
|  |  | 1.41 | Diketopiperazine[f] |
| C—O | 1.43 | 1.43 | Methyl nitrate |
|  | (1.42) | 1.44 | O-Methylhydroxylamine |
|  |  | 1.42 | Dimethyl ether |
|  |  | 1.46 | Dioxane |
| C—S | 1.81 | 1.82 | Dimethylsulfide |
|  | (1.81) |  |  |
| C—Cl | 1.76 | 1.755 | Carbon tetrachloride |
|  | (1.71) | 1.73 | Fluorodichloromethane |
|  |  | 1.77 | Methyl chloride |
|  |  | 1.78 | t-Butyl chloride |
| C—Br | 1.91 | 1.91 | Carbon tetrabromide |
|  | (1.88) | 1.92 | t-Butyl bromide |
| C—I | 2.10 | 2.12 | Iodoform |
|  | (2.09) |  |  |
| C=C | 1.34 | 1.33 | Ethylene |
| C=O | 1.24 | 1.21 | Formaldehyde |
| C≡C | 1.20 | 1.20 | Acetylene |
| C≡N | 1.15 | 1.154 | Hydrogen cyanide |

[a] In angstrom units. The values not in parentheses are obtained from Pauling's atomic radii (see reference 20), with the use of equation 1; the values in parentheses are obtained with Schomaker and Stevenson's atomic radii (see reference 21), with the use of equation 2. See Table 4·2.

[b] In angstrom units. For probable errors, statements of experimental methods, and references to the original literature see the Appendix.

[c] This value applies to the distance between one of the methyl carbon atoms and the central carbon atom to which it is joined.

[d] This value applies to the distance between the two central carbon atoms.

[e] This value applies to the distance between one of the methyl carbon atoms and the atom of the benzene ring to which it is joined.

[f] This value applies to the distance between one of the methylene carbon atoms and the nitrogen atom adjacent to it,

range, 1.06–1.09 A, in a series of different molecules; that of the carbon-chlorine bond varies similarly within the range, 1.73–1.78 A; and so on. However, a number of exceptions do exist, in which the variations are larger than the foregoing. For example, the length of a carbon-carbon single bond, which has a very nearly constant value of 1.54 A in diamond and in most of the other substances investigated, is decreased to 1.49 A in methyl cyanide, and to 1.47 A in dimethylacetylene and diketopiperazine; in general it seems to be true that a carbon-carbon single bond is shortened appreciably when it is adjacent to a triple bond or to a carbon-oxygen double bond, but, strangely enough, not when it is adjacent to a carbon-carbon double bond as in *i*-butene or hexamethylbenzene. The deviations from constancy in all these substances are apparently greater than any uncertainties in the experimental data. Similar systematic variations may be expected to occur with other types of bond as well; the shortening of two of the carbon-nitrogen bonds in diketopiperazine from the expected value of 1.47 A to only 1.41 A may be an example of this effect, but more data than are now available would be desirable.

In all the above molecules, the observed deviations from constancy can perhaps be accounted for with the aid of the idea of hyperconjugation, as will be shown at the end of this section; for the present however we shall regard them merely as empirical facts. In other molecules, the deviations may be due to more obvious causes. For example, the lengthening of the carbon-nitrogen bond in trimethylamine oxide to 1.54 A may be merely a result of the change in the valence state of the nitrogen atom (but it is strange that an apparently similar change produces a *shortening* to 1.39 A in glycine). Furthermore, the lengthening of the central carbon-carbon bond in hexamethylethane to 1.58 A is hardly surprising in view of the steric repulsions between the bulky methyl groups.

Although it is inconvenient that systematic deviations from the rule of constant bond length are sometimes observed, the rule is not thereby rendered useless. This is because such deviations can usually be anticipated and allowed for, so that the possibility still remains of predicting, with fair accuracy, the length of any pure single, double, or triple bond.

A further useful generalization in regard to interatomic distances is that the length, $r_{AB}$, of a bond between any two atoms, $A$ and $B$, can be expressed as

$$r_{AB} = r_A + r_B \tag{1}$$

where $r_A$ and $r_B$ are the so-called radii of $A$ and $B$, respectively. It is found empirically that the atomic radii are usually constant from molecule to molecule to about the same extent that the bond lengths themselves are, provided that the values of the radii of the various atoms are allowed to depend not only upon the natures of the atoms in question but also upon the types of bond formed (i.e., single, double, or triple, and ionic or covalent). In ethylene, for example, each carbon atom must be considered to have two different radii — a covalent single-bond radius for each of its links with hydrogen atoms and a covalent double-bond radius for its link with the other carbon atom. These two carbon radii are different from each other and, of course, also from the hydrogen radius.

Of the several sets of covalent radii that have been proposed by various authors on the basis of the simple equation 1, we shall refer only to the one of Pauling.[20] A number of these radii are listed as the values which are not in parentheses in Table 4·2. The significance of the

TABLE 4·2

COVALENT RADII[a]

|  | H |  |  |  |
|---|---|---|---|---|
| Single-bond radius | 0.30 |  |  |  |
|  | (0.37) |  |  |  |
|  | C | N | O | F |
| Single-bond radius | 0.77 | 0.70 | 0.66 | 0.64 |
|  | (0.77) | (0.74) | (0.74) | (0.72) |
| Double-bond radius | 0.67 | 0.61 | 0.57 | 0.55 |
| Triple-bond radius | 0.60 | 0.55· | 0.51 | — |
|  | P | S | Cl |  |
| Single-bond radius | 1.10 | 1.04 | 0.99 |  |
|  | (1.10) | (1.04) | (0.99) |  |
| Double-bond radius | 1.00 | 0.95 | 0.90 |  |
| Triple-bond radius | 0.93 | 0.88 | — |  |
|  | Br |  |  |  |
| Single-bond radius | 1.14 |  |  |  |
|  | (1.14) |  |  |  |
| Double-bond radius | 1.05 |  |  |  |
|  | I |  |  |  |
| Single-bond radius | 1.33 |  |  |  |
|  | (1.33) |  |  |  |
| Double-bond radius | 1.24 |  |  |  |

[a] In angstrom units. The figures not in parentheses are those of Pauling, reference 20; the ones in parentheses are those of Schomaker and Stevenson, reference 21.

[20] For the complete list in its most recent form, see L. Pauling, *The Nature of the Chemical Bond*, Cornell University Press, Ithaca, N. Y., 1st ed., 1939, p. 154; 2nd ed., 1940, p. 164.

double-bond radii of fluorine, chlorine, etc., and of the triple-bond radii of oxygen, sulfur, etc., will become clearer in the following section. (Ionic radii will not be considered in this book, because they are of relatively little interest in connection with organic molecules.) The method of using these atomic radii for the prediction of bond lengths can be illustrated with a few examples. The calculated lengths of the carbon-carbon single, double, and triple bonds are, of course, just twice the carbon single-, double-, and triple-bond radii, or $2 \times 0.77 = 1.54$, $2 \times 0.67 = 1.34$, and $2 \times 0.60 = 1.20$ A, respectively; that of a carbon-chlorine single bond is the sum of the carbon and chlorine single-bond radii, or $0.77 + 0.99 = 1.76$ A; that of a carbon-oxygen double bond is the sum of the carbon and oxygen double-bond radii, or $0.67 + 0.57 = 1.24$ A; and so on. The agreement between the observed bond lengths and the calculated ones is shown by a comparison of the second and third columns of Table 4·1. It will be seen that the agreement is usually to within 0.02–0.03 A, which is about the order of magnitude of the uncertainty in the experimental values.

It has been found that small, but significant, discrepancies often occur if a single set of atomic radii is used to calculate the lengths of bonds between atoms of the same or similar electronegativity and also between atoms of widely different electronegativity. Consequently, a slight modification in Pauling's scheme has been proposed by Schomaker and Stevenson,[21] who replace equation 1 by the slightly more complicated expression

$$r_{AB} = r_A + r_B - 0.09 \, | \, x_A - x_B \, | \, \text{A} \tag{2}$$

Here, the quantity $| \, x_A - x_B \, |$ is the absolute magnitude of the difference between the electronegativities of the atoms $A$ and $B$ (see Table 3·10). The atomic radii, $r_A$ and $r_B$, to be used in conjunction with equation 2 are frequently different from those employed by Pauling; they are given by the values in parentheses in Table 4·2. The interatomic distances calculated with their aid, which are listed in the second column of Table 4·1, in parentheses, are often in somewhat better agreement with the experimental values than are those derived from Pauling's radii, but the difference is seldom great. The Schomaker and Stevenson scheme suffers, however, from the fact that it has not yet been extended to double and triple bonds, and so it is not of sufficiently general applicability to be of great use to us in the following discussions. For this reason, we shall hereafter make use only of the simpler treatment of Pauling.

We have seen above that we can, with some assurance, predict the distance between any two given atoms in a molecule, provided that they are joined by a bond that is definitely single, double, or triple. We

[21] V. Schomaker and D. P. Stevenson, *J. Am. Chem. Soc.*, **63**, 37 (1941).

turn now to a consideration of those cases in which the bond of interest is of a hybrid type. In benzene, for example, each carbon-carbon bond resonates between a single and a double bond. Its length, therefore, might be expected to be intermediate between the single-bond value of 1.54 A and the double-bond value of 1.34 A. Indeed, since the two Kekulé structures are equivalent to each other and so are equally important in the resonance, we might, as a first approximation, anticipate a bond length of 1.44 A, just halfway between the extremes. Spectroscopic data show, however, that a double bond is always stiffer than a comparable single bond[22] or, in other words, that more energy is required to stretch a double bond by a given amount than to contract a single bond by that same amount. Consequently, as a second approximation, we could anticipate that the actual bond length should be somewhat less than the simple mean. This prediction is in complete agreement with the observed distance of 1.39 A.

The frequently encountered statement that resonance " shortens " bond distances is not quite strictly correct. In benzene, for example, the observed length of 1.39 A is indeed less than the normal single-bond length of 1.54 A, but it is also greater than the normal double-bond length of 1.34 A. There is no more logical reason for comparing the observed length with one of the extremes than with the other. The observed *average* bond length is less, however, than would correspond to a Kekulé structure.

The situation is similar in other molecules in which a bond resonates between single and double, between double and triple, or among all three types of bond. The observed distance is always intermediate between the extremes but is closer to the lower extreme than would correspond to a simple weighted mean. This fact makes it possible to obtain considerable information in regard to the detailed structure of a molecule from a study of its interatomic distances. Such information is subject to some uncertainty since, as we have already seen, the various bond lengths are not always strictly constant even in the absence of resonance. However, if due attention is paid to the known deviations from constancy, and if, moreover, the present method of investigation is used in conjunction with other independent data, an accumulation of evidence can often be obtained which appears to be quite incontrovertible.

In Table 4·3 the observed bond lengths in a number of resonating molecules are compared with the values calculated for pure single, double, or triple bonds. (Similar data for a considerable number of further substances can be found in the Appendix.) In all the substances

[22] See, for example, J. H. Hibben, *Chem. Rev.*, **18**, 1 (1936). Cf. also Section 6·5.

## TABLE 4·3

### Lengths of Hybrid Bonds

| Atoms Bonded | Lengths of Pure Bonds[a] | Lengths Obs[b] | Substance | Type of Resonance[c] |
|---|---|---|---|---|
| CC | 1.54 | 1.42 | Graphite | F |
|  | 1.34 | 1.47 | Glyoxal | B |
|  | 1.20 | 1.37 | Cyanogen | B |
|  |  | 1.29 | Carbon suboxide | H |
|  |  | 1.36 | Diacetylene[d] | B |
|  |  | 1.46 | Butadiene[d] | B |
|  |  | 1.46 | Furan[d] | E |
|  |  | 1.44 | Thiophene[d] | E |
|  |  | 1.39 | Pyrazine | F |
|  |  | 1.39 | Benzene | F |
|  |  | 1.39 | Resorcinol | F |
|  |  | 1.41 | Naphthalene | F |
|  |  | 1.39 | Hexamethylbenzene[d] | F |
|  |  | 1.40 | Diphenylacetylene[e] | B |
| CN | 1.47 | 1.34 | Diazomethane | D |
|  | 1.28 | 1.37 | Urea | A |
|  | 1.15 | 1.18 | Methyl isocyanide[l] | G |
|  |  | 1.19 | Methyl isocyanate | C |
|  |  | 1.35 | Pyrazine | F |
|  |  | 1.45 | Picryl iodide[f] | B |
|  |  | 1.35 | Picryl iodide[g] | B |
| CO | 1.43 | 1.313 | Calcium carbonate | A |
|  | 1.24 | 1.129 | Carbon monoxide | G |
|  | 1.11 | 1.27 | Sodium formate | A |
|  |  | 1.159 | Carbon dioxide | C |
|  |  | 1.18 | Methyl isocyanate | C |
|  |  | 1.29 | Formic acid (dimeric)[m] | A |
|  |  | 1.20 | Carbon suboxide | H |
|  |  | 1.40 | Furan | E |
|  |  | 1.36 | Resorcinol | J |
| CCl | 1.76 | 1.67 | Cyanogen chloride | J |
|  | 1.57 | 1.68 | Phosgene | A |
|  |  | 1.73 | Tetrachloroethylene | J |
|  |  | 1.68 | Monochloroacetylene | J |
|  |  | 1.69 | Vinyl chloride | J |
|  |  | 1.69 | Chlorobenzene | J |

## TABLE 4·3 (Continued)

### LENGTHS OF HYBRID BONDS

| Atoms Bonded | Lengths of Pure Bonds[a] | Lengths Obs[b] | Substance | Type of Resonance[c] |
|---|---|---|---|---|
| CBr | 1.91 | 1.79 | Cyanogen bromide | J |
| | 1.72 | 1.80 | Dibromoacetylene | J |
| | | 1.86 | Vinyl bromide | J |
| | | 1.84 | 1,3,5-Tribromobenzene | J |
| CI | 2.10 | 2.03 | Vinyl iodide | J |
| | 1.91 | 2.02 | p-Diiodobenzene | J |
| NN | 1.40 | 1.13 | Diazomethane | D |
| | 1.22 | 1.24 | Methyl azide[h] | C |
| | 1.10 | 1.10 | Methyl azide[i] | C |
| NO | 1.36 | 1.21 | Nitromethane | A |
| | 1.18 | 1.36 | Methyl nitrate[j] | A |
| | 1.06 | 1.26 | Methyl nitrate[k] | A |
| | | 1.21 | Sodium nitrate | A |

[a] In angstrom units. The first value given for each pair of atoms refers to a single bond, the second to a double bond, and the third to a triple bond.

[b] In angstrom units. For probable errors, statements of experimental methods, and references to the original literature, see the Appendix.

[c] The symbols in this column have the following meanings:

  A. See structures XX–XXIX of Section 4·1.
  B. Conjugation between multiple bonds.
  C. See structures III, IV, and V of this section.
  D. See structures XVI and XVII of this section.
  E. Resonance as in furan. See structures XXI–XXVI of Section 3·2.
  F. Resonance between Kekulé (and Dewar) structures and their analogs.
  G. See structures IX and X of this section.
  H. See structures VI, VII, and VIII of this section.
  J. Resonance as in vinyl chloride. Cf. structure II of this section.

[d] The value given for this substance applies only to the bond which, in the conventional structure, is represented as single and as lying between two multiple bonds.

[e] The value for this substance applies only to the bonds between the triple bond and the benzene rings.

[f] This value applies only to the bonds ortho to the iodine atom.

[g] This value applies only to the bond para to the iodine atom.

[h] This value applies only to the bond nearer to the methyl group.

[i] This value applies only to the bond farther from the methyl group.

[j] This value applies only to the bond linking the nitrogen atom to the methoxyl oxygen atom.

[k] This value applies only to the bonds linking the nitrogen atom to one of the oxygen atoms not in the methoxyl group.

[l] This value applies only to the bond linking the nitrogen atom to the carbon atom that is not part of the methyl group.

[m] For more recent and more precise values of the carbon-oxygen distances in formic acid and in several further simple carboxylic acids, see J. Karle and L. O. Brockway, J. Am. Chem. Soc., 66, 574 (1944).

listed, the measured interatomic distances are in agreement with the conclusions reached above. In butadiene, for example, the structure I can make only a small contribution to the state of the molecule, and yet its effect is apparently sufficient to decrease the length of the central

$$\text{H}_2\dot{\text{C}} - \text{CH} = \text{CH} - \dot{\text{C}}\text{H}_2$$

I

carbon-carbon bond from 1.54 A to only 1.46 A. (It is important here that a single bond adjacent to only one double bond, as in $i$-butene and hexamethylbenzene, is not shortened appreciably.) Similarly in vinyl chloride, the relatively unimportant structure II is apparently responsible for the reduction of the carbon-chlorine distance from 1.76 A to

$$\text{H}_2\text{C} - \text{CH} = \overset{+}{\text{Cl}}$$

II

1.69 A. In the remaining substances listed in Table 4·3, the same situation is encountered; a bond represented as single in the most stable structure is always shorter than would be expected on the basis of the single-bond radii if, in that structure, it lies either between two multiple bonds, as in butadiene, or between one multiple bond and an atom with an unshared pair of electrons, as in vinyl chloride.

Other types of grouping, in which a double bond partakes of some triple-bond character, are illustrated by carbon dioxide, methyl isocyanate, carbon suboxide, carbon monoxide, methyl isocyanide, methyl azide, and diazomethane. It is of interest that in carbon dioxide, for example, in which each carbon-oxygen bond receives as much single- as triple-bond character from resonance among the structures III, IV, and V, the length is only slightly greater than that expected for a pure triple bond. This, of course, can be related to the fact that the triple

$$: \text{O}=\text{C}=\text{O} :  \qquad : \overset{-}{\text{O}}-\text{C}{\equiv}\overset{+}{\text{O}} :  \qquad : \overset{+}{\text{O}}{\equiv}\text{C}-\overset{-}{\text{O}} :$$

III                    IV                    V

bond is so much stiffer than the single. The resonance in methyl isocyanate is apparently similar to that in carbon dioxide. In carbon suboxide, which resonates among the structures VI, VII, and VIII, equal contributions of single- and triple-bonded structures make the lengths of both the carbon-carbon and the carbon-oxygen bonds shorter

$$: \text{O}=\text{C}=\text{C}=\text{C}=\overset{+}{\text{O}} :  \qquad : \text{O}{\equiv}\text{C}-\text{C}{\equiv}\text{C}-\overset{-}{\text{O}} :  \qquad : \overset{-}{\text{O}}-\text{C}{\equiv}\text{C}-\text{C}{\equiv}\overset{+}{\text{O}} :$$

VI                    VII                    VIII

than would have been expected for pure double bonds.

In carbon monoxide, the bond length again has practically the triple-bond value, but the interpretation is not so clear in view of the anomalous valence state of the carbon atom. Pauling has estimated[23] that the double-bonded structure IX should correspond to a length of 1.15 A, which is already considerably shorter than the 1.24 A characteristic of

$$: C = O :$$
$$\overset{..}{}$$
IX

$$: \overset{-}{C} = \overset{+}{O} :$$
X

the carbonyl group in an aldehyde or the like. The small further shortening to the observed length of 1.13 A may then be due to the contribution of the structure X.

In methyl isocyanide, the predicted length of the carbon-nitrogen bond of the isocyanide group is 1.19 A for structure XI and 1.15 A for structure XII. (In the first of these values, the same correction has

$$CH_3 - \overset{..}{N} = C :$$
XI

$$CH_3 - \overset{+}{N} = \overset{-}{C} :$$
XII

been made for the anomalous valence state of the carbon atom as in the corresponding value for carbon monoxide.) The observed length of 1.18 A is indeed intermediate between the extremes, but the actual deviation from either extreme is probably no greater than the experimental uncertainty. Although no definite conclusion can therefore be drawn from the bond *length*, the fact that the C–N–C bond *angle* is 180° provides considerable information. Such a linear arrangement of the atoms is in agreement with structure XII, whereas an angle of about 120° would have seemed more reasonable for structure XI. Consequently, it seems reasonable to suppose that a triple-bonded structure makes a fairly large contribution to the state of this substance and, from analogy, to that of carbon monoxide as well.

In methyl azide, the two nitrogen-nitrogen bonds are not of the same length. The data are in agreement with the supposition that resonance occurs between the structures XIII and XIV, but that the further

$$CH_3 - \overset{..}{N} = \overset{+}{N} = \overset{..}{\overset{-}{N}} :$$
XIII

$$CH_3 - \overset{..}{N} - \overset{+}{N} = N :$$
$$\overset{..}{}$$
XIV

$$CH_3 - \overset{+}{N} = \overset{+}{N} - \overset{..}{\overset{--}{N}} :$$
$$\overset{..}{}$$
XV

structure XV is too unstable, on account of its unfavorable distribution of electric charge, to make an appreciable contribution. In diazomethane, the facts are consistent with resonance between XVI and XVII, which are analogous to XIII and XIV, respectively. (No struc-

[23] L. Pauling, reference 20, 1st ed., 1939, p. 180; 2nd ed., 1940, p. 195.

ture analogous to XV can be drawn for this substance.)  For the remaining substances in Table 4·3, the types of resonance involved

$$H_2C\overset{+}{=}N\overset{\cdot\cdot}{=}N : \qquad\qquad H_2C\overset{\cdot\cdot}{-}N\overset{+}{\equiv}N :$$

$$\text{XVI} \qquad\qquad\qquad\qquad \text{XVII}$$

should be apparent from the entries made in the last column.  Some further points of interest are taken up again in greater detail in the following section.

If hyperconjugation is taken into account, a number of the variations in bond length, which were referred to above as occurring apparently in the absence of resonance, may perhaps find an explanation in terms of resonance.  It has been suggested,[24] for example, that in methylacetylene the relatively unstable structure XVIII makes an appreciable

$$\overset{H\cdots\cdots}{H_2C = C = CH}$$

$$\text{XVIII}$$

contribution and so gives some double-bond character to the carbon-carbon bond that is represented as single in the conventional structure.  In a similar manner, the fact that the carbon-carbon and carbon-nitrogen single bonds are shortened when adjacent to a carbonyl group is readily understandable.  On this basis, however, it is not clear why the carbon-hydrogen bond is also slightly shorter than usual in acetylene or why an ethylenic linkage has no apparent effect upon neighboring single bonds.  The situation is still obscure, evidently, and probably nothing is to be gained by trying to extend the present interpretation too far.

**4·4  Per Cent Double-Bond Characters and Fractional Bond Orders.**
In the preceding section we saw in a qualitative way that, when a bond resonates between single and double, its length is intermediate between the extremes.  It would be useful if a more quantitative correlation could be made between the observed lengths of the various bonds and the relative contributions of the singly and doubly bonded structures.  Two essentially different schemes for effecting such a correlation have been proposed.  The first of these, which is due to Pauling and his co-workers,[25] defines the *per cent double-bond character*, $p$, of a bond by

[24] L. Pauling, H. D. Springall, and K. J. Palmer, *J. Am. Chem. Soc.*, **61**, 927 (1939)
R. S. Mulliken, C. A. Rieke, and W. G. Brown, *ibid.*, **63**, 41 (1941).
[25] L. Pauling, L. O. Brockway, and J. Y. Beach, *J. Am. Chem. Soc.*, 57, 2705 (1935).  L. Pauling and L. O. Brockway, *ibid.*, **59**, 1223 (1937).

means of the equation

$$r = r_s - (r_s - r_d) \frac{3p}{2p + 100} \tag{1}$$

or

$$p = \frac{100(r_s - r)}{2r + r_s - 3r_d} \tag{2}$$

where $r$ is the observed length of the actual bond, and $r_s$ and $r_d$ are the lengths of pure single and pure double bonds, respectively, between the two atoms in question. It is seen that $p$ assumes the values of 0 for $r = r_s$, and of 100 for $r = r_d$. The significance of the interpolation for intermediate values of $r$ and of $p$ becomes apparent from a consideration of the carbon-carbon bond, for which $r_s = 1.54$ A and $r_d = 1.34$ A. In benzene, with $r = 1.39$ A, and in graphite, with $r = 1.42$ A, the bonds are found to have 50 and 33⅓ per cent double-bond character, respectively. These values seem quite reasonable if all structures which have formal bonds are ignored. In benzene, for example, the two Kekulé structures, being equivalent, must make equal contributions to the state of the molecule, so that each bond can be considered just halfway between a single and double bond. Similarly in graphite, each bond is represented as single in two-thirds of the structures, and as double in one-third of the structures, without formal bonds. (This statement follows from the fact that the carbon atoms in graphite are arranged in parallel planes, each of which is essentially a single giant molecule resonating among a tremendously large number of structures of the type indicated by I. The individual planes are separated from each other

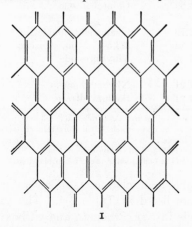

I

by such great distances — 3.41 A between adjacent planes — that the only effective interactions between them can be the van der Waals forces.   See the table in the Appendix.)   The precise forms of the equations 1 and 2 were indeed chosen in order to bring out these suggestive relationships.

TABLE 4·4

PER CENT DOUBLE-BOND CHARACTERS

| Atoms Bonded | Observed Bond Length[a] | Substance | Per Cent Double-Bond Character |
|---|---|---|---|
| CC | 1.39 | Benzene | 50 |
|  | 1.42 | Graphite | 33⅓ |
|  | 1.36 | Diacetylene[b] | 75 |
|  | 1.41 | Naphthalene[c] | 38 |
|  | 1.46 | Cyclopentadiene[b] | 18 |
|  | 1.47 | Glyoxal | 15 |
|  | 1.48 | Biphenyl[d] | 12½ |
| CN | 1.34 | Diazomethane | 42 |
|  | 1.35 | Pyrazine | 36 |
|  | 1.37 | Urea | 27 |
|  | 1.37 | Pyridine | 27 |
| CO | 1.27 | Sodium formate | 64 |
|  | 1.31 | Calcium carbonate | 36 |
|  | 1.25 | Urea | 86 |
|  | 1.28 | Phosgene | 56 |
|  | 1.28 | Acetamide | 56 |
| CCl | 1.67 | Cyanogen chloride | 23 |
|  | 1.68 | Phosgene | 19½ |
|  | 1.69 | Vinyl chloride | 16 |
|  | 1.69 | Chlorobenzene | 16 |
| CBr | 1.79 | Cyanogen bromide | 36 |
|  | 1.84 | 1,3,5-Tribromobenzene | 16 |
|  | 1.86 | Vinyl bromide | 11 |
| NO | 1.21 | Nitromethane | 62½ |
|  | 1.21 | Sodium nitrate | 62½ |

[a] In angstrom units.   These values are taken from Table 4·3 and from the Appendix.

[b] This value applies only to the bond which, in the conventional structure, is represented as single and lying between multiple bonds.

[c] This value is the average length of all carbon-carbon bonds.

[d] This value applies only to the bond joining the two benzene rings.

The per cent double-bond characters of several representative bonds of varying types are listed in Table 4·4.   The values found for the carbon-oxygen bonds in the carbonate and carboxylate ions are fairly close to the values of 33⅓ and 50 per cent, respectively, which might have been anticipated in view of the natures of the structures involved in the resonance.   The value of 62½ per cent for the nitrogen-oxygen bond in both the analogous nitrate ion and nitro group, however, is less satisfactory.   The suggestion has been made[6] that the difficulty here may be due to the presence of formal positive charges upon the nitrogen atoms.   A further possible explanation is that the assumed length of the pure double bond may be in error.   The remaining values given in Table 4·4 are of quite reasonable magnitude, but it is doubtful if much quantitative significance can be assigned to them.   In all cases, the fact that variations in bond length are often observed even when no reasonable resonating structures can be written introduces considerable uncertainty.   This difficulty is especially serious in bonds like the carbon-carbon bond in diacetylene, the carbon-nitrogen bond in urea, and the carbon-chlorine bond in cyanogen chloride, because these bonds occur in such environments that one would expect them to be shortened whether resonance is involved or not.   (Of course, if the " anomalous " shortening in question is really due to hyperconjugation, as was suggested above, then the calculated per cent double-bond characters may still be significant even in these dubious cases.)   Moreover, with such bonds as the nitrogen-oxygen bond, for which the length of the pure double bond is not accurately known, the uncertainties are still greater; and finally, with the carbon-halogen bonds, which never occur as pure double bonds, the assumed values of $r_d$, and hence the conclusions reached, are little better than mere guesses.   In spite of these objections, however, the present treatment, as long as it is not assigned a more quantitative significance than it actually possesses, is a useful and helpful aid in the discussion of structural problems.

The second method of correlating interatomic distances and bond character is due to Penney.[26]   In this treatment, which rests upon a rather better theoretical basis than Pauling's, the *order* of a bond is defined in such a way that it assumes the values 1, 2, and 3 for pure single, double, and triple bonds, respectively, and is a linear function of the bond energy for bonds of intermediate type.   In benzene, for example, each carbon-carbon bond would be of order 1.5 if the resonance energy were zero, since then the energy of each bond would be just the average between the energies of a pure single and a pure double bond.   The resonance energy, however, actually stabilizes the molecule by some 36 kcal per mole, so that each carbon-carbon bond is strengthened to the extent of about 6 kcal per mole.   The bond order is therefore somewhat greater than 1.5.   Similarly, the bond order in graphite is somewhat greater than 1⅓.   The exact numerical values of the bond orders in these and in other substances can be found only by elaborate, but still crudely approximate, quantum-mechanical calculations which cannot be described here.   (However, see Section 3·5.)   Penney's complete procedure for

[26] W. G. Penney, *Proc. Roy. Soc.* (*London*), **A158**, 306 (1937).

calculating bond lengths is, in outline, as follows: The orders of the carbon-carbon bonds in ethane, graphite, benzene, ethylene, and acetylene are (by definition or by calculation) 1.000, 1.45, 1.623, 2.000, and 3.000, respectively,

### TABLE 4·5

CALCULATED ORDERS AND LENGTHS OF BONDS IN HYDROCARBONS

| | Bond Order | | Bond Length[e] | | | |
|---|---|---|---|---|---|---|
| Substance[a] | P[b] | C[c] | P[b] | C[c] | LJ[d] | Obs[f] |
| Benzene | 1.623 | 1.67 | (1.39) | (1.39) | 1.37 | 1.39 |
| Graphite | 1.45 | 1.53 | (1.42) | (1.42) | — | 1.42 |
| Butadiene A | 1.33 | 1.45 | 1.43 | 1.43 | 1.41 | 1.46 |
| B | 1.91 | 1.89 | 1.34 | 1.35 | 1.34 | (1.34) |
| Hexatriene A | 1.81 | 1.79 | 1.36 | 1.37 | 1.35 | — |
| B | 1.37 | 1.48 | 1.42 | 1.42 | 1.40 | — |
| C | 1.88 | 1.87 | 1.35 | 1.35 | 1.35 | — |
| Octatetraene A | 1.46 | 1.53 | 1.41 | 1.42 | 1.40 | — |
| B | 1.76 | 1.76 | 1.37 | 1.37 | 1.35 | — |
| C | 1.37 | 1.50 | 1.42 | 1.42 | 1.40 | — |
| D | 1.88 | 1.86 | 1.35 | 1.35 | 1.35 | — |
| Naphthalene A | 1.43 | 1.52 | 1.42 | 1.42 | 1.37 | 1.41 |
| B | 1.52 | 1.56 | 1.40 | 1.40 | 1.39 | 1.41 |
| C | 1.69 | 1.73 | 1.38 | 1.38 | 1.37 | 1.41 |
| D | 1.53 | 1.60 | 1.40 | 1.40 | 1.39 | 1.41 |
| Biphenyl A | — | 1.37 | — | 1.45 | 1.44 | 1.48 |
| B | — | — | — | — | 1.40 | 1.42 |
| Styrene A | 1.92 | — | 1.34 | 1.34 | 1.34 | — |
| B | 1.31 | — | 1.45 | 1.44 | 1.44 | — |
| C | 1.58 | — | 1.40 | 1.37 | 1.37 | — |
| D | 1.63 | — | 1.39 | 1.38 | 1.38 | — |
| E | 1.62 | — | 1.39 | 1.37 | 1.37 | — |

[a] The identity of the bonds in the various compounds is as follows: In the open-chain conjugated systems (butadiene, hexatriene, and octatetraene) the bond A is the one in the center of the molecule, the bond B is the one adjacent to it, and so on to the terminal bond; in naphthalene, the bond A is the central one, the bond B is the one adjacent to it, the bond C is the one between atoms $C_1$ and $C_2$, and the bond D is the one between the atoms $C_2$ and $C_3$; in biphenyl, the bond A is the one joining the two rings and bond B is any one in either of the rings; and in styrene, the bond A is the terminal one represented as double in the conventional structure, the bond B is the one linking A to the ring, and the bonds C, D, and E are the bonds in the benzene ring, taken in sequence.

[b] W. G. Penney, reference 26. The values for styrene were obtained by Penney and Kynch. (See note d.)

[c] C. A. Coulson, reference 27.

[d] J. E. Lennard-Jones, reference 28. The calculations for styrene were made by W. G. Penney and G. J. Kynch, Proc. Roy. Soc. (London), A164, 409 (1938).

[e] In angstrom units.

[f] In angstrom units. See Table 4·3 and also the table in the Appendix.

whereas the corresponding distances are 1.54, 1.42, 1.39, 1.33, and 1.20 A, respectively. A smooth curve showing the relation between bond order and bond length is drawn. Then, for any further molecule, such as butadiene, the orders of the various bonds are calculated theoretically, and the predicted lengths are read off from the empirical curve. The results obtained in this way for a number of hydrocarbons are listed in Table 4·5. Also listed in this table are the results of similar treatments that have been carried through by Coulson[27] for the same substances. These additional values of both the bond orders and the bond lengths have been derived by a method which is essentially the same as Penney's, but which differs in the quantum-mechanical approximations introduced into the theoretical calculations of the bond orders. The agreement of the two procedures with each other and with the meager experimental data is as satisfactory as could have been anticipated.

The calculations for naphthalene are of particular interest in that they predict an appreciable difference among the various carbon-carbon bonds. Pauling's method of treatment also leads to a similar conclusion,[25] for, if all structures containing formal bonds are neglected, the bonds between the $\alpha$ and their adjacent $\beta$ carbon atoms have 66⅔ per cent double-bond character and a predicted length of 1.37 A, whereas all the other carbon-carbon bonds have 33⅓ per cent double-bond character and predicted lengths of 1.42 A. Although all the measured bond lengths are reported to have the constant value of 1.41 A, a reexamination of the published data[25] suggests that the predicted differences do, nevertheless, exist.

The methods of Penney and of Coulson, although they are superior to that of Pauling on theoretical grounds, suffer from two handicaps which limit their usefulness. In the first place, they are restricted to the treatment of hydrocarbons, and, in the second place, they can be applied to new problems only by persons who are familiar with the quantum-mechanical methods employed in the calculations. These same limitations apply also to still a further method, due to Lennard-Jones,[28] by which bond lengths can be calculated directly without explicit reference to bond orders and without use of the observed lengths of the bonds in benzene and graphite. The results obtained by this method, which are also listed in Table 4·5, are seen to be in satisfactory agreement with those mentioned before.

**4·5 Miscellaneous Applications.** (*a*) It was pointed out in Section 4·2 that a molecule like butadiene should exist preferentially in a completely planar configuration as a result of the partial double-bond character of the central carbon-carbon bond. Conversely, the length of that bond should be less if the molecule were actually planar than it would be if the molecule were held in some way in a non-planar configuration. Similar considerations apply generally to all molecules having conjugated double bonds. The experimental evidence bearing upon this point is meager and not completely conclusive. In solid picryl iodide, for example, the nitro group *para* to the iodine atom is coplanar

---

[27] C. A. Coulson, *Proc. Roy. Soc. (London)*, **A169**, 413 (1939); *Proc. Roy. Soc. (Edinburgh)*, **A61**, 115 (1941). J. E. Lennard-Jones and C. A. Coulson, *Trans. Faraday Soc.*, **35**, 811 (1939).

[28] J. E. Lennard-Jones, *Proc. Roy. Soc. (London)*, **A158**, 280 (1937). J. E. Lennard-Jones and J. Turkevitch, *ibid.*, **A158**, 297 (1937).

with the benzene ring, but the two nitro groups *ortho* to the iodine are forced by steric repulsions to lie in planes nearly perpendicular to that of the ring.   The corresponding carbon-nitrogen distances are 1.35 and 1.45 A, respectively, in agreement with expectation.   (See Table 4·3 and the table in the Appendix.)   In solid *cis* azobenzene, the molecule departs considerably from planarity, and the length of the carbon-nitrogen bond is 1.46 A, or very nearly that of a pure single bond.   A smaller effect is observed in solid *trans* azobenzene, in which the molecules are not all crystallographically equivalent but belong to two types. In one of these, the molecule is completely planar and the carbon-nitrogen bond length is 1.40 A; in the other, the molecule is not completely planar, and the carbon-nitrogen distance is 1.43 A.   The situation is similar in *trans* stilbene, the corresponding carbon-carbon bond lengths being 1.44 and 1.45 A, respectively.   The reported variations in distance in these last substances are in the correct direction, but are too small to be trustworthy.   Especially with stilbene, the uncertainties in the experimental values are greater than the observed effects.   Further data of high accuracy would be necessary before any conclusions could be drawn.

(*b*) If the partial double-bond character of the central bond in butadiene holds the molecule in a single plane, then two geometrically isomeric forms, represented by I and II, should be possible.   The energy

$$CH_2=CH \qquad\qquad CH_2=CH$$
$$|\qquad\qquad\qquad |$$
$$CH_2=CH \qquad\qquad HC=CH_2$$
$$\text{I}\qquad\qquad\qquad\text{II}$$

required for a molecule to pass from one form to the other should be small, however, and so we could not expect an isolation of stable isomers

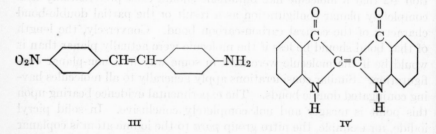

$$O_2N-\bigcirc-CH=CH-\bigcirc-NH_2$$

III                          IV'

to be possible.   Actually no examples are known in which isomers of this type have been separated from each other (unless the existence of such substances as *cis* cinnamic acid in several crystalline modifications should prove to be due to such an effect).   Conversely, the partial single-bond character of the central double bond in stilbene should make rotation easier about that bond.    Indeed, Calvin and Buckles have brought forward evidence that the *cis-trans* interconversion is so labile in *p*-nitro-*p'*-aminostilbene, III, that only a single form can be isolated.[29] Similarly in indigo, it appears that one form (probably the *cis* form, IV), reverts spontaneously to its isomer in a few hours even in the solid state.[30] The available evidence is not completely conclusive, however, and the problem deserves further investigation.

[29] M. Calvin and R. E. Buckles, *J. Am. Chem. Soc.*, **62**, 3324 (1940).
[30] G. Heller, *Ber.*, **72**, 1858 (1939).

## Chapter 5

## RESONANCE AND DIPOLE MOMENTS

**5·1  General Discussion.**[1]  In the same way in which we define the center of mass (or center of gravity) of a material object, we can define also the centers of the positive, and of the negative, charges of a molecule. If, in a given molecule, these centers of the positive and negative charges do not coincide with each other, the substance is said to be polar; if they do coincide, the substance is said to be non-polar.  Evidently, the molecules of a polar substance are distinguished from those of a non-polar one by the fact that the former, but not the latter, have positive and negative ends.  For example, in the typically polar substance, hydrogen chloride, the centers of the positive and negative charge undoubtedly lie in the direction of the hydrogen and chlorine nuclei, respectively, so that the hydrogen and chlorine atoms can be considered to carry net positive and negative charges, respectively; on the other hand, in the typically non-polar substance, molecular hydrogen, each atom must be electrically neutral.

The quantitative measure of the polarity of a substance is its electric dipole moment, $\mu$, which is defined by the equation

$$\mu = Er \tag{1}$$

The letter $E$ represents here the magnitude of the total positive, or negative, charge, and $r$ is the distance between the two centers of charge. (This definition of the electric dipole moment is unique only for neutral molecules, since only then are the magnitudes of the total positive and negative charges equal.  Consequently, we shall restrict ourselves in the future to the discussion of neutral molecules, and we shall not consider the dipole moments of ions.  Moreover, since we shall have no occasion in this chapter to refer to *magnetic* dipole moments, we shall adopt the common procedure of describing the electric dipole moments simply as

[1] For further details than can be given here, the reader is referred to the many excellent general discussions that have been published in the past.  For example, see C. P. Smyth, *Dielectric Constant and Molecular Structure*, Chemical Catalog Company, New York, 1931; J. H. Van Vleck, *The Theory of Electric and Magnetic Susceptibilities*, Oxford University Press, Oxford, 1932; N. V. Sidgwick, *Some Physical Properties of the Covalent Link in Chemistry*, Cornell University Press, Ithaca, N. Y., 1933, Chapter V.

"dipole moments" or, more simply still, as "moments.") The dipole moment of a non-polar substance is equal to zero, because the distance $r$ is equal to zero, whereas that of a polar substance cannot be zero, because neither $E$ nor $r$ can be zero; this fact suggests an alternative way of stating the distinction between polar and non-polar substances.

An idea of the magnitude of the dipole moment of a polar substance can be obtained in the following manner. The charges of the particles contained in the molecule, that is, the charges of the nuclei and the electrons, are of the order of $10^{-10}$ electrostatic unit; and the intramolecular distances are of the order of $10^{-8}$ cm. Consequently, the dipole moments should be of the order of $10^{-10} \times 10^{-8} = 10^{-18}$ electrostatic unit. This quantity, $10^{-18}$ esu, is a convenient unit in terms of which dipole moments may be expressed; it is called the Debye unit, or simply the Debye, and it is represented by the symbol $D$. Thus, a non-polar substance can be described as one with a moment equal to $0.00D$.

From its definition in equation 1, a dipole moment is seen to have a direction as well as a magnitude, because the distance $r$ between the two centers of charge has a definite direction. A dipole moment is therefore a vector quantity and can be represented by an arrow. The convention has been adopted of drawing this arrow so that it is parallel to the line joining the centers of charge, and so that its head and tail are pointed in the directions of the negative and positive centers, respectively. The tail is commonly crossed, as in $+\!\!\longrightarrow$, in order to emphasize the fact that it represents the positive end of the dipole. The length of the arrow is proportional to the magnitude of the moment, that is, to the magnitude of the product, $Er$, which is, of course, always a positive quantity.

It is frequently convenient to think of the total dipole moment of a molecule as the sum of partial moments, which may be either localized in different parts of the molecule, or due to different causes. Since a dipole moment is a vector, the sum in question must be a vector sum, or a resultant. The method of forming such a vector sum is illustrated in the diagram

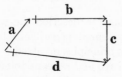

which represents the vector equation

$$\mathbf{a} + \mathbf{b} + \mathbf{c} = \mathbf{d}$$

The procedure is simply to arrange the arrows that represent the individual vectors to be summed ($\mathbf{a}$, $\mathbf{b}$, and $\mathbf{c}$ in the present example) so that the head of the first is coincident with the tail of the second, the head of the second is coincident with the tail of the third, and so on. For this purpose, the arrows can be moved to any necessary positions, but their directions (and of course their lengths) must be left unchanged; this means that they must be kept always parallel to their original directions or, what amounts to the same thing, to the dipole moments which they represent. The sum of the vectors, or their resultant, is then represented in magnitude and direction by the arrow **d**, which is drawn with its head, and tail, coincident with the head of the last, and tail of the first, of the component vectors, respectively. It can be shown that the order of addition is immaterial, so that, for example,

$$\mathbf{a} + \mathbf{b} + \mathbf{c} = \mathbf{a} + \mathbf{c} + \mathbf{b} = \mathbf{c} + \mathbf{b} + \mathbf{a}, \text{ and so on}$$

Several important corollaries can be drawn from the above graphical scheme for the representation of vector addition. In the first place, the two arrows which represent a vector, **a**, and its negative, −**a**, are of the same length and are parallel to each other, but they point in opposite directions, as

Moreover, the sum of a set of vectors is equal to zero if, in the diagram from which the sum is computed, the head of the last arrow coincides with the tail of the first. And finally, the magnitude of the sum of two vectors is equal to the sum of the magnitudes if the vectors are parallel and pointed in the same direction; it is equal to the magnitude of the difference between the magnitudes if the vectors are parallel and pointed in opposite directions; and it has an intermediate value if the vectors make an angle with each other. In general, the magnitude of a sum of vectors is greater the more nearly the vectors point in the same direction. The method of vector addition and its above-mentioned corollaries will be illustrated further in the following sections.

It will not be possible here to describe the ways in which the values of dipole moments can be measured experimentally. Brief mention may be made, however, of the basic principles involved.[1] As has already been noted, a polar molecule has a positive and a negative end; in an electrostatic field, therefore, it tends to be oriented so that its dipole moment lies parallel to the field. This tendency toward a definite orientation is opposed, however, by the thermal motion, which favors a completely random orientation. Some sort of compromise between the competing effects must be reached, of course. Obviously, at low temperatures, at which the thermal energy is small, the orientation along the direction of the field should be more nearly complete than at high temperatures, at which the thermal energy is large. Moreover, since the degree of orientation is reflected in the dielectric constant, $\varepsilon$, of the substance, it follows that the dielectric constant of a polar substance should vary with temperature. Indeed, calculation has led to equation 2,

$$\frac{\varepsilon - 1}{\varepsilon + 2} \cdot \frac{M}{d} = P_E + P_A + \frac{4\pi N\mu^2}{9kT} \tag{2}$$

where $M$ is the molecular weight and $d$ is the density of the substance, $N$ is Avogadro's number, $k$ is Boltzmann's constant, $T$ is the absolute temperature, and $P_E$ and $P_A$ are the so-called electron and atom polarizations, respectively. (Actually, $P_E$ and $P_A$ are *polarizabilities* rather than *polarizations*, but the latter term seems to be generally adopted for them in dipole moment work.) It is important that the dipole moment, $\mu$, appears in equation 2 only in the form of the square of its magnitude, which is no longer a vector. Consequently, the direction of the moment cannot be measured.

Some discussion of the fundamental equation 2 is desirable here, in order that its significance and its methods of application may be made clear. In the first place, it should be remarked that the equation applies strictly only to a substance in the form of a highly attenuated gas. The experimental study of such a gas is difficult, because its dielectric constant is always only slightly greater than unity, so that the term $\varepsilon - 1$ in the numerator on the left side of equation 2 is a small difference between larger quantities and cannot be measured very precisely. Moreover, many substances of interest cannot be vaporized without decomposition. For these reasons, most of the measurements of dipole moments have been carried out in dilute solution in some non-polar solvent like benzene or carbon tetrachloride. Equation 2 then has to be replaced by the more general one, 2′,

$$\frac{\varepsilon - 1}{\varepsilon + 2} \cdot \frac{f_1 M_1 + f_2 M_2}{d} = f_1(P_{E1} + P_{A1}) + f_2(P_{E2} + P_{A2}) + \frac{4\pi f_2 N\mu_2^2}{9kT} \tag{2′}$$

in which the subscripts 1 and 2 refer to the non-polar solvent and to the solute, respectively; $f_1$ and $f_2$ are the mole fractions of the appropriate components; and the other symbols have the same meanings as in equation 2. The value of the term $P_{E1} + P_{A1}$ is determined by measuring the dielectric constant of the pure solvent, for which $f_1 = 1$ and $f_2 = 0$. Equation 2′, which cannot be derived as rigorously as equation 2, seems to be fairly, but not absolutely, satisfactory. As a result, dipole moments measured in solution may be in error by several tenths of a Debye unit. In the future, therefore, we shall use the values obtained in the gas phase whenever possible; when such values are not available, we shall try to limit ourselves to comparisons of the moments obtained for substances of similar structure under comparable conditions.

Since $P_E$ and $P_A$ are found experimentally to be practically independent of temperature, it follows from equation 2 that, when the quantity $\dfrac{\varepsilon - 1}{\varepsilon + 2} \cdot \dfrac{M}{d}$

is plotted against the reciprocal of the absolute temperature, a straight line with a slope of $4\pi N\mu^2/9k$ should be obtained, provided that the dipole moment, $\mu$, does not itself vary with temperature. (For the sake of simplicity, we shall assume in the following that we are dealing with a gaseous substance, so that we can employ equation 2.) In principle, this fact provides the most precise method for the evaluation of $\mu$. In practice, however, the accurate determination of the slope of the line often requires that the dielectric constant be measured over an impracticably great temperature range; moreover, the method cannot be used at all if $\mu$ is a function of temperature. For these reasons, a different procedure (the *optical*, as distinguished from the *temperature-variation*, method) has been commonly adopted. The electron polarization, $P_E$, can be calculated directly from the index of refraction, $n$, of the substance, with the aid of the Lorenz-Lorentz equation

$$\frac{n^2 - 1}{n^2 + 2} \cdot \frac{M}{d} = R_M = P_E \tag{3}$$

for the molecular refraction, $R_M$. Since the index of refraction depends upon the wavelength of the light used, the value of $P_E$ measured for visible light should be extrapolated to infinite wavelength. The atom polarization, $P_A$, is usually small and is ordinarily either ignored or else arbitrarily assigned a value equal to some definite factor, say one-tenth, times that of $P_E$. In this manner, the dipole moment can be obtained from a measurement of the dielectric constant at a single temperature. An error of uncertain magnitude and sign, however, is introduced by the approximations and assumptions in the calculation. This error can sometimes be quite large,[2] but it is usually assumed to be at most only a few tenths of Debye unit.

**5·2  The Origin of Dipole Moments.**  For our present purposes, we shall find it convenient to think of the measured moment of a given substance as the vector sum of contributions, known as bond moments, that are made by all the bonds that are present in the molecule. By adopting this procedure, we can first deal with each bond separately, and then consider the combination of the various bond moments into the resultant moment of the molecule as a whole.

The existence of a dipole moment can frequently be correlated with the presence of formal charges in the molecule. Trimethylamine oxide, I, for example, has a moment of $5.02D$, in benzene solution,[3] which undoubtedly resides largely in the nitrogen-oxygen bond. The nitrogen and oxygen atoms, of course, lie at the positive and negative ends, respectively, of this bond moment. Similarly, nitromethane, which resonates between structures II and III, probably owes its moment of

---

[2] I. E. Coop and L. E. Sutton, *J. Chem. Soc.*, 1269 (1938). For a general discussion of atom polarization, see L. E. Sutton, *Annual Reports on the Progress of Chemistry*, **37**, 57 (1940).

[3] E. P. Linton, *J. Am. Chem. Soc.*, **62**, 1945 (1940).

3.50$D$ in the gas phase (Table 5·2), largely to the formal charges; again, the nitrogen and oxygen atoms are undoubtedly positive and negative, respectively. Very frequently, however, appreciable dipole moments

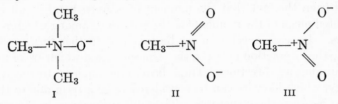

exist in molecules in which no formal charges are present; under such circumstances, the resonance theory gives considerable insight into the factors involved.

It was pointed out in Section 2·7 that any actual bond must resonate between purely ionic and purely covalent structures, and it was mentioned that this fact provides a qualitative picture of the origin of dipole moments. It seems evident, for example, that in hydrogen chloride, in which resonance occurs among the structures IV, V, and VI, the hydrogen atom must be positive relative to the chlorine, because structure V is certainly more stable and so must make a larger contribution than structure VI. In the hydrogen molecule, on the other hand, the

$$\underset{\text{IV}}{\text{H—Cl}} \qquad \underset{\text{V}}{\overset{+\quad-}{\text{H}\quad\text{Cl}}} \qquad \underset{\text{VI}}{\overset{-\quad+}{\text{H}\quad\text{Cl}}}$$

resonance among the three corresponding structures, VII, VIII, and IX, leads to zero moment. The two ionic structures, VIII and IX, being

$$\underset{\text{VII}}{\text{H—H}} \qquad \underset{\text{VIII}}{\overset{+\quad-}{\text{H}\quad\text{H}}} \qquad \underset{\text{IX}}{\overset{-\quad+}{\text{H}\quad\text{H}}}$$

equivalent, must make the same contribution to the state of the molecule, and therefore their effects upon its moment exactly cancel each other.

It has not yet been possible to develop a completely satisfactory quantitative theory of bond moments on the above basis, since, in the attempt to do so, several difficulties arise which have so far not been resolved. In the first place, it is possible that even a purely covalent structure may correspond to a non-vanishing dipole moment, and, in fact, approximate calculations have suggested that this may be the rule rather than the exception when the bond in question is between dissimilar atoms.[4] Such a covalent moment should lie with its positive end at the larger of the two atoms, and therefore it might tend either to increase or to

[4] R. S. Mulliken, *J. Chem. Phys.*, **3**, 573 (1935).

diminish that due to the ionic structures. In any event, its exact effect upon the observed bond moment could not be determined without detailed and laborious numerical computation. A second difficulty arises from the fact that the moment of a given bond is not simply a weighted mean of the moments of the structures among which resonance occurs. Instead, account must be taken of further terms, which are due to the interaction between the structures, and which are of uncertain magnitude and direction. These bear some analogy to the resonance energy, which likewise can be considered to be a term due to the interaction between the structures. They differ, however, in the significant regard that they may either increase or decrease the moment (or they may possibly even leave it unchanged), whereas the resonance energy can never increase the energy content.

Still a further factor which makes a quantitative treatment difficult is that experiment gives only the total dipole moment of the molecule as a whole, and not the moments of the individual bonds. In some

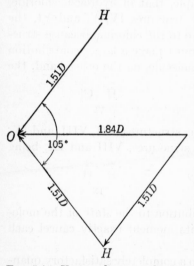

FIG. 5·1. Vector diagram showing the dipole moment of a water molecule as the sum of the moments of the two O–H bonds.

especially simple molecules, to be sure, the bond moments can be inferred unambiguously from the measured moments of the substances. A trivial example of this is encountered in any diatomic molecule, such as that of hydrogen chloride, because then only one bond is present, and consequently the bond moment and the measured moment are identical. A more interesting example is provided by water. Since the two oxygen-hydrogen bonds are equivalent, they must have the same bond moment. This fact, when combined with the measured moment of $1.84D$[5] for the substance, and with the measured value of $105°$ for the H–O–H bond angle,[6] shows that the oxygen-hydrogen bond moment must be $1.51D$. In the calculation, the principle of which should be apparent from Figure 5·1, the further reasonable assumption must be made that

[5] Except as otherwise noted, all numerical values of dipole moments given in this chapter are for the substance in the gaseous state and are taken from a compilation which appears in *Trans. Faraday Soc.*, **30** (1934) in an Appendix inserted between pages 904 and 905.

[6] D. M. Dennison, *Rev. Modern Phys.*, **12**, 175 (1940).

the bond moments lie along their respective bond axes. Similarly, from the facts that the total moment of ammonia is $1.46D$, and that each of the H–N–H bond angles is $107°$,[6] the moment of the nitrogen-hydrogen bond is found to be $1.31D$. In each of these examples, the hydrogen is presumably positive with respect to the central atom. On the other hand, the measured moment of methane is $0.00D$. This value is a direct consequence merely of the tetrahedral symmetry of the molecule and sheds no light whatever upon the moment of the carbon-hydrogen bond. In the following discussion, we shall assume that the carbon-hydrogen bond moment is equal to $0.4D$, with the hydrogen positive.[7] With more complex molecules, further difficulties arise. For example, in methyl ether, the total moment is the resultant of two carbon-oxygen, and six carbon-hydrogen bond moments. If the moments of the carbon-hydrogen bonds are the same as in methane, and if the H–C–C and C–O–C bond angles are tetrahedral, then the observed moment of $1.3D$ for the molecule requires that the moment of each carbon-oxygen bond be $0.8D$. In a similar manner, the moments of other types of bond can be obtained. The values of several representative bond moments, calculated in this way, are given in Table 5·1. It should be apparent that the exact values of these are subject to some uncertainty if they have had to be derived in the rather indirect manner illustrated above in connection with the carbon-oxygen bond moment. Moreover, the value derived for the moment of a given type of bond is often found to vary slightly from substance to substance.

Although the above-mentioned complications make a completely satisfactory quantitative treatment impossible at the present time, results of some significance can nevertheless be obtained by ignoring them and proceeding on the simplest possible basis. Thus, for the purposes of the present discussion, we shall assume that the magnitude of the moment of any purely covalent structure is zero, that that of any purely ionic structure is equal to the product of the electronic charge $(4.80 \times 10^{-10}$ esu$)$ by the internuclear distance, that the actual moment of the bond is the weighted mean of the two, and that the "observed" bond moments of Table 5·1 are correct. For hydrogen chloride, for example, the covalent, ionic, and actual moments are 0.00, 6.14, and $1.03D$, respectively, so that the bond must be 83 per cent covalent and 17 per cent ionic. This conclusion is not unreasonable, but obviously, in view of the considerations of the preceding paragraphs, it must be regarded only as the roughest sort of approximation.

The results of similar calculations for several further kinds of single

---

[7] See C. A. Coulson, *Proc. Cambridge Phil. Soc.*, **36**, 509 (1940), and references to the earlier literature given there.

## TABLE 5·1

BOND MOMENTS AND PARTIAL IONIC CHARACTERS OF BONDS

| Bond | Moment[a] (D) | $r$[b] (A) | $er$[c] (D) | Per Cent Ionic Character | Difference in Electronegativities[d] |
|---|---|---|---|---|---|
| C—H | (0.4) | 1.07 | 5.1 | 8 | 0.4 |
| N—H | 1.31 | 1.00 | 4.8 | 27 | 0.9 |
| O—H | 1.51 | 0.96 | 4.6 | 33 | 1.4 |
| S—H | 0.68 | 1.34 | 6.4 | 11 | 0.4 |
| H—Cl | 1.03 | 1.27[e] | 6.1 | 17 | 0.9 |
| H—Br | 0.78 | 1.41[e] | 6.8 | 11 | 0.7 |
| H—I | 0.38 | 1.61[e] | 7.7 | 5 | 0.4 |
| C—N | 0.45[f] | 1.47 | 7.1 | 6 | 0.5 |
| C—O | 0.8 | 1.43 | 6.8 | 12 | 1.0 |
| C—Cl | 1.5 | 1.76 | 8.4 | 18 | 0.5 |
| C—Br | 1.4 | 1.91 | 9.2 | 15 | 0.3 |
| C—I | 1.2 | 2.10 | 10.1 | 12 | 0.0 |
| K—Cl | 6.3[e] | 2.79[e] | 13.4 | 47 | 2.2[g] |

[a] L. Pauling, *The Nature of the Chemical Bond*, Cornell University Press, Ithaca, N. Y., 1st ed., 1939, p. 68; 2nd ed., 1940, p. 68.

[b] Except as noted, the values of the internuclear distance, $r$, given here are the sums of Pauling's covalent radii. See Table 4·2.

[c] The quantities listed in this column are the products of the magnitude of the electronic charge $e(= 4.80 \times 10^{-10})$ by the distances $r$.

[d] Pauling's values are used. See Table 3·10.

[e] O. K. Rice, *Electronic Structure and Chemical Binding*, McGraw-Hill Book Company, New York, 1940, p. 199.

[f] C. P. Smyth, *J. Am. Chem. Soc.*, **60**, 183 (1938).

[g] L. Pauling (reference a, 1st ed., 1939, p. 64; 2nd ed., 1940, p. 64) gives the electronegativity of potassium as 0.8.

bond are given in Table 5·1. These also seem quite reasonable in the majority of cases, although some exceptions do occur. The comparatively large value of the carbon-iodine bond moment, for example, seems surprising since the electronegativities listed in Table 3·10 indicate that the ionic structures X and XI should make only small, and approximately equal, contributions. Moreover, it can hardly be explained as

$$\overset{+}{R_3C} \quad \overset{-}{I} \qquad\qquad \overset{-}{R_3C} \quad \overset{+}{I}$$

$$\text{X} \qquad\qquad\qquad\qquad \text{XI}$$

due to an especially large moment of the covalent structure, inasmuch as the iodine should then be at the positive end of the dipole instead of at the negative end, where it appears to be. In the gaseous potassium chloride molecule, on the other hand, the observed moment seems unreasonably small since here, if anywhere, an almost completely ionic bond should be found. These examples illustrate the difficulties encountered in the application of the present treatment and the uncertainties inherent in the interpretation of the results obtained with its aid.

A different sort of quantitative approach, which seems to suffer from similar difficulties, consists in correlating the observed bond moments with the differences in electronegativities of the two atoms in question.[8] It is found empirically that usually the magnitude of a bond moment, when expressed in Debye units, is approximately equal to the difference between the values of the electronegativities listed in Table 3·10. The observed moment of hydrogen chloride, for example, is $1.03D$, whereas the difference in electronegativities, $x_{Cl} - x_H$, is 0.9. Data for several further bonds are also given in Table 5·1. Discrepancies again occur with the carbon-iodine and potassium-chlorine bonds, as before, so that the quantitative aspects of the treatment still leave much to be desired.

In spite of the fact that no completely satisfactory quantitative treatment has as yet been devised, the purely qualitative features of the theory remain a helpful aid in the understanding of the origin of dipole moments. In the following sections we shall show how a similar treatment leads to a logical, but still qualitative, explanation of certain variations in bond moments.

**5·3 Polarization.** All the alkyl chlorides, $C_nH_{2n+1}Cl$, might be expected to have exactly the same dipole moment; experimentally,

TABLE 5·2

EFFECT OF POLARIZATION ON DIPOLE MOMENTS[a]

| Alkyl Group | Substituent | | | | | |
|---|---|---|---|---|---|---|
| | F | Cl | Br | I | NO$_2$ | CN[b] |
| Methyl | 1.81 | 1.87 | 1.78 | 1.59 | 3.50 | 3.94[c] |
| Ethyl | 1.92 | 2.05 | 2.02 | 1.90 | 3.70[d] | 4.04[c] |
| n-Propyl | — | 2.10 | 2.15 | 2.01 | 3.72 | 4.05[c] |
| n-Butyl | — | 2.09 | 2.15 | 2.08 | 3.55[e] | 4.09[c] |
| n-Amyl | — | 2.12 | — | — | — | — |
| n-Heptyl | — | — | 2.15 | — | — | — |
| i-Propyl | — | 2.15 | 2.19 | — | 3.73 | — |
| i-Butyl | — | 2.04 | — | — | — | — |
| s-Butyl | — | 2.12 | 2.20 | — | — | — |
| t-Butyl | — | 2.13 | — | — | 3.71 | — |

[a] The quantities listed in the body of this table are the dipole moments (expressed in Debye units) of the gaseous molecules RX, where the alkyl group R is given at the left of the row, and the substituent X is given at the top of the column. Except where noted, the data are taken from R. H. Wiswall, Jr., and C. P. Smyth, *J. Chem. Phys.*, **9**, 356 (1941). A number of the individual values quoted by Wiswall and Smyth in this paper are due to L. G. Groves and S. Sugden, *J. Chem. Soc.*, 158 (1937).

[b] These substances are cyanides and not isocyanides.

[c] L. G. Groves and S. Sugden, note a.

[d] E. C. Hurdis and C. P. Smyth, *J. Am. Chem. Soc.*, **64**, 2829 (1942).

[e] This value obtained by L. G. Groves and S. Sugden (note a) is probably too low, because these authors reported low values for several other aliphatic nitro compounds as well.

J. G. Malone, *J. Chem. Phys.*, **1**, 197 (1933).

however, small variations are found to occur. It will be seen, in fact, from the data of Table 5·2 that the observed moments increase in magnitude as the alkyl groups become either larger or more highly branched. The moments are affected appreciably, however, only by structural changes in the fairly immediate neighborhood of the chlorine atom.

The proof of the initial statement of the preceding paragraph can be obtained by application of the rule of vector addition, provided that all carbon-hydrogen bonds are assumed to have the same moment, all carbon-carbon bonds are assumed to have zero moment, and all bond angles are assumed to have the same values from molecule to molecule. A simpler proof, which is based upon the same assumptions, is as follows: The dipole moment of methane is zero. Therefore, the resultant of the moments of any three of its carbon-hydrogen bonds must be equal in magnitude and opposite in direction to the moment of the fourth. Therefore, the dipole moment of a substance should not be changed if a hydrogen atom *joined to carbon* is replaced by a methyl group, or vice versa. Since any alkyl chloride can be made (in thought) from any other by a succession of such replacements, it follows at once that all alkyl chlorides should have the same dipole moment.

The above deviations from the strict constancy of bond moments find a simple explanation in the polarization of the hydrocarbon radicals by the carbon-chlorine dipoles. In methyl chloride, for example, the existence of the large carbon-chlorine moment requires that the carbon atom be relatively positive. This atom therefore exerts a larger than usual attraction for the electrons which it shares with the hydrogen atoms, and so pulls them in closer than normal. In other words, a small dipole is induced in the methyl group by the large moment of the carbon-chlorine bond, and the observed moment is the sum of the two. Since the primary and the induced dipoles are at any rate roughly in the same direction, the effect of the polarization must be to increase the magnitude of the moment of the molecule. In ethyl chloride the situation is similar. On account of its greater size, however, the ethyl group is more polarizable than the methyl group, and so both the induced and the total moments must be larger for ethyl chloride than for methyl chloride.

In *n*-propyl chloride, a further increase in the observed moment occurs, but it is smaller than that noted in passing from methyl to ethyl chloride. The reason for this leveling off is that the additional methylene group in *n*-propyl chloride is at a considerable distance from the carbon-chlorine bond; it is therefore in a region of relatively low electrostatic potential and is only slightly polarized. For a similar reason, the observed moment of *n*-butyl chloride is not appreciably greater than that of *n*-propyl chloride.

The moment of *i*-propyl chloride is slightly larger than that of *n*-propyl chloride. This difference is probably due not to any intrinsically greater polarizability of the *i*-propyl group, but rather to the fact that it is more closely bunched about the carbon-chlorine bond and so has a more favorable steric arrangement for polarization. The difference is small, however, and may be no greater than the uncertainties in the experimental data. Similarly, no reliance can be put in the reported small difference between the moments of *s*- and *t*-butyl chlorides.

The phenomenon of polarization is, of course, not restricted to the alkyl chlorides but occurs generally whenever a strongly polar group is present in the neighborhood of another, polarizable group. A number of further examples, also taken from the aliphatic series, are included in Table 5·2. It will be seen that the general situation is always closely parallel to that encountered above with the alkyl chlorides, so that a single explanation accounts satisfactorily for a considerable body of data. It seems strange, however, that the very large nitro *group moment* apparently produces less polarization than the smaller carbon-chlorine bond moment. The explanation is perhaps that the nitro group moment may lie largely in the nitrogen-oxygen bonds, as is indeed suggested by the formal charges. If this supposition is correct, then the large primary dipoles are farther away from the polarizable groups, upon which they act, in the nitro compounds than in the alkyl halides, and so they have relatively smaller effects.

The significance of a group moment is the following: In nitromethane, for example, the total moment that can be referred to the nitro group is the sum of the moments of the carbon-nitrogen and nitrogen-oxygen bonds. Since there is no way of determining the values of the individal bond moments separately, and no advantage in doing so anyhow, we shall lump them together and call their sum the nitro group moment. The group moments of other polyatomic substituents can be defined in completely analogous manners. Obviously, group moments can be handled in just the same way as the bond moments characteristic of monatomic substituents, *provided that* they lie along the bond joining the substituent to the rest of the molecule. If this condition is satisfied, as with the nitro, cyano, methyl, and numerous other groups (including, of course, all monatomic groups), the moment or the corresponding group is said to be axial; if the condition is not satisfied, as with the hydroxy, amino, and many other groups, the moment or the group is said to be non-axial. The treatment of non-axial group moments is comparatively difficult, because the angles between the different component vectors in the complete molecule not only may be unknown but also may vary as the group rotates about the bond which links it to the rest of the molecule. For example, whereas the dipole moment of *p*-dinitrobenzene must be zero because the nitro group moment is axial,[2] that of the dimethyl ether of hydroquinone cannot be predicted because the methoxy group moment is non-axial. (Actually the moment of the substance in solution is $1.7D$, as compared with $1.2D$ for anisole.) For these reasons, we shall restrict ourselves, throughout the remainder of this chapter, to axial groups to as great an extent as possible.

Polarization, which has been treated hitherto as a purely classical effect, can also be discussed from the point of view of resonance. The example of methyl chloride will again serve to illustrate the principles involved. In this substance, the partially ionic structures I and II (among many others) must make small contributions to the state of the molecule. Now, the carbon atom is relatively positive on account of the large carbon-chlorine bond moment. The effect of such a positive charge on the carbon must be to increase the stability of structure I and to decrease that of structure II. Thus, these must make larger and smaller contributions, respectively, than do the corresponding struc-

tures for methane. In other words, the carbon-hydrogen bond that is under discussion here is polarized by the carbon-chlorine moment. Similar considerations apply, naturally, also to the remaining carbon-hydrogen bonds, as well as to any further bonds that may be present in more complex molecules. By an obvious extension of the argument, it can easily be shown that the present method of treatment accounts for the rapid decrease in polarizing power with distance, and consequently for the qualitative features discussed above and summarized in Table 5.2.

**5.4  Dipole Moments and Resonance.**  In Section 5.2 we found that the dipole moments of essentially covalent bonds can be explained qualitatively as resulting from resonance between purely covalent and purely ionic structures. We turn now to a consideration of the effect of resonance among structures of more conventional type, in which each valence bond is considered already to possess its own characteristic bond moment. A simple example is provided by carbon dioxide, which apparently resonates among the structures I, II, and III. (See Sec-

$$O\!=\!C\!=\!O \qquad\qquad \overset{+}{O}\!=\!C\!-\!\overset{-}{O} \qquad\qquad \overset{-}{O}\!-\!C\!\equiv\!\overset{+}{O}$$

I                              II                              III

tions 3·3 and 4·3.)   Of these, structure I corresponds to zero dipole moment, since the two carbon-oxygen bond moments exactly cancel each other.   The remaining structures, II and III, have large moments on account of their formal charges, when considered separately; however, they must make equal contributions, and so they also lead to a zero moment when considered together.   As a result of the resonance among all three structures, therefore, the molecule is completely nonpolar.

It will be interesting and instructive to consider at this point the changes in the above discussion which would have been required if carbon dioxide were a tautomeric substance, consisting of molecules with the structures I, II, and III.   Two extreme situations can be taken up separately.   In the first place, the molecules might undergo transitions from one structure to another so readily that the average time which they spend between transitions is small compared with the time required for them to be oriented in an electrostatic field, say $10^{-7}$–$10^{-12}$ sec.   Under such circumstances, the molecules could not be oriented in the field; they would therefore behave like nonpolar molecules, and the measured dipole moment would be zero, as it actually is.   However, this could hardly be the real state of affairs, because it would not correspond to a true tautomerism, but rather to a resonance of the sort described in paragraph A2i of Section 1·5.   The substance would then not have a definite energy content.   Consequently, this possibility can be excluded.   The second extreme situation would arise if the average time which the molecules spend between transitions is large compared with the time required for them to be oriented.   Under such circumstances, carbon dioxide would behave like an ordinary mixture of substances with the structures I, II, and III.   The measured dipole moment would therefore have a *magnitude* intermediate among those of the structures involved.   Consequently, since the structures II and III have moments of large magnitude, the measured moment could not be zero if these were involved to any appreciable extent. It follows, then, that this second possibility also is excluded, unless we should choose to ignore the structures II and III, and to assume that carbon dioxide is completely represented by the single structure I.[9]

A rather more interesting example of the effect of resonance upon dipole moments is provided by nitrous oxide, $N_2O$.   The most stable structures for this substance are presumably IV and V.   (The further structure VI is probably too unstable, on account of its especially

$$\overset{-}{N}{=}\overset{+}{N}{=}O \qquad\qquad N{\equiv}\overset{+}{N}{-}\overset{-}{O} \qquad\qquad {}^{--}N{-}\overset{+}{N}{\equiv}\overset{+}{O}$$
$$\text{IV} \qquad\qquad\qquad \text{V} \qquad\qquad\qquad\qquad \text{VI}$$

unfavorable charge distribution, to require consideration.)   As a result of their formal charges, the structures IV and V must correspond

[9] Cf. L. E. Sutton, *Trans. Faraday Soc.*, **30**, 789 (1934).

separately to large moments in opposite directions. However, the observed moment is zero to within the experimental uncertainty. This value can be explained on the assumption that the two structures IV and V make approximately equal contributions, so that the negative charge which structure IV imparts to the terminal nitrogen atom is almost exactly counterbalanced by that which structure V imparts to the oxygen. Such a qualitative discussion as the present would not have enabled us to predict the actual magnitude of the moment, but it does permit an interpretation of the experimental data, which would otherwise have appeared entirely anomalous. It is of particular interest that the zero dipole moment of this substance, unlike that of carbon dioxide, cannot be accounted for on the basis of any single structure but requires the consideration of resonance between two structures. Moreover, the facts are completely inconsistent with the assumption of any sort of tautomerism between the structures.

In the azide group, the resonance is similar to that in nitrous oxide. For phenyl azide, for example, the structures VII and VIII presumably make the largest contributions. (Again a third structure, IX can be written, but is probably too unstable to make a significant contribution.) Although the observed moment of $1.55D^{10}$ (in benzene solution) is rather larger than that of nitrous oxide, it is still so small that it can be explained only on the basis of resonance between the structures VII and VIII.

$$C_6H_5—\overset{+}{N}=\overset{-}{N}=N \qquad C_6H_5—\overset{-}{N}—\overset{+}{N}\equiv N \qquad C_6H_5—\overset{+}{N}\equiv\overset{+}{N}—N^{--}$$

$$\text{VII} \qquad\qquad\qquad \text{VIII} \qquad\qquad\qquad \text{IX}$$

It is known that in this substance the phenyl group is at the positive end of the dipole, so that apparently structure VII is more important than VIII. The method by which the direction of the moment is determined is as follows. The moments of nitrobenzene, X, and of $p$-nitrophenyl azide, XI, are $3.95D^{11}$ and $2.96D,^{10}$ respectively (in benzene solution). Since the moment of nitro-

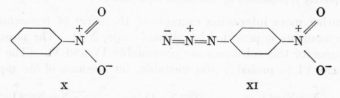

X                                              XI

benzene must be due largely to the formal charges on the nitrogen and oxygen atoms, it is certain that the nitro and phenyl groups lie in the negative and

$^{10}$ E. Bergmann and W. Schütz, Z. physik. Chem., **B19**, 389 (1932). See also N. V. Sidgwick, L. E. Sutton, and W. Thomas, J. Chem. Soc., 406 (1933).

$^{11}$ R. H. Birtles and G. C. Hampson, J. Chem. Soc., 10 (1937).

positive directions, respectively. Moreover, since the moment of nitro-benzene is *decreased* by the introduction of the azide group, it follows that the moments due to the two substituents in *p*-nitrophenyl azide must be in approximately (although probably not exactly) opposite directions. From analogy, then, the conclusion is drawn that in phenyl azide itself the direction of the moment is as stated above.

Carbon monoxide presents a difficult problem on account of the anomalous valence state of the carbon. In Sections 3·3 and 4·3, some not entirely conclusive evidence was brought forward which purported to show that this substance resonates between the structures XII and XIII. The first of these structures probably corresponds to a dipole

$$C{=}O \qquad\qquad \overset{-}{C}{\equiv}\overset{+}{O}$$

$$\text{XII} \qquad\qquad\qquad \text{XIII}$$

moment of considerable magnitude, which lies in such direction that the carbon atom is positive and the oxygen is negative. This conclusion follows from the fact that oxygen is a more electronegative element than carbon. Although the substances are hardly comparable, it is interesting and probably significant in this connection that aldehydes and ketones have moments of the order of 2.5–3.0*D*, with the oxygen nega-tive. The second structure, XIII, on the other hand, must have a large moment in the opposite direction, on account of the formal charges. The actual moment of the substance is 0.1*D* (of unknown direction). This value, although it could not have been predicted in advance, is entirely reasonable as a result of resonance between XII and XIII, and it provides perhaps the most satisfactory evidence for the existence of the resonance. It seems probable that here, as with nitrous oxide, no single structure could account for the observed moment.

In the isocyanides, the situation is similar to that in carbon monoxide. The moment of phenyl isocyanide (in solution) is 3.5*D*, and its direction is such that the phenyl group is at its positive end. (For the method of establishing the direction of the moment, see the above discussion of phenyl azide.) This result is consistent with resonance between the structures XIV and XV, with the latter perhaps predominating. The

$$C_6H_5{-}N{=}C \qquad\qquad C_6H_5{-}\overset{+}{N}{\equiv}\overset{-}{C}$$

$$\text{XIV} \qquad\qquad\qquad \text{XV}$$

fact that the moment of the isocyanide group is apparently axial also supports a large contribution from structure XV.

In Section 5·3, attention was called to those variations in the dipole moments of the alkyl halides and similar compounds which are due to differing polarizabilities of the alkyl groups. On the basis of the con-

siderations discussed there, the moment of vinyl chloride, XVI, would
be expected to be particularly large, possibly about 2.2 or 2.3*D*, since
the vinyl radical is known to have a larger polarizability than any

$$H_2C{=}CH$$
$$\vert$$
$$Cl$$
XVI

$$H_2\overset{-}{C}{-}CH$$
$$\Vert$$
$$Cl^+$$
XVII

comparable saturated radical.    The observed moment, however, is only
1.44*D*, which is smaller than even that of methyl chloride.    (See Tables
5·2 and 5·3.)    The explanation of this apparent discrepancy is presumably that resonance occurs between the structures XVI and XVII.
The second of these can make only a small contribution to the state of
the molecule, but, on account of the presence of the formal charges, it
must have a very large moment in a direction approximately the opposite of that of structure XVI.    The effect of the resonance must therefore
be to decrease the value of the actual moment of the substance, in
agreement with the observation.    The present considerations are, of
course, completely consistent with those of Section 4·3, in which the
shortness of the carbon–chlorine bond in vinyl chloride was attributed to
a partial double-bond character of the bond.

In chloroacetylene, XVIII and XIX, the resonance effect is still

$$HC{\equiv}C{-}Cl$$
XVIII

$$\overset{-}{H}C{=}C{=}\overset{+}{Cl}$$
XIX

greater, and the dipole moment is reduced further to 0.44*D*, even though
the ethynyl group is known to be highly polarizable.    (See Table 5·3.)
Moreover, bromoacetylene has zero dipole moment, so that apparently
the ionic structure analogous to XIX makes an even greater contribution when the electronegativity of the halogen is decreased.    We might
anticipate, therefore, that iodoacetylene would have a non-vanishing
moment with the iodine at the positive end.    Although this substance
seems not to have been investigated, the expectation is confirmed by the
fact that in phenyliodoacetylene, $C_6H_5C{\equiv}CI$, the iodine atom has been
found to be positive.[12]    (For the method of establishing the direction
of the moment, see the above discussion of phenyl azide.)

In chlorobenzene also, the observed moment of 1.73*D* seems lower
than that expected from analogy with the aliphatic chlorides, since the
phenyl group, like the vinyl and ethynyl groups, is highly polarizable.
The explanation again presumably involves the idea of resonance.    In

[12] C. J. Wilson and H. H. Wenzke, *J. Am. Chem. Soc.*, **56**, 2025 (1934).

this case, the two Kekulé structures XX and XXI are doubtless the most important, but the less stable quinoid structures XXII, XXIII, and XXIV have such large moments that, even though their contribu-

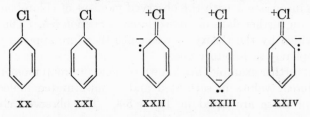

tions are small, they are apparently able to decrease the resultant moment of the substance to an appreciable extent.

It is probable that resonance is not the only factor causing the above variations in the moments of the unsaturated halogen compounds. There are reasons to believe that an ethylenic, or especially an acetylenic, carbon atom may be more electronegative than a saturated one. Consequently, even the conventional structures, XVI, XVIII, XX, and XXI, may correspond to less negative halogen atoms than usual. It is impossible at the present time to compare the importance of this further effect with that of the resonance.

In nitrobenzene, the effect of the resonance would be expected to increase the moment, because the large moments of the relatively unstable structures, XXIX, XXX, and XXXI, are in the same (or nearly the same) direction as those of the Kekulé structures, XXV–XXVIII. As a result, although the dipole moment of even *t*-nitrobutane is only

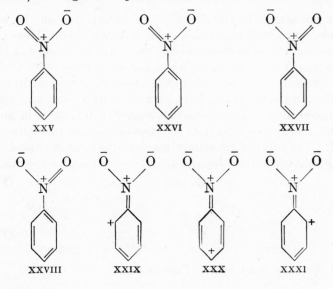

3.71$D$, that of nitrobenzene (in the gas phase) is 4.24$D$. The facts here could be accounted for on the assumption of an unexpectedly large polarizability of the phenyl group; such an explanation, however, would be inconsistent with the observed moment of chlorobenzene and with certain further data discussed later in Section 5.5. The explanation provided by the theory of resonance therefore appears to be the only completely satisfactory one.

Several further examples are known of bond or group moments which have different values in saturated and in unsaturated molecules. A number of these are listed in Table 5.3. The observed changes in

### TABLE 5.3

#### EFFECT OF RESONANCE ON BOND AND GROUP MOMENTS[a]

| X | RX[b] | H₂C=CHX[c] | HC≡CX[c] | C₆H₅X[c] |
|---|---|---|---|---|
| | | Substance | | |
| Cl | 2.15 | 1.44 | 0.44 | 1.73 |
| Br | 2.20 | 1.41 | 0.0 | 1.71 |
| I | 2.08 | 1.26 | — | 1.50 |
| NO₂ | 3.73 | — | — | 4.24[d] |

[a] The quantities listed in the body of the table are the values (in $D$) of the dipole moments of the substances in question in the vapor phase.

[b] Some arbitrariness necessarily exists in the choice of the alkyl compound used in this column for comparison. The values given for each substituent, X, are the largest reported for any of the alkyl groups, R. This choice is made in order that the polarizabilities may be as nearly comparable as possible. The data for these alkyl compounds are taken from Table 5.2.

[c] J. A. C. Hugill, I. E. Coop, and L. E. Sutton, *Trans. Faraday Soc.*, **34**, 1518 (1938).

[d] L. G. Groves and S. Sugden, *J. Chem. Soc.*, 971 (1935).

moment are always in the directions to be expected on the basis of resonance, and are of reasonable order of magnitude. (However, see the discussion of the moments of the unsaturated cyanides at the end of this section.) Similar tables, which are not directly comparable with this one because they refer to dipole moments measured in solution rather than in the gas phase, have been given by various authors.[9,13]

Additional interesting information regarding resonance in aromatic molecules can be obtained from the dipole moment of *p*-nitroaniline, XXXII. The effect of resonance in aniline itself, as in chlorobenzene, is to shift electrons from the substituent to the ring, whereas the effect

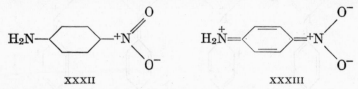

XXXII                    XXXIII

[13] C. P. Smyth, *J. Org. Chem.*, **1**, 17 (1936).

of the resonance in nitrobenzene is to shift electrons from the ring to the substituent. In $p$-nitroaniline, these two effects can occur simultaneously and reinforce each other, since the structure XXXIII may make a fairly large contribution. That the situation actually is as suggested can be shown in the following manner. In this substance, the amino and nitro group moments cannot lie in the same direction, because the former is non-axial, and so the magnitude of their vector sum must be less than the sum of their magnitudes. Since the moments of aniline and of nitrobenzene (in benzene solution) are 1.53 and 3.95$D$,[11] respectively, we should therefore expect that the moment of $p$-nitroaniline would be less than 1.53 + 3.95 = 5.48$D$. (The values of the moments in solution must be used for these substances, because no data are available for $p$-nitroaniline in the vapor phase. Since solvent effects of several tenths of a Debye unit are often observed, significant comparisons can be made only between moments measured under the same conditions.) The observed value, however, is 6.10$D$ so that interaction of the sort represented by structure XXXIII is apparently an important feature of the molecule. A similar effect might be expected to occur also in $p$-nitrochlorobenzene, since a structure quite analogous to XXXIII can be written for this substance. However, the rule of vector addition is obeyed here, so that the interaction must be small. In Section 8·11 we shall find independent evidence to support the view that the electrons of an amino group are much freer to be shifted into an attached benzene ring than are those of a chlorine atom.

The moment of toluene may be due in part to a resonance effect. If all the carbon-carbon bonds had strictly zero moments, and if all the carbon-hydrogen bonds had exactly the same moment, then this substance would necessarily be non-polar. Actually, however, it is found to have a dipole moment of 0.4$D$, with the methyl group positive with respect to the phenyl.[14] It is possible, of course, that the moment of a $C_{aromatic}$—$C_{aliphatic}$ bond may not be zero, and that the moment of a $C_{aromatic}$—H bond may not be equal to that of a $C_{aliphatic}$—H bond. Such an effect would actually be anticipated, since, as was mentioned above, an unsaturated carbon atom probably is more electronegative than a saturated one. This fact probably provides at least a part, and possibly all, of the complete explanation of the moment of toluene, but a further factor also requires consideration. Hyperconjugation of the methyl group with the ring may be a significant feature. That is to say, structures of the sort represented by XXXIV and XXXV (which are merely the ionic analogs of XXXVI) may make small contributions.

[14] For example, see J. W. Williams, *Fortschr. Chem., Physik physik. Chem.*, **20** 257 (1930), Table 11.

If resonance with such structures does occur, and if, moreover, the structures like XXXIV are more important than those like XXXV, then a small moment in the observed direction would be produced. It is

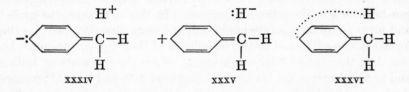

XXXIV XXXV XXXVI

difficult, however, to estimate the relative importance of these two effects (i.e., variations in the values of bond moments and hyperconjugation) or, indeed, to show conclusively that either one is involved at all. This is a point that will require further clarification before it can be considered settled.

A further type of structure in which resonance affects the dipole moment is contained in the $\alpha,\beta$-unsaturated aldehydes and ketones.[9,15] Crotonaldehyde, XXXVII, for example, has a moment of 3.67$D$, which is considerably larger than the customary value of 2.5–3.0$D$ for saturated

$$CH_3—CH{=}CH—CH{=}O \qquad CH_3—\overset{+}{C}H—CH{=}CH—\overset{-}{O}$$
XXXVII XXXVIII

carbonyl compounds. The difference can be considered due to the possibility of resonance with the less stable structure XXXVIII. The correctness of this explanation is strongly supported by the moments of 3,5-dimethylcyclohexenone, XXXIX, and of pulegone, XL. In these substances, the conjugated systems are held by the six-membered rings

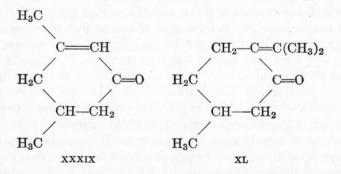

XXXIX XL

more or less rigidly in the *trans* and *cis* configuration, respectively. The geometries of the molecules, therefore, are such that the moment of the

[15] E. C. Hurdis and C. P. Smyth, *J. Am. Chem. Soc.*, **65**, 89 (1943).

normal structure and that of the less stable structure analogous to XXXVIII are more nearly in the same direction in the former compound than in the latter. The actually observed moments are 3.79 and 2.95$D$, respectively (in solution), in agreement with expectation.

A somewhat similar situation is encountered with dimethyl-$\gamma$-pyrone.[16] The resonance here involves not only the normal structure XLI and the less stable one XLII (which are analogous to XXXVII and XXXVIII, respectively) but also two further ones of the type represented by XLIII.

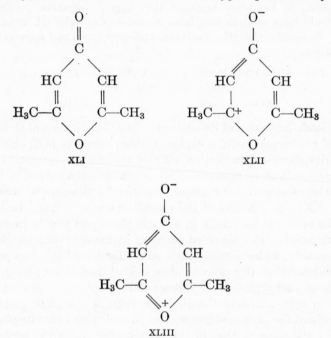

The resonance between these last Kekulé-like structures must counterbalance their unfavorable distribution of charge to a considerable extent and so must increase their contribution to the state of the molecule. As a result, the dipole moment is increased from a calculated value of about 1.75$D$ for the structure XLI to the observed value of 4.05$D$ (in solution).

Anomalous dipole moments have been found in certain cyanides.[15] Thus, although the moment of *n*-butyl cyanide is 4.09$D$ (Table 5·2), that of acrylonitrile, XLIV, is only 3.88$D$. From analogy with the similarly constituted aldehydes and ketones, the unsaturation might have been expected here also to result in an increase, rather than in a decrease, in the moment. The explanation has been offered that the structure XLV for some reason makes

[16] E. C. E. Hunter and J. R. Partington, *J. Chem. Soc.*, 87 (1933).

a larger contribution to the state of the acrylonitrile molecule than the corresponding structure, XLVI, does to the state of the crotonaldehyde molecule. If this explanation is correct, acrylonitrile would be more analogous to vinyl chloride than to crotonaldehyde. On the other hand, the moment of

$$H_2C{=}CH{-}C{\equiv}N \qquad H_2\overset{-}{C}{-}CH{=}C{=}N^+ \qquad CH_3{-}\overset{-}{C}H{-}CH{=}CH{-}O^+$$

XLIV　　　　　　　　　　XLV　　　　　　　　　　XLVI

*trans* crotononitrile, XLVII, is 4.50*D*, which is 0.62*D* greater than that of acrylonitrile. It has been suggested that hyperconjugation, involving an unexpectedly large contribution from structures like XLVIII, must be involved. Evidently, the situation is still rather confused and requires further investigation.

$$CH_3{-}CH{=}CH{-}C{\equiv}N \qquad\qquad CH_2{=}CH{-}CH{=}C{=}N^-$$
$$\phantom{CH_3{-}CH{=}CH{-}C{\equiv}N \qquad\qquad} {}^+H$$

XLVII　　　　　　　　　　　　XLVIII

**5·5 Steric Inhibition of Resonance.** The phenomenon of steric inhibition of resonance provides evidence which supports both the rule of coplanarity discussed in Section 4·2 and also the interpretation of the dipole moments of nitrobenzene and of *p*-nitroaniline given in Section 5·4. In nitrobenzene, for example, the effect of the quinoid structures, XXIX, XXX, and XXXI of the preceding section, should be both to make the molecule lie wholly in a single plane and also to increase its dipole moment. The expected increase in moment can be observed experimentally, as has already been pointed out, and this fact provides some evidence that the molecule does indeed tend to be planar. As a corollary of this argument, it follows that the moment should be decreased to approximately the aliphatic value if the nitro group were rotated about the carbon-nitrogen bond in such a way that its plane was no longer the same as that of the benzene ring. This is because the above quinoid structures would then be made even less stable by the departure of the nitro group from coplanarity with the ring, so that their contributions would be greatly reduced.

In nitrodurene, I, the methyl group moments cancel in pairs; con-

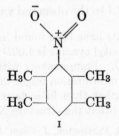

I

sequently, a strict application of the rule of additivity would lead to the prediction that the dipole moment of the molecule should be the same as that of nitrobenzene, that is, about $3.95D^{11}$, because in this latter substance the four corresponding carbon-hydrogen bond moments also cancel in pairs. (In order to have a common basis of comparison, we shall refer in this section only to dipole moments measured in solution in benzene.) There is reason to believe, however, that in nitrodurene the nitro group cannot lie in the plane of the ring because of the presence of the bulky substituents in the two positions *ortho* to it. If the molecule were planar, each oxygen atom would be at a distance of about 2.5 A from a methyl carbon atom, whereas the usual distance of closest approach of an oxygen atom and a methyl carbon atom to which it is not bonded is about 3.4 A.[17] It is evident, therefore, that there must be large repulsive forces in operation, which twist the nitro group about the carbon-nitrogen bond, so that one oxygen atom lies above, and the other lies below, the plane of the ring. The dipole moment of nitrodurene, if these arguments are correct, should then be less than that of nitrobenzene, and approximately equal to that of an aliphatic nitro compound. The observed value[11] is only $3.39D$, in agreement with expectation. (The moments of the aliphatic nitro compounds are less in solution than in the vapor phase and are usually in the neighborhood of $3.3D$.) This fact provides strong support for the interpretation of the data in this, and in the preceding section.

Further evidence can be brought forward which also supports the views expressed above. In bromodurene, II, for example, no inhibition of resonance by steric factors can occur, because no reasonable deformation of the molecule by the methyl groups can decrease the stability of the quinoid structures analogous to XXII, XXIII, and XXIV of Section 5·4. Consequently, the dipole moment of bromodurene should

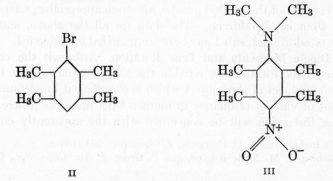

II                                     III

[17] L. Pauling, *The Nature of the Chemical Bond*, Cornell University Press, Ithaca, N. Y., 1st ed., 1939, p. 176; 2nd ed., 1940, p. 189.

be approximately the same as that of bromobenzene.   This expectation
is, in fact, found to be correct, the observed values being 1.55 and 1.52$D$,
respectively.[11]   It is apparent, therefore, that the methyl groups do not
*directly* alter the moment of the molecule to any significant extent.
With aniline and aminodurene, similarly, the observed moments are
nearly the same (1.53 and 1.39$D$, respectively), so that apparently there
is no important inhibition of resonance in the latter substance.   This
fact also might have been anticipated in view of the small size of the
amino group.   In nitrodimethylaminodurene, III, on the other hand,
the contribution of the quinoid structure must be greatly decreased by
the steric interference of both the nitro and the dimethylamino groups
with their neighbors.   As a result, the moment is reduced to only 4.11$D$[18]
as compared with 6.87$D$ for $p$-nitrodimethylaniline.   Also in nitromesity-
lene, IV, the moments of the methyl groups cancel each other, as they

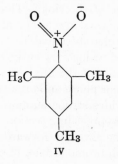

IV

do in nitrodurene.   Consequently, if it were not for the inhibition of
resonance, this substance too should have the same moment as nitrobenzene.   Actually, its moment has been found[19] to be 3.64$D$, so that
the steric effect of the methyl groups, although appreciable, seems to be
smaller than in nitrodurene.   The data for all the above, and for a
number of additional, substances are summarized in Table 5·4.

**5·6  Dipole Moments and Free Rotation.**   Although the complex
problem of free rotation lies outside the scope of the present book,[20]
there is one aspect of the subject which is of sufficient importance from
the point of view of resonance to merit a brief description here.   The
following discussion will be concerned with the apparently complete

---

[18] C. E. Ingham and G. C. Hampson, *J. Chem. Soc.*, 981 (1939).

[19] F. Brown, J. M. A. de Bruyne, and P. Gross, *J. Am. Chem. Soc.*, **56**, 1291
(1934).

[20] For a discussion, see N. V. Sidgwick, reference 1.

## TABLE 5·4

Effect of Steric Inhibition of Resonance on Dipole Moment[a]

| X | Y | Benzene Derivative $p\text{-}C_6H_4XY$ | Durene Derivative $C_6(CH_3)_4XY$ | Mesitylene Derivative $C_6H_2(CH_3)_3X$ |
|---|---|---|---|---|
| NO$_2$ | H | 3.95[c] | 3.39[c] | 3.64[b] |
| N(CH$_3$)$_2$ | H | 1.58[d] | — | 1.03[d] |
| NH$_2$ | H[f] | 1.53[c] | 1.39[c] | 1.40[d] |
| OH | H[f] | 1.61[d] | 1.68[d] | — |
| F | H[f] | 1.46[b] | — | 1.36[b] |
| Cl | H[f] | 1.56[b] | — | 1.55[b] |
| Br | H[f] | . 1.52[c] | 1.55[c] | 1.52[b] |
| I | H[f] | 1.27[b] | — | 1.42[b] |
| NO$_2$ | N(CH$_3$)$_2$ | 6.87[d] | 4.11[d] | — |
| NO$_2$ | OC$_2$H$_5$ | 4.76[d,e] | 3.69[d] | — |
| NO$_2$ | NH$_2$ | 6.10[c] | 4.98[c] | — |
| NO$_2$ | OH | 5.04[d] | 4.08[d] | — |
| NO$_2$ | Br | 2.65[c] | 2.36[c] | — |

[a] The quantities listed in the body of the table are the dipole moments (in $D$) of the indicated compounds in benzene solution and, except as noted, at 25°.

[b] F. Brown, J. M. A. de Bruyne, and P. Gross, reference 19. These measurements were made at 30°.

[c] R. H. Birtles and G. C. Hampson, reference 11.

[d] C. E. Ingham and G. C. Hampson, reference 18.

[e] This value applies to *p*-nitroanisole.

[f] No inhibition of resonance is to be expected in this substance.

coplanarity of the atoms forming the carboxyl group in an ester.[21] (See Section 4·2.)

The dipole moment of any ester formed between a saturated monohydric alcohol, ROH, on the one hand, and a saturated monocarboxylic acid, R'CO$_2$H, on the other, is found to be approximately equal to 1.7–1.9$D$. This independence of the natures of the radicals R and R' is, of course, to be expected on the basis of the rule of vector addition of bond moments, just as in the alkyl halides and the like. More important from our present point of view, however, is the fact that these moments do not vary appreciably with the temperature over temperature ranges of as much as 190°. Now, if rotation could occur about all bonds that are represented as single bonds in the conventional structure, an ester molecule could assume the two extreme geometrical configurations represented by I and II, as well as an infinite number of intermediate ones. Since a carbon-oxygen bond is associated with a moment of about 0.8$D$ (Table 5·1) it is evident that the moments of the molecule

[21] The following discussion is taken from R. J. B. Marsden and L. E. Sutton, *J. Chem. Soc.*, 1383 (1936).

in the two extreme configurations must be widely different. In fact, a calculation based upon the usual bond angles and upon the values of the bond moments found in other aliphatic compounds leads to predicted moments of 1.53 and 3.53$D$ for I and II, respectively. The fact that the

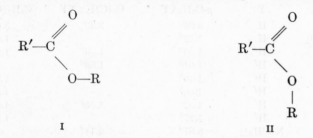

I          II

observed moment is independent of temperature can be explained in only two ways. The first possibility is that rotation about the carbon-oxygen bond is completely free, and that no forces are operative which favor one (or more) of the possible configurations over the others. Under these circumstances, the molecule would spend the same fraction of the time in any one configuration as in any other, regardless of temperature, and the observed moment would be an average, with equal weights (actually, the root mean square), of the moments corresponding to all the various configurations. The second possible explanation is that the molecule is held rigidly in some definite configuration by forces that are too strong to be overcome by the thermal motion at the temperatures investigated. Under these circumstances, the observed moment would be just that of the favored configuration. That the second alternative is the correct one is strongly suggested by the fact that the observed moment is in satisfactory agreement with the value calculated for configuration I, but seems much too small to be any sort of average of the values for I and II. This conclusion is supported further by the fact that the moment of $\gamma$-butyrolactone, III, in which the configuration is uniquely determined by the five-membered ring, is 4.12$D$, in fair agree-

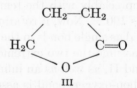

III

ment with the value calculated for the configuration II.

From the foregoing discussion, it follows that an acyclic ester of a carboxylic acid is held rigidly in the planar configuration I. The problem still remains of deciding the nature of the forces responsible for this rigidity.   One explanation, which has already been discussed in Section 4·2, is that resonance with the structure IV gives considerable

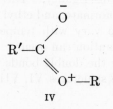

IV

double-bond character to the carbon-oxygen bond under discussion and so prevents rotation about it.   The question which of the two possible configurations, I or II, is the more stable is then presumably determined by specific dipole or van der Waals interactions between the alkyl radical R and the carbonyl group (or, in the γ-lactone, by the formation of the ring).   An alternative explanation is that a particularly powerful attraction may exist between the alkyl group and the carbonyl oxygen, and that this is strong enough, except in the lactone, to hold the molecule rigidly in the configuration I.   It would be difficult, however, to account satisfactorily for an attraction powerful enough to produce such a large effect.   More direct evidence against this second explanation has been obtained from an investigation of the ε-lactone, V.   The seven-membered ring in this substance is of sufficient size so that it does not necessarily hold the ester grouping in the configuration II, nor even very close to it, but it is not large enough to permit the molecule to achieve the configuration I.   Consequently, if an exceedingly powerful attraction does exist between the alkyl radical and the carbonyl

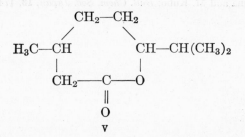

V

oxygen atom, the actual configuration, and hence the dipole moment, should be intermediate between those characteristic of a γ-lactone and an ordinary, acyclic ester.   In fact, calculation has led to an estimated value of 2.7D or less for such a situation.   The observed moment, 4.33D, is instead practically the same as that of γ-butyrolactone, and so only the first explanation, based on resonance, remains.   This conclusion supports the belief, reached originally in Section 3·3, that the resonance energy of a carbalkoxy group must be quite large.

Not all esters show this rigidity. The dipole moments of methyl carbonate, methyl chloroformate, and ethyl chloroformate, for example, have been reported[22] to vary with temperature, so that apparently some not entirely free rotation can occur. The explanation is possibly that in these substances the double bonds must be distributed among *three* positions, as in the structures VI, VII, and VIII. They cannot,

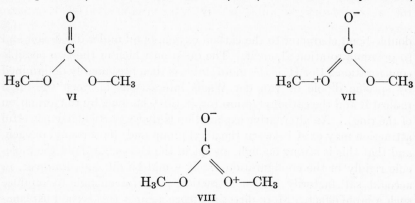

therefore, impart as much rigidity to the carbon-oxygen bonds as in the simple esters, where they are distributed between only *two* positions. In this connection, it is significant that the carbon-oxygen bond is somewhat longer, and so has less double-bond character, in the carbonate ion than in a carboxylate ion.     (See Table 4·4.)

[22] S. Mizushima and M. Kubo, *Bull. Chem. Soc. Japan*, **13**, 174 (1938).

# Chapter 6

## RESONANCE AND MOLECULAR SPECTRA

**6·1   Types of Spectra.**   Spectroscopic data have long been used in the study of structural problems.   Even the most superficial attempt to survey the entire field here would be out of place, however, and so the following discussion, after a brief preliminary introduction, will be limited to a few aspects in which the concept of resonance has proved especially helpful.[1]

Spectra are classified as emission or absorption spectra.   (For our purposes, the fluorescence and Raman spectra can be regarded merely as special cases of these general types.)   In the former type of spectrum, the molecules of the substance in question undergo transitions from states of higher, to states of lower, energy, and the energy lost by the molecules is emitted in the form of light; in the latter type, the molecules absorb light and are thereby raised to states of higher energy.   In both kinds of spectrum, the relation between the energy changes in the molecules and the frequencies of the light emitted or absorbed are given by the Bohr condition:

$$h\nu_{12} = E_2 - E_1 \tag{1}$$

where $h$ is Planck's constant, the magnitude of $\nu_{12}$ is the frequency, and $E_1$ and $E_2$ are the energies per molecule in the initial and final states, respectively.   It will be seen that a positive value of $\nu_{12}$ corresponds to absorption, whereas a negative value corresponds to emission, of light.

The following figures are of interest in connection with the orders of magnitude of the quantities involved.   A wavelength of 4000 A, which lies approximately at the blue end of the visible spectrum, corresponds to an energy change of about 71 kcal per mole, whereas a wavelength of 8000 A, which lies approximately at the red end of the visible spectrum, corresponds to an energy change of half that magnitude.

---

[1] For further details regarding diatomic molecular spectra, see G. Herzberg, *Molecular Spectra and Molecular Structure, I, Diatomic Molecules* (translated by J. W. T. Spinks), Prentice-Hall, Inc., New York, 1939.   A fairly complete bibliography is given in this book, pp. 535ff.   For polyatomic molecular spectra, see H. Sponer, *Molekülspectren und ihre Anwendung auf chemische Probleme*, Springer, Berlin, vol. I, 1935, vol. II, 1936; D. M. Dennison, *Rev. Modern Phys.*, **12**, 175 (1940); H. Sponer and E. Teller, *ibid.*, **13**, 75 (1941); Conference on Spectroscopy, *ibid.*, **14**, 57–340 (1942).   The question of intensities in molecular spectra is discussed in some detail by R. S. Mulliken and C. A. Rieke, reference 4.

We shall be concerned only with absorption spectra; these can be further classified into three types. The first of these, the pure rotation spectrum, is associated with changes which occur in the rotational states of the molecules without simultaneous changes in the vibrational and electronic states. Since the separations in energy between the various rotational levels are relatively small, it follows from equation 1 that the corresponding frequencies are relatively low or, in other words, that the wavelengths are relatively great. Actually, the pure rotation spectra of all substances occur in the far infrared in an experimentally difficult region of the spectrum and, for that reason, have been comparatively little investigated. The second type of spectrum, the rotation-vibration spectrum, is associated with transitions in which the vibrational, and usually also the rotational, states of the molecules are altered, but in which the electronic states remain unchanged. The energy differences are rather greater here than in the pure rotation spectrum and, accordingly, the absorption occurs at somewhat shorter wavelengths, actually in the near infrared region. And finally, the eletronic spectrum, in which we shall be principally interested, arises from transitions between electronic states, usually accompanied by simultaneous changes in both the vibrational and rotational levels. (The significance of the term " electronic state " will be explained more fully in the following section.) Relatively large energy differences are involved in the electronic spectra, which therefore occur at relatively short wavelengths, actually in the ultraviolet, or sometimes in the visible, region.

The relation among the various energy levels and the corresponding spectra can be seen from Figure 6·1, which represents schematically the two lowest electronic levels of a diatomic molecule. (For polyatomic molecules, the corresponding diagrams would be similar in general nature, but much more complicated.) In this figure, the heights of the various horizontal lines above some appropriate base line represent the energy contents of the corresponding states of the molecule. The two heavy lines at the left of the figure represent the electronic energies of the two states, that is, the energies which would obtain if the nuclei were held in fixed positions. The lines in the center of the figure represent the energies of a few of the lowest vibrational states associated with each electronic state, that is, the energies which would obtain if no rotation of the molecule were allowed. Since the molecule must have at least the " half quantum " of zero-point vibrational energy, the lowest of these vibrational levels in either electronic state lies above the corresponding electronic level; the remaining levels lie above these at approximately constant intervals. The lines at the right of the figure represent a few of the lowest rotational levels associated with the various electronic and vibrational levels, that is, the actual energies which the molecule can have when all types of motion are taken into account.    For the sake of clarity, the lowest (non-rotating) levels are represented by full lines, and the other (rotating) levels by broken lines.    (To be rigor-

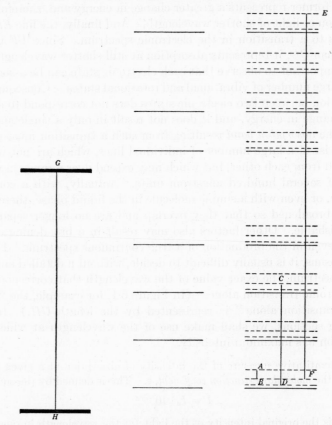

**Fig. 6·1.**   Diagram in which the heights of the various horizontal lines above some arbitrary base-line correspond to the energies of a diatomic molecule in the corresponding electronic, vibrational, and rotational states.   The heavy lines at the left correspond to two electronic states; the lines in the center correspond to a few of the lowest vibrational states associated with each electronic state; and the lines at the right correspond to a few of the lowest rotational states associated with each of the electronic and vibrational states.

ously correct, we ought to consider also the motion of the molecule as a whole through space.   This translational motion is of little spectroscopic interest, however, and so we shall ignore it.)

We can now consider the three types of spectrum enumerated above in the light of the energy level diagram.   The vertical line *AB* in Figure

6·1, for example, corresponds to one of the transitions in the pure rotation spectrum of the substance, since the electronic and vibrational levels do not change.    The line *CD*, on the other hand, corresponds to a transition in the vibration-rotation spectrum.    Since *CD* is longer than *AB*, the former represents a greater change in energy and, therefore, an absorption of light of shorter wavelength.    And finally, the line *EF* corresponds to a transition in the electronic spectrum.    Since *EF* is still longer than *CD*, it represents absorption at still shorter wavelengths.

It is important to observe that each electronic state can be associated with a large number of vibrational and rotational states.    Consequently, a transition between two electronic states does not correspond to only a single change in energy, and it does not result in only a single spectral line.    The *absorption band* resulting from such a transition must therefore consist of a large number of individual lines, which are not widely separated from each other, but which may extend over a range in wavelength of several hundred angstrom units.    Actually, with a complex molecule, or even with a simple molecule in the liquid phase, these lines may be broadened so that they overlap and are no longer separately distinguishable.    Other factors also may result in a broadening of the lines or even in the production of a true continuous spectrum.    For all these reasons, it is usually difficult to decide, without a detailed analysis of the spectrum, the exact value of the wavelength that corresponds to the electronic transition alone.    (In Figure 6·1, for example, the " electronic transition alone " is represented by the length *GH*.)    In the following sections, we shall make use of the wavelength at which the absorption has maximum intensity.

The quantitative measure of the intensity of absorption at a given wavelength is the *molecular extinction coefficient*, $\varepsilon$.    This is defined by the equation

$$I = I_0 \cdot 10^{-dc\varepsilon} \tag{2}$$

where $I_0$ is the original intensity of the light (at the wavelength in question) and $I$ is the intensity of the light (at the same wavelength) after it has passed through $d$ centimeters of the substance (or of a solution of the substance) at a concentration of $c$ moles per liter.    The more intense the absorption, the larger is the value of $\varepsilon$.    Absorption spectra are usually reported in the form of curves, in which the extinction coefficients (or their logarithms) are plotted as ordinates against the wavelength (or the frequency) as abscissa.    Such a method of representation is most useful, of course, when the individual lines of the spectrum overlap, so that only a continuous region of absorption of varying intensity is observed.

**6·2    Ground and Excited Electronic States.**    The nature of a transition between two electronic states can be discussed most easily with reference to a specific example, which can be conveniently taken as ethylene. The most stable structures that can be written for this

$$H_2C=CH_2 \qquad H_2\overset{+}{C}-\overset{-}{C}H_2 \qquad H_2\overset{-}{C}-\overset{+}{C}H_2$$
$$\text{I} \qquad\qquad\qquad \text{II} \qquad\qquad\qquad \text{III}$$

substance are doubtless I, II, and III, with the first, of course, much more stable than the other two. As a result of resonance among these three structures, there arise, as was pointed out in Section 1·5, altogether three states (i.e., electronic states) of the molecule, each of which can possess varying amounts of vibrational and rotational energy. The most stable of these, the ground state, is essentially that represented by the structure I, with small equal contributions from II and III; the two remaining states, the excited states, on the other hand, are essentially resonance hybrids of the structures II and III, with only a small contribution from I (but with probably larger contributions from still further structures not considered here).

The situation discussed above for ethylene is similar to that encountered generally in all other types of molecule. The ground state can often be described with considerable accuracy by a single structure, but the excited states almost invariably require a consideration of resonance among several structures. Indeed, it frequently happens that the structures involved in the excited states are themselves of such nature that they cannot be expressed at all with the conventional symbols. This is hardly surprising inasmuch as these symbols were devised largely by organic chemists, who were interested in representing molecules in their chemically realizable ground states and were not concerned with spectroscopic matters. However, if we restrict ourselves to a consideration of only a few of the very most stable of the innumerable excited states, we can often obtain a satisfactory representation of these in terms of resonance among structures of familiar types. The attempt will be made in the two succeeding sections to carry through such treatments for a small number of representative substances.

A spectroscopic system of nomenclature has been developed for the description of all, and not merely the most stable, of the excited states.[2] The so-called molecular orbital treatment of molecular structure, upon which this system of nomenclature is based, is apparently somewhat better suited to the discussion of excited states than is the valence-bond treatment, which we are employing implicitly in this book. In particular, such a point of view avoids some of the difficulties described in the following section. However,

[2] See, for example, R. S. Mulliken, *Phys. Rev.*, **43**, 279 (1933) and numerous earlier, as well as more recent, papers in the *Physical Review*, the *Journal of Chemical Physics*, and the *Journal of the American Chemical Society*.

we shall discuss neither this more general nomenclature, nor the molecular orbital treatment itself, because neither makes explicit use of the concepts of structure or of resonance.

**6·3  Spectra of Organic Substances.**[3]  It is found empirically that a compound with conjugated double bonds absorbs light of longer wavelength than an analogous compound with only one or more isolated double bonds.   Thus, whereas ethylene does not absorb light of wavelength greater than about 1900–2000 A, butadiene absorbs at about 2100 A.   Moreover, as the number of double bonds in the conjugated system increases, the absorption comes to progressively greater wavelengths, so that 2,4,6,8,10,12-tetradecahexaene, I, for example, absorbs in the visible and is, therefore, colored.

$$CH\!=\!CH\!-\!CH\!=\!CH\!-\!CH\!=\!CH\!-\!CH\!=\!CH\!-\!CH\!=\!CH\!-\!CH\!=\!CH$$
$$| \qquad\qquad\qquad\qquad\qquad\qquad\qquad\qquad\qquad\qquad\qquad |$$
$$CH_3 \qquad\qquad\qquad\qquad\qquad\qquad\qquad\qquad\qquad\qquad CH_3$$

The above facts are readily understood when the types of resonance in the various molecules are considered.   Thus, for ethylene, as we have seen, we can discuss the most stable of the excited states on the basis of resonance among the structures I, II, and III of the preceding section. For butadiene, on the other hand, we must take into account not only the structure II, analogous to the first of these, and several structures like III and IV, analogous to the remaining two, but also the further structure V, with a formal bond.   All the less stable structures, of the type of III–V, for this substance contain the same numbers of the same kinds

$$CH_2 = CH - CH = CH_2 \qquad \overset{+}{C}H_2 - \overset{-}{C}H - CH = CH_2$$
$$\text{II} \qquad\qquad\qquad\qquad \text{III}$$

$$\overset{+}{C}H_2 - CH = CH - \overset{-}{C}H_2 \qquad \overset{..........}{C}H_2 - CH = CH - \overset{.}{C}H_2$$
$$\text{IV} \qquad\qquad\qquad\qquad \text{V}$$

of bond, but V doubtless has a lower energy content than any of the others because it is the only one which does not require a separation of charge.   Although the ground state of the molecule is stabilized in the usual manner by the resonance among these various structures, the resonance energy must be small since the structures like III–V have much higher energies than II.   The actual structure of the molecule in its ground state is therefore essentially II with only small contributions from the other structures.   The first excited state, however, is formed

[3] Cf. C. R. Bury, *J. Am. Chem. Soc.*, **57**, 2115 (1935).

largely from the structures like III–V.   Since these, as a group, are not of widely different energy, the resonance among them alone must produce considerable stabilization.   Consequently, although the effect of structure II is to raise the energy of this first excited state by a small amount, the net effect of the resonance as a whole must be to make the state more stable than it would otherwise have been.   Furthermore, the stabilization so produced must be greater here than in the ground state. It follows then that the energy of excitation is lower, and hence the absorption occurs at longer wavelengths, than if there were no resonance. Moreover, since the resonance in butadiene is considerably more extensive than that in ethylene, but at the same time is rather similar in type, the further conclusion can be drawn that the conjugation should result in an increased wavelength of absorption, as it actually does.

Since V is presumably the most stable of the structures of the types illustrated by III–V, we might suppose that it should make a particularly large contribution to the first excited state of the butadiene molecule.   There is reason to believe, however, that such a supposition is not correct.[4]   The argument leading to this conclusion is too complicated to be given here in full, but its essential features are, in outline, the following.   It can be shown, by an application of the so-called selection rules, that an electronic transition from the ground state of the substance to any low-lying excited state, receiving an appreciable contribution from V, should lead to very weak absorption. The actual absorption at 2100 A, however, is extremely intense, so that the corresponding excited state must be a hybrid of principally the ionic structures like III and IV.   This unexpected fact has at least two possible explanations. In the first place, it is conceivable that the absorption band of longest wavelength really is a very weak one which lies close to, and is completely obscured by, a much more intense one of somewhat shorter wavelength.   There is no experimental evidence supporting such an interpretation, however.   A more probable explanation is that, since the first excited state must certainly receive contributions from a large number of further structures in addition to those we have considered so far, it is quite possible that these additional structures may be able to interact with the ionic structures like III and IV more effectively than they can with V.   If this second explanation is correct, then the state to which V makes a large contribution may, after all, not be the most stable of the excited ones.   The problem is of such complexity that no very definite conclusion can be drawn theoretically.

The foregoing discussion illustrates the types of difficulty that may be encountered when the present simple treatment is applied to the excited states of molecules.   In general, great care must be exercised to make sure that the observed absorption band is actually the one to which the theoretical considerations refer.   Since the necessary identifications cannot be made

[4] R. S. Mulliken, *J. Chem. Phys.*, **7**, 121 (1939).   R. S. Mulliken and C. A. Rieke, *Reports on Progress in Physics*, **8**, 231 (1941).

with any assurance at the present time, except for some comparatively simple substances, the treatment obviously can be only an extremely crude one, and only the gross qualitative features of the conclusions to which it leads can be considered significant.

For hexatriene, a number of structures like VI and VII and their ionic analogs, can be written. The first excited state should be stabilized,

$$CH_2 = CH - CH = CH - CH = CH_2$$

VI

$$CH_2 = CH - CH - CH = CH - CH_2$$

VII

relative to the ground state, by the resonance among these structures, and this stabilization should be greater than in butadiene on account of the larger number of structures. Consequently, the increase in the length of the conjugated system should result in a displacement of the absorption to longer wavelengths, as it actually does. Furthermore, *hyper*conjugation is apparently responsible in a similar way for the fact that alkyl substituents on unsaturated atoms displace the absorption somewhat further toward longer wavelengths.[5]

In benzene, the most important resonance is that between the two Kekulé structures, VIII and IX. This resonance gives rise to two states of the molecule, of which one is the ground state and the other is an

VIII                                   IX

excited state.    (If the three Dewar structures are considered in addition to the two Kekulé structures, the resonance then leads to altogether four excited states in addition to the ground state; and if all the corresponding ionic structures are taken into account, the number of excited states becomes very large.)    It would be difficult, on the basis of the kind of qualitative arguments used above, to predict whether benzene should absorb light of shorter or of longer wavelengths than, say, hexatriene. The fact that absorption occurs in about the same region of the spectrum for both substances is not unreasonable, however.

The comparison of other aromatic hydrocarbons with benzene can be carried through in a straightforward manner.    Thus, substances in

[5] R. S. Mulliken, C. A. Rieke, and W. G. Brown, *J. Am. Chem. Soc.*, **63**, 41 (1941). References to previous papers are given there.

which phenyl groups are conjugated either with each other or with ethylenic linkages should absorb at longer wavelengths than analogous substances in which such conjugation is not present.    This prediction follows from the same sort of reasoning that was used above to show that the conjugation of double bonds with each other should have a similar effect.    Some experimental data bearing upon this point are summarized in Table 6·1.    The fact that the absorption maximum of benzene occurs at a slightly longer wavelength than that of biphenyl is contrary to

TABLE 6·1

ABSORPTION OF LIGHT BY POLYPHENYLS[a]

| Substance | $\lambda_{max}(A)$[b] |
|---|---|
| Benzene | 2550[c] |
| Biphenyl | 2515 |
| p-Terphenyl | 2800 |
| p-Quaterphenyl | 3000 |
| p-Quinquiphenyl | 3100 |
| p-Sexiphenyl | 3175 |
| m-Terphenyl | 2515 |
| m-Noviphenyl | 2530 |
| m-Deciphenyl | 2530 |
| m-Quindeciphenyl | 2540 |

[a] A. E. Gillam and D. H. Hey, *J. Chem. Soc.*, 1170 (1939).

[b] The values listed in this column are the wavelengths at which the absorptions of the indicated substances are at a maximum, in solution in chloroform.

[c] In ethyl alcohol.

expectation and may perhaps be due to an overlapping of two different absorption bands in the biphenyl spectrum, in consequence of the existence of two excited electronic levels with not very different energies. It is possibly significant that the absorption *starts* at longer wavelengths for biphenyl than for benzene, but, on the other hand, this fact may be due merely to the more intense absorption by the biphenyl.    A further possibility, which it now seems is probably the correct one, is that, on account of the uncertainty in the identification of the absorption bands of biphenyl (see above), the band at 2515 A for this substance should be compared, not with the weak absorption by benzene at 2550 A, but instead with the much more intense absorption by the latter substance at shorter wavelengths.    On the other hand, the data for the various polyphenyls are in complete qualitative agreement with expectation. In the *para* series, the wavelength of absorption increases continuously with the number of phenyl groups, but, in the *meta* series, the wavelength remains practically unchanged.    The reason for this striking difference in behavior is presumably that, in the former series, each phenyl group can interact with all the others, whereas, in the latter, each is conjugated effectively with only its immediate neighbors.   For example, in *p*-terphenyl, structures like X (and its ionic analogs) could be expected to make appreciable contributions; but, in *m*-terphenyl, no corresponding structures can be drawn, except for some relatively very unstable ones like XI (and its ionic analogs) with at least two formal

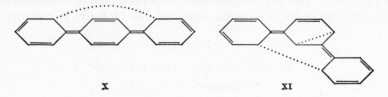

X                                             XI

(or ionic) bonds.   Further data of interest in the present connection are contained in Table 6·2 on page 159.

In the condensed aromatic ring systems also, such as naphthalene, anthracene, and so on, the increased conjugation again results in absorption at progressively greater wavelengths.   (See Table 6·2.)

The dyes, as a class, are more interesting than are the hydrocarbons considered up to the present, but they are more complex in structure and so are more difficult to deal with theoretically.   Many of the most familiar dyes are salts in which the colored cations or anions resonate among structures that differ widely in the distribution of electric charge. For example, in the ion of crystal violet, the most important structures are presumably ones like XII, XIII, and XIV, although numerous

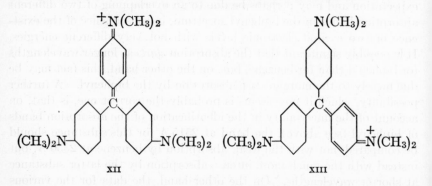

XII                                             XIII

further structures like XV, XVI, and XVII must also be involved. Indeed, if these latter structures were not possible, the resonance could be of only minor importance, since then condition 2 of Section 1·4 would not be satisfied.   As a result, the states of the ion arising from the resonance among only the structures like XII, XIII, and XIV would have practically identical energy; the absorption of light that would occur during a transition from one of these states to another would therefore be at a tremendously longer wavelength than observed.

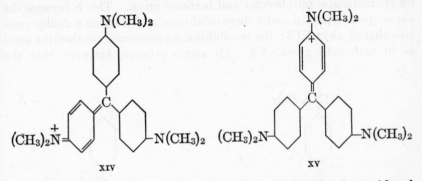

XIV                                   XV

When the further structures like XV, XVI, and XVII are considered, however, the difficulty is removed, because structure XII, for example,

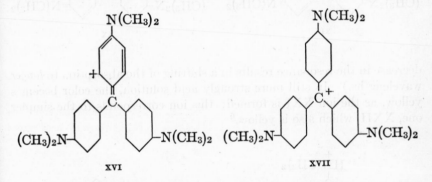

XVI                                   XVII

can resonate effectively with XV, which in turn can resonate with XVI, and so on until the structures XIII and XIV are finally reached.

The carbinol, XVIII, is the color base corresponding to the dye,

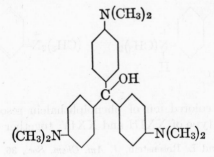

XVIII

crystal violet. The possibilities for resonance are much more restricted here than in the dye, and the substance is colorless. A further interesting fact in regard to crystal violet is that in strongly acid solution it loses its characteristic purple color and becomes green. This is because the ion acquires a proton under these conditions and takes on a double positive charge, as in XIX; the possibilities for resonance are then the same as in malachite green, XX. (It seems strange, however, that the

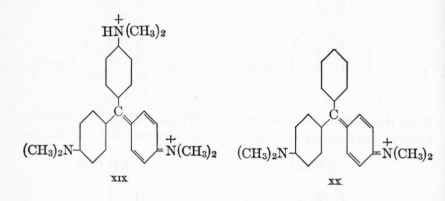

decrease in the resonance results in a shifting of the absorption to *longer* wavelengths.) In still more strongly acid solution, the color becomes yellow, as the ion XXI is formed; this ion corresponds to the simpler one, XXII, which also is yellow.[6]

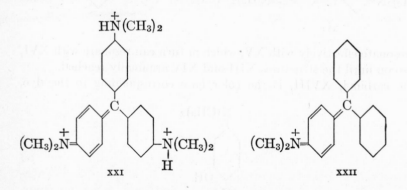

Similarly, the colored ion of phenolphthalein resonates among the structures of the type of XXIII and XXIV, together with a number of

[6] E. Q. Adams and L. Rosenstein, *J. Am. Chem. Soc.*, **36**, 1452 (1914). J. B. Conant and T. H. Werner, *ibid.*, **52**, 4436 (1930).

intermediate ones, whereas the parent substance XXV and the ion XXVI are colorless, and the further ion, XXVII, is only slightly colored.[7]

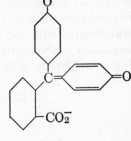

XXIII                        XXIV

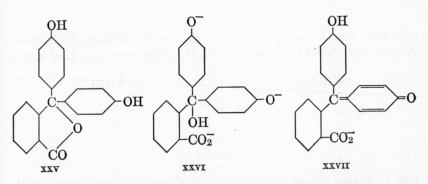

XXV             XXVI             XXVII

On the other hand, numerous dyes, such as indigo, XXVIII, consist of neutral molecules, so that the ionic charge is not a prerequisite for

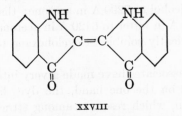

XXVIII

dye character. With these substances also, resonance is important and can be considered the cause of the absorption at relatively long wavelengths. In dyes of this sort, the resonance which is most important for the production of the color presumably involves the relatively unstable structures with formal bonds, as in V, and those with separated

---

[7] S. F. Acree and E. A. Slagle, *Am. Chem. J.*, **42**, 115 (1909). E. Vogt, *Z. physik. Chem.*, **132**, 101 (1928).

charges, as in III and IV. The significance of the latter type of structure can be seen from a study of the effect of solvent upon the position of absorption. Thus, the maximum absorption of the neutral phenol blue, XXIX, is at 5520 A in cyclohexane, at 5820 A in acetone, at 6120 A in methyl alcohol, and at 6680 A in water.[8] This trend toward longer wavelengths with increasing dielectric constant of the medium can be explained as the result of an increasing stability, and hence an increasing contribution, of the ionic structures like XXX in the more polar

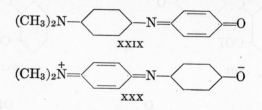

XXIX

XXX

solvents. On the other hand, the very similar Bindschedler's green, XXXI, and phenol indophenol, XXXII, which have their most impor-

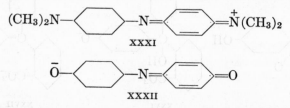

XXXI

XXXII

tant resonance among equivalent or nearly equivalent structures without separation of charge, do not show any corresponding effect of solvent. The absorption maximum of Bindschedler's green varies only from 7260 A in methyl alcohol to 7290 A in acetone; that of phenol indophenol, only from 6280 A in water to 6420 A in acetone. (Neither of these latter dyes is sufficiently soluble in cyclohexane to be studied in that solvent.)

Brooker and his associates have made a very interesting study of the transition between, on the one hand, the dyes like crystal violet or Bindschedler's green, which resonate among structures that have the same stability, and, on the other hand, the dyes like indigo or phenol blue, which resonate among structures that differ greatly in stability.[9] The substances investigated were the members of several different series of cyanine dyes; typical examples are provided by the dyes for which the extreme structures XXXIII and XXXIV (as well as a con-

[8] L. G. S. Brooker and R. H. Sprague, *J. Am. Chem. Soc.*, **63**, 3214 (1941).

[9] L. G. S. Brooker, G. H. Keyes, and W. W. Williams, *J. Am. Chem. Soc.*, **64**, 199 (1942).   L. G. S. Brooker, *Rev. Modern Phys.*, **14**, 275 (1942).

siderable number of intermediate ones) can be written. Although both
XXXIII and XXXIV represent simple ions with no separation of charge,
they are not equivalent, and presumably the former is the more stable of
the two. If the groups at the ends of the molecules are varied, the difference between the energies of the two extreme structures can also be

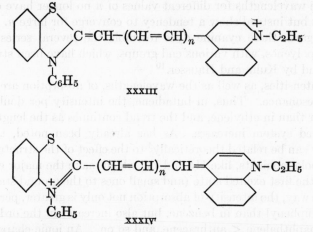

XXXIII

XXXIV

varied within wide limits, from zero, when these groups are identical,
to a value perhaps as great as in, say, phenol blue. In this way, several
important generalizations have been found to hold. If the end groups
are different, but are of approximately the same " basicity," so that the
structures corresponding to XXXIII and XXXIV are of approximately
the same stability, then the wavelength of maximum absorption is very
close to the mean of the wavelengths for the two related symmetrical
dyes. (For example, the symmetrical dyes related to XXXIII are
XXXV and XXXVI.) Moreover, as the number, $n$, of vinylene groups

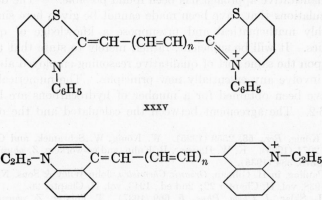

XXXV

XXXVI

increases, the wavelength of maximum absorption increases by an approximately constant amount of about 1000 A for each additional vinylene group. On the other hand, if the two end groups differ greatly in " basicity," the wavelength of maximum absorption is less than the mean (showing a decreased effectiveness of the resonance) and, moreover, the wavelengths for different values of $n$ no longer have constant intervals but instead show a tendency to converge for large $n$. In this latter regard, these cyanine dyes resemble the several series of conjugated polyenes, with various end groups, which have been studied by König and by Kuhn and Hausser.[10]

The intensities, as well as the wavelengths, of absorption are affected by the resonance. Thus, in butadiene, the intensity per double bond is greater than in ethylene, and the trend continues as the length of the conjugated system increases. As has already been noted, this high intensity can be related theoretically[4] to the effect of the structures with large dipole moments, like III and IV, which make the major contributions to the first excited state (and small ones to the ground state). In the same way, the intensity of absorption not only is greater, per benzene ring, in biphenyl than in benzene, but also increases in the order: benzene < naphthalene < anthracene, and so on. An ionic charge, which occupies different positions in the various resonating structures, as in crystal violet, for example, is also associated with intense absorption. This fact can be shown[11] theoretically to be due to the marked difference in the distribution of charge in the various structures.

Although, as we have just seen, the idea of resonance leads to a rough understanding of some of the major trends in the absorption spectra of organic substances, the picture is still much too crude to be of very wide applicability. For a few restricted series of compounds, a somewhat more quantitative approach has been found possible.[12] The details of the calculations that have been made cannot be given here since they are highly mathematical and presuppose a knowledge of quantum mechanics. It will be sufficient, rather, merely to state that they are based upon the same sort of qualitative reasoning employed above and do not involve any essentially new principles. The numerical results that have been obtained for a number of hydrocarbons are listed in Table 6·2. The agreement between the calculated and the observed

[10] W. König, Ber., 58, 2559 (1925). W. König, W. Schramek, and G. Rösch, ibid., 61, 2074 (1928). K. W. Hausser, R. Kuhn, and co-workers, Z. physik. Chem., B29, 371, 378, 384 (1935).

[11] L. Pauling, in H. Gilman, Organic Chemistry, John Wiley & Sons, New York, 1st ed., 1938, vol. II, Chapter 22; 2nd ed., 1943, vol. II, Chapter 26.

[12] A. L. Sklar, J. Chem. Phys., 5, 669 (1937). T. Förster, Z. physik. Chem., B41, 287 (1938).

## TABLE 6·2

ULTRAVIOLET ABSORPTION SPECTRA OF SOME HYDROCARBONS

Wavelength (A) of First Absorption Maximum

| Substance | Calcd $S^a$ | Calcd $F^b$ | Obs |
|---|---|---|---|
| Butadiene | 1900 | — | 2100[c] |
| Benzene | 2470 | 2450 | 2550[d] |
| Fulvene | 3645 | — | 3650[e] |
| Hexatriene | 2460 | — | 2610[f] |
| Phenylmethyl | 3060 | — | — |
| Styrene | 2570 | — | 2850[g] |
| Naphthalene | 2680 | 2950 | 2750[h] |
| Azulene | 6914 | 7800 | 7000[i] |
| Biphenyl | 2570 | — | 2515[d] |
| Anthracene | — | 3650 | 3700[h] |
| Phenanthrene | — | 3000 | 3400[h] |
| Pyrene | — | 3450 | 3300[h] |
| Naphthacene | — | 4500 | 4600[b] |
| Pentacene | — | 5450 | 5800[b] |

[a] A. L. Sklar, reference 12.  Some of the values in this column are taken from unpublished calculations of the present author.

[b] T. Förster, reference 12.  The value for azulene was calculated by the present author.

[c] G. Scheibe and H. Grieneisen, *Z. physik. Chem.*, **B25**, 52 (1934).

[d] A. E. Gillam and D. H. Hey, *J. Chem. Soc.*, 1170 (1939).

[e] *Handbuch der Physik*, Springer, Berlin, 1929, vol. 21, p. 105;  quoted by A. L. Sklar, reference 12.  See J. Stark and W. Steubing, *Physik. Z.*, **9**, 661 (1908).

[f] M. S. Kharasch, W. Nudenberg, and E. Sternfeld, *J. Am. Chem. Soc.*, **62**, 2034 (1940).  The value listed is for 2,5-dimethylhexatriene.  Hexatriene itself would doubtless absorb at somewhat shorter wavelengths.

[g] M. Pestemer and L. Wiligut, *Monatsh.*, **66**, 119 (1935).

[h] W. V. Mayneord and E. M. F. Roe, *Proc. Roy. Soc. (London)*, **A152**, 299 (1935).

[i] P. A. Plattner and A. St. Pfau, *Helv. Chim. Acta*, **20**, 224 (1937).

positions of the first electronic absorption bands is fairly good in all cases and, in fact, is better than could have been anticipated in view of the mathematical approximations made in the calculations.  Certain features come out of this more elaborate treatment that could hardly have been foreseen from qualitative considerations.  For example, the fact is accounted for that fulvene, XXXVII, azulene, XXXVIII, and the phenylmethyl radical, XXXIX, absorb light of surprisingly long

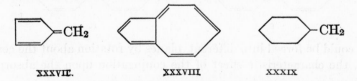

XXXVII.          XXXVIII          XXXIX

wavelengths in comparison with other analogous substances.  The last example is of particular interest in connection with the observed colors of the more stable triarylmethyl radicals, although, of course, the color of the phenylmethyl radical itself is not known.   Rather similar calculations for a number of dyes of the crystal violet and indigo types are reported also to have been made with satisfactory results, but no details are given.[13]   Further calculations for more restricted groups of compounds have been reported by Mayer and McCallum[14] and by Herzfeld and Sklar.[15]   The last calculations are of interest in that they provide a qualitative theoretical interpretation of the experimental data and empirical generalizations of Brooker.[9]

A brief further discussion of the calculations by Sklar[12] and by Förster[12] is desirable in order that the limitations to which they are subject may be made clearer.   In both treatments, only the purely covalent structures are taken into account, and all structures containing ionic bonds are ignored. For this reason, the treatments are unable to provide information regarding *all* the excited states.   Consequently, just as with butadiene (see above) there is no assurance that the calculations actually apply to the *first* absorption bands; and for a number of substances it seems fairly certainly established that they do not do so.[4]   The significance of the agreement between the observed and calculated wavelengths is therefore somewhat obscured. It seems reasonable, however, to suppose that, since the calculations should at any rate refer to the second, third, or some subsequent absorption band, if not to the first, then the absorption should start at a wavelength at least as great as that calculated.   Consequently, the calculations for azulene and pentacene, for example, are probably significant in showing that these substances should be deeply colored.

**6·4   Steric Inhibition of Resonance and Spectra.**   In the preceding section, it was pointed out that when two phenyl groups are conjugated with each other, as in biphenyl, the absorption lies at a different wavelength and is more intense (per benzene ring) than in benzene itself. Both of these effects can be considered due to the conjugation or, in other words, to the possibility of writing structures like I and II, in which the rings are joined by a double bond.   If, therefore, the two

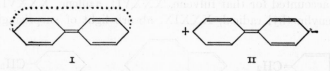

I                                       II

rings could be forced into different  planes by rotation about the **central** bond, the characteristic effect of the conjugation upon the absorption

[13] L. Pauling, *Proc. Natl. Acad. Sci.*, U. S., **25**, 577 (1939).
[14] M. G. Mayer and K. J. McCallum, *Rev. Modern Phys.*, **14**, 248 (1942).
[15] K. F. Herzfeld and A. L. Sklar, *Rev. Modern Phys.*, **14**, 294 (1942).

should vanish.   This prediction has been verified by studies of a number of substituted biphenyls in which the planar arrangement is made impossible by steric interactions.   The absorption spectrum of bimesityl, III, for example, is almost identical (per aromatic ring) with that of

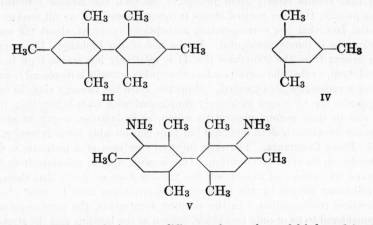

mesitylene, IV, but it is very different from that of biphenyl itself.[16] This fact is in accordance with expectation, since the optical activity of 3,3'-diaminobimesityl, V, for example, shows that methyl groups in the 2,6,2',6' positions are able to hold the two rings in different planes.[17] A large number of further examples have been given by Rodebush and his co-workers[16,18] who have studied the effect of the size of the substituents in the *ortho* positions, and have found that in general the alteration in the absorption spectrum is most pronounced when the blocking groups are largest.   These facts lend support to the beliefs both that the planar configuration is necessary for the resonance to be completely effective and also that the molecules do indeed tend to be planar in the absence of steric interactions.   Further examples have been given by Jones.[19]

An interesting fact regarding the effect of inhibition of resonance upon the absorption spectrum of the biphenyls is that the decrease in the intensity is much more pronounced than the change in the wavelength of maximum absorption.   In fact, the position of the maximum is not noticeably displaced at all in these substances.   The explanation of this apparently anomalous situation is probably the following.[4,20]   The first absorption band of bi-

[16] L. W. Pickett, G. F. Walter, and H. France, *J. Am. Chem. Soc.*, **58**, 2296 (1936). M. T. O'Shaughnessy and W. H. Rodebush, *ibid.*, **62**, 2906 (1940).
[17] W. W. Moyer and R. Adams, *J. Am. Chem. Soc.*, **51**, 630 (1929).
[18] B. Williamson and W. H. Rodebush, *J. Am. Chem. Soc.*, **63**, 3018 (1941).
[19] R. N. Jones, *J. Am. Chem. Soc.*, **63**, 1658 (1941).
[20] R. S. Mulliken, private communication.

phenyl, which is of high intensity, is probably due to a transition to an excited state that results from resonance principally, if not entirely, among ionic structures like II; on the other hand, the first absorption band of benzene, which is of low intensity, is almost certainly due to a transition to an excited state that results largely from resonance between the Kekulé structures. Consequently, the two excited states in question are not at all analogous, and the fact that the corresponding absorptions occur at about the same wavelengths is purely accidental.    In the non-planar biphenyls, the excited state arising from the structures like II is relatively less stable than in biphenyl itself, so that the corresponding absorption actually is displaced toward shorter wavelengths, as expected.    However, since the benzene rings in such compounds are no longer effectively conjugated with each other, they now give rise to their normal absorption which, as in benzene, occurs at about the same wavelength as in biphenyl but is of considerably lower intensity.

**6·5  Force Constants.**    The near infrared spectrum of a molecule is due to changes in its state of vibration.    One is often able to calculate from the observed frequencies of absorption the various *force constants* that describe the resistance offered by the molecule to deformation from its most stable geometrical configuration.    In the simplest treatments, the force constants are considered to be of only two kinds, known as the bending and the stretching force constants, respectively.    Of these, the former refer to alterations in the values of bond angles, whereas the latter refer to alterations in the values of bond lengths.

In the following discussion, we shall be interested only in the stretching force constants, $k$, which are defined by the equation[21]

$$W_d = \tfrac{1}{2}k(r - r_e)^2 \tag{1}$$

$W_d$ represents here the energy of distortion that is necessary to stretch (or to contract) the bond in question from its most stable length $r_e$ to the length $r$.    It is found that the force constant, $k$, like the bond length, $r_e$, is roughly constant for a bond of a given type and varies only slightly from molecule to molecule.    The value of $k$ is dependent, however, upon the atoms bonded, and it is more or less proportional to the bond order for pure single, double, and triple bonds between the same two atoms.

When a bond is not a pure single, double, or triple bond, but is of intermediate character as a result of resonance, its force constant may be expected to have an intermediate value.    Although this prediction appears to be in agreement with the facts, the difficulties that are encountered in determining accurate values of force constants from the spectra and other data in any but the very simplest molecules are so great that the conclusions reached are not beyond question.    It may be hoped, however, that, if comparisons are made only between values obtained by the same investigators, the errors inherent in the treatment may be minimized.    In Table 6·3 are listed the values taken

[21] This equation is only roughly approximate and is not closely obeyed when $r$ is very different from $r_e$.    For better, but more complicated, expressions for $k$ and $W_d$, see P. M. Morse, *Phys. Rev.*, **34**, 57 (1929).

by Thompson and Linnett[22] as best representing the force constants of bonds of pure types and also the values found by them for the force constants of bonds of intermediate types. The observed deviations are indeed always in

TABLE 6·3

STRETCHING FORCE CONSTANTS[a]

|  | Atoms Bonded | | | |
|---|---|---|---|---|
| Substance | CC | CN | CO | CCl |
| (Pure single bond) | 4.9 | — | 4.98 | 4.38 |
| (Pure double bond) | 9.5 | — | 13.0 | — |
| (Pure triple bond) | 15.8 | 18.10 | — | — |
| Cyanogen chloride | — | 16.65 | — | 5.15 |
| Carbon monoxide | — | — | 18.6 | — |
| Carbon dioxide | — | — | 15.24 | — |
| Tetrachloroethylene | 5.8 | — | — | 5.2 |
| Cyanogen | 6.69 | 17.51 | — | — |
| Carbon suboxide | 14.87 | — | 14.15 | — |

[a] The quantities listed in the body of the table are the stretching force constants, expressed in units of $10^5$ dynes per centimeter, for the bonds in the molecules given at the left of the row between the atoms given at the top of the column. The data are taken from H. W. Thompson and J. W. Linnett, reference 22. For the nature of the resonance which is presumed to occur in the various molecules, see Table 4·3.

the expected directions but are sometimes of too small magnitude to be of certain significance in view of the large probable errors. It is evident that this problem deserves further careful study.

[22] H. W. Thompson and J. W. Linnett, *J. Chem. Soc.*, 1291, 1384 (1937). J. W. Linnett and H. W. Thompson, *ibid.*, 1399 (1937); *Nature*, **139**, 509 (1937).

## Chapter 7

### RESONANCE AND CHEMICAL EQUILIBRIUM

**7·1 General Discussion.** The study of chemical equilibrium and of the way in which it is related to the structures of the various reactants involved has long attracted the attention of both practical and theoretical chemists. This has been due partly to the rigor and elegance of the thermodynamic methods that can be used in such a study, and partly also to the intrinsic importance of the subject itself. From the practical point of view, a knowledge of the values of equilibrium constants is of the utmost importance, because it enables one to know whether or not the reactions in question are capable of proceeding to appreciable extents in the desired directions under any realizable experimental conditions, and it shows how the most favorable conditions are to be chosen. From the theoretical point of view, such knowledge is of equal importance, because it aids in the understanding of the *reasons why* structural changes have their observed effects, and it often makes possible a prediction of the effects of as yet uninvestigated changes. These theoretical aspects provided part of the impetus for the development of the prequantum mechanical theories of intermediate stages and of mesomerism (Section 1·2) and will form the basis for most of the discussion in this chapter.

In the reversible reaction

$$A + B \rightleftarrows X + Y \tag{1}$$

the equilibrium constant, $K$, and the standard free energy change, $\Delta F°$, are given by the familiar thermodynamic equations[1]

$$K = \frac{[X][Y]}{[A][B]} = \frac{(X)(Y)\gamma_X\gamma_Y}{(A)(B)\gamma_A\gamma_B} \tag{2}$$

and

$$\Delta F° = -RT \ln K \tag{3}$$

The expressions in square brackets are the activities of the substances in question; the ones in parentheses are the respective concentrations; the $\gamma$'s are the activity coefficients; and $R$ and $T$ are the gas constant

---

[1] For discussions of these, and subsequent, equations, see any textbook of physical chemistry. For example, F. H. Getman and F. Daniels, *Outlines of Physical Chemistry*, John Wiley & Sons, New York, 7th ed., 1943, pp. 286 ff.

and the absolute temperature, respectively. Similarly, in a second reaction

$$A' + B' \rightleftarrows X' + Y' \tag{4}$$

the corresponding equations

$$K' = \frac{[X'][Y']}{[A'][B']} = \frac{(X')(Y')\gamma_{X'}\gamma_{Y'}}{(A')(B')\gamma_{A'}\gamma_{B'}} \tag{5}$$

and

$$\Delta F^{\circ\prime} = -RT \ln K' \tag{6}$$

also obtain. From equations 2, 3, 5, and 6, it follows that

$$\Delta\Delta F^{\circ} \equiv \Delta F^{\circ} - \Delta F^{\circ\prime} = -RT \ln \frac{K}{K'} = -RT \ln \frac{[X][Y][A'][B']}{[A][B][X'][Y']}$$

$$= -RT \ln \frac{(X)(Y)(A')(B')}{(X')(Y')(A)(B)} \frac{\gamma_X\gamma_Y\gamma_{A'}\gamma_{B'}}{\gamma_{X'}\gamma_{Y'}\gamma_A\gamma_B} \tag{7}$$

If the reactions of equations 1 and 4 are very similar in type (for example, if each of them is the neutralization of a monocarboxylic acid by a certain specified base in a certain specified solvent) then two simplifications in the treatment are immediately suggested. In the first place, it seems reasonable that the distinction between the activities and the concentrations can be ignored, and that the quantity $\Delta\Delta F^{\circ}$ can be expressed directly in terms of concentrations without reference to activities or activity coefficients. The reason for this is that the activity coefficients of $A$, $B$, $X$, and $Y$ should not differ significantly from those of $A'$, $B'$, $X'$, and $Y'$, respectively, so that the expression involving the activity coefficients at the extreme right of equation 7 should be very nearly unity. This approximation, which considerably simplifies all the subsequent discussion of equilibria, is probably a fairly good one, although it is of course not rigorously correct.

The second simplification which we shall make is a much less justifiable one. Equation 7 relates the ratio $K/K'$ of the equilibrium constants of the two reactions to the difference $\Delta\Delta F^{\circ}$ between the standard free energy changes. However, from a consideration of the resonance in the various molecules we can usually draw conclusions only in regard to the differences $\Delta\Delta E \equiv \Delta E - \Delta E'$ between the corresponding changes in internal energy (not free energy). Since

$$\Delta\Delta F^{\circ} = \Delta\Delta E + P\Delta\Delta V - T\Delta\Delta S^{\circ} \tag{8}$$

for reactions at constant pressure $P$ and temperature $T$, we can identify $\Delta\Delta E$ and $\Delta\Delta F^{\circ}$ only if the remaining terms are negligible. The first of these, $P\Delta\Delta V$, is probably sufficiently small to be ignored, since the volume changes, $\Delta V$ and $\Delta V'$, for the two reactions must be not only small individually but also approximately equal to each other. The second term, $T\Delta\Delta S°$, which involves the difference between the entropy changes, may be rather large, however. In fact, in some series of apparently very similar reactions that have been carefully studied, this term has been found to be more important than $\Delta\Delta E$ in determining the relative values of the equilibrium constants.[2]

For the reasons just outlined, it would seem to be highly dangerous for us to assume that variations in the positions of chemical equilibria can be predicted by a method requiring the identification of $\Delta\Delta F°$ and $\Delta\Delta E$. Nevertheless, we are often forced to make this assumption if we wish to discuss these variations at all, because we do not have sufficient experimental data to attempt a more rigorous treatment, except for a few extremely restricted groups of reactions. To as great an extent as possible, therefore, we shall limit ourselves to comparisons of reactions for which $\Delta\Delta F°$ is large, with the hope that thereby we can be fairly certain of the *direction* of the effect due to resonance, even though we cannot predict its exact magnitude. We shall find that we are often able in this way to obtain simple and logical explanations of the sometimes striking variations in the positions of equilibrium in analogous reactions.[3]

The reasoning which underlies the arguments in the following sections can be illustrated with the reactions of equations 1 and 4. First, let us suppose that $X'$ is the only one of all the reactants and products in these equations that is stabilized to any appreciable extent by resonance. If the two reactions are so similar that all further factors cancel out in the comparison, then it follows that $\Delta E$ is greater algebraically than $\Delta E'$. This means that $\Delta\Delta E$ is positive, as is also presumably $\Delta\Delta F°$, so that reaction 4 goes farther to the right than reaction 1. Conversely, of course, if $A'$ is the only substance so stabilized, reaction 1 goes farther to the right than reaction 4; and, in general, the reaction for which the gain in resonance energy is largest, or for which the loss in resonance energy is smallest, goes the most nearly to completion. These conclusions are justified, of course, only in so far as all further factors capable of affecting the equilibrium actually do cancel out in the comparison.

In certain classes of reaction the difficulties in the treatment, which were described above, can be shown to be negligible. This seems to be fairly generally true, for example, when the substances $A$, $B$, $X$, and $Y$ of equation

---

[2] L. F. Fieser and C. C. Price, *J. Am. Chem. Soc.*, **58**, 1838 (1936).

[3] For a more complete and more rigorous discussion of the difficulties referred to above, see L. P. Hammett, *Physical Organic Chemistry*, McGraw-Hill Book Company, New York, 1940, Chapter III.

1 differ from $A'$, $B'$, $X'$, and $Y'$, respectively, only in regard to substitution at points far removed from the reaction centers. Thus, for the equilibrium between, on the one hand, *meta* or *para* (but not *ortho*) substituted anilines plus formic acid and, on the other hand, the corresponding formanilides plus water, we might expect $\Delta\Delta S°$ to be very small, so that $\Delta\Delta F°$ and $\Delta\Delta E$ are approximately equal. This expectation is apparently in accord with experiment.[4]

A more complicated situation of a rather different type, in which the value of $\Delta\Delta S°$ again causes no trouble, arises in, for example, a comparison of the ionization constants of *meta* and *para* substituted benzoic acids. The major effect of substituents here seems to consist in an electrostatic interaction with the ionizable proton. Since this coulombic energy is a form of " reversible work," it contributes directly to the free energies, rather than to the internal energies, of the substances. Consequently, it can legitimately be used in the discussion of the changes in ionization constant, without apology for the neglect of entropy terms. It can be shown theoretically, and it has been verified experimentally,[3] that the temperature dependence of the dielectric constant of the solvent introduces a variation in the entropy of ionization. As a result, $\Delta\Delta F°$ and $\Delta\Delta E$ are not equal, but this fact causes no difficulty because $\Delta\Delta F°$ (or, rather, that part of it which is directly due to the electrostatic interactions under discussion) is the quantity that is actually being dealt with in the theoretical treatment. As in the previous example of the formanilides, substituents that are close to the centers of reaction introduce further effects that cannot at present be allowed for, so that, for example, no treatment of the *ortho* substituted benzoic acids can be carried through with any assurance.

## 7·2 Acid Strengths.[5]

There are at least two independent factors that cause variations in the strengths of acids of the same general type. The first of these, which has been recognized and understood for many years,[6] is electrostatic in nature. In $\alpha$-chlorobutyric acid, for example, the ionizable proton is in a region of relatively high positive potential, since it is closer to the positive, than it is to the negative, end of the large carbon-chlorine dipole. For this reason, less work is required to remove the proton to infinity (or, in other words, to ionize the molecule) than in unsubstituted butyric acid, in which no such effect exists. As a result, $\alpha$-chlorobutyric acid is a stronger acid than butyric acid, the ionization constants[7] being $1.45 \times 10^{-3}$ and $1.50 \times 10^{-5}$, respectively. In a similar manner, the facts that $\beta$-chlorobutyric acid, with a constant of $8.8 \times 10^{-5}$, is weaker than its $\alpha$ isomer, and that $\gamma$-chlorobutyric

[4] O. C. M. Davis, *Z. physik. Chem.*, **78**, 353 (1911). See also L. P. Hammett, page 190 of reference 3.

[5] Cf. G. Schwarzenbach and K. Lutz, *Helv. Chim. Acta*, **23**, 1162 (1940).

[6] For example, see N. Bjerrum, *Z. physik. Chem.*, **106**, 219 (1923).

[7] Except as otherwise noted, all dissociation constants cited in this and the following section are taken from *International Critical Tables*, McGraw-Hill Book Company, New York, 1929, vol. VI, pp. 259 ff. They refer to 25°.

acid, with a constant[8] of $3 \times 10^{-5}$, is weaker still, find a ready explanation in the steadily increasing distance between the proton and the carbon-chlorine dipole in the un-ionized molecule. Similar qualitative interpretations of the empirical data can be made, by obvious extensions of the reasoning, for a large number of further acids, and with many acids a semiquantitative approach has led to completely satisfactory results.[9] However, in spite of the great importance of this treatment, we shall have little further to say about it, except incidentally, since it does not directly involve the idea of resonance.

It should be apparent that, just as in the *meta* and *para* substituted benzoic acids which were mentioned at the end of Section 7·1, these purely electrostatic effects contribute directly to the free energy of ionization. Consequently, unless the polar group is close to the ionizable proton, no complications are introduced by the fact that the entropy of ionization is not known.

The second important factor influencing acid strength directly involves the theory of resonance. Phenol, for example, is an acid with a dissociation constant of $1.06 \times 10^{-10}$. The fact that this value is tremendously greater than that of any comparable alcohol cannot be explained on the basis of electrostatic interactions of the type that are important in the chlorobutyric acids. A consideration of the possibilities for resonance, however, leads at once to a simple interpretation of the facts. Thus, with a saturated alcohol, neither the undissociated molecule, ROH, nor the negative ion, RO⁻, is stabilized by resonance to any appreciable extent, since only one reasonable structure can be written for each. With phenol, on the other hand, both the undissociated molecule and the negative ion can resonate among the Kekulé and the *ortho* and *para* quinoid structures, of which I, II, III, and IV represent typical examples. (As usual, the Dewar and other similar

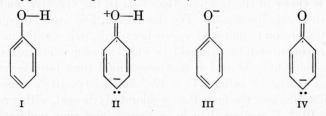

I          II          III          IV

[8] This value is taken from Landolt-Börnstein, *Physikalisch-Chemische Tabellen*, Springer, Berlin, 1923, vol. II, p. 1125.

[9] J. G. Kirkwood and F. H. Westheimer, *J. Chem. Phys.*, **6**, 506 (1938). F. H. Westheimer and J. G. Kirkwood, *ibid.*, **6**, 513 (1938). A simpler, but almost purely empirical, method of calculation has been given by C. G. Derick, *J. Am. Chem. Soc.*, **33**, 1152 (1911). For a recent, detailed discussion of this latter method, see G. E. K. Branch and M. Calvin, *The Theory of Organic Chemistry*, Prentice-Hall, Inc., New York, 1941, pp. 217 ff.

structures with formal bonds make further small contributions. They will be ignored here, however, because they would merely complicate the following discussion without leading to anything essentially new and without altering the conclusions in any significant way.) The Kekulé structures, I and III, are of course the most stable and hence the most important in the resonance, but the quinoid structures, II and IV, are of particular interest in the present connection and require special consideration. It will be observed that in structure II a wide separation of charges has been effected, whereas in IV the negative ionic charge has merely been transferred from the oxygen to a carbon atom. As a result, IV is doubtless considerably more stable, relative to its corresponding Kekulé structure III, than II is relative to I. This implies that structure IV makes a larger contribution to the state of the ion than structure II does to that of the neutral molecule, and that, moreover, the resonance energy of the ion must be greater than that of the neutral molecule. It follows then that the resonance facilitates ionization, and that phenol should be a stronger acid than a saturated alcohol, in which no such resonance exists.

This same conclusion can be obtained in a different, but more or less equivalent, way which does not make explicit use of the idea of resonance energy. In the quinoid structure II of the undissociated molecule, the oxygen atom carries a positive formal charge. The effect of this charge is to make the oxygen atom more positive, or less negative, than a corresponding oxygen atom in a saturated alcohol. The resonance, therefore, creates an electrostatic effect, which then increases the degree of ionization just as in the chlorobutyric acids. In most, but not all, of the remaining examples discussed in this and in the succeeding section, these same two points of view can be adopted. The second of these possible points of view has the advantage of relating the effect to a purely electrostatic interaction and so of decreasing to some extent the difficulty regarding the changes in entropy. However, we shall make use of only the former one, based upon the idea of resonance energy, because it is the more general of the two and can be applied to a wider variety of problems.

The structural feature of the phenol molecule which gives rise to the above-described effects is the enolic grouping, $C{=}C{-}OH$. It is evident, then, that the relatively great acidities of the various substituted phenols, the naphthols, and so on can be explained in an entirely analogous manner. Moreover, the same type of reasoning leads to the further conclusion that the non-phenolic enols should also be considerably more acidic than comparable saturated alcohols. This prediction cannot be tested directly by comparison with experiment, because the simplest enols, like vinyl alcohol, V, rearrange immediately and, for all practical purposes, irreversibly to the corresponding aldehydes or ketones, VI; and the more complex ones, like the enol forms of aceto-acetic ester, VII, and acetylacetone, VIII, contain highly polar groups

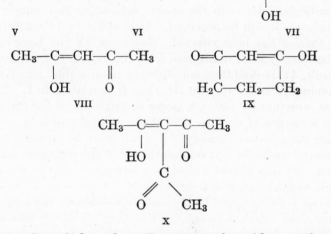

which exert large independent effects upon the acid strengths.    From the evidence which is available, however, it seems evident that the predicted effect does exist.[5,10]    In the enol form of acetylacetone, VIII, for example, the reported ionization constant of $5.8 \times 10^{-9}$ is definitely too large to be due merely to an electrostatic interaction with the adjacent carbonyl group.    Moreover, in the enol forms of 1,3-cyclohexanedione (dihydroresorcinol), IX, and of triacetylmethane, X, with constants of $5.5 \times 10^{-6}$ and $1.55 \times 10^{-6}$, respectively, the acid strengths are even greater.    And finally, in the enol form of glutaconic dialdehyde, XI, the observed constant of $1.75 \times 10^{-6}$ is of the same order of magnitude, although the electrostatic interaction should be considerably smaller.

$$HO—CH=CH—CH=CH—CH=O$$
XI

It is of interest that acetylacetone, dihydroresorcinol, glutaconic dialdehyde, and triacetylmethane give rise to negative ions in which the resonance should be especially effective, since it occurs between two equivalent structures in the first three ions, and among three such structures in the last one.    This fact, which does not obtain with the simple enols like phenol, may be partly responsible for the somewhat greater acidity of these dicarbonyl compounds.

[10] G. Schwarzenbach and K. Lutz, *Helv. Chim. Acta*, **23**, 1147 (1940).

The values of the ionization constants of the above enols are based upon the assumptions that, in aqueous solution, acetylacetone is 19.6 per cent enolic,[11] whereas 1,3-cyclohexanedione, triacetylmethane, and glutaconic dialdehyde are each 100 per cent enolic. If the last three of these substances actually contain some of the keto forms in aqueous solution, the true ionization constants of the enol forms are correspondingly greater than the values given.

The foregoing discussion of the phenols and enols can be generalized to include all other types of substance containing the characteristic grouping $X = Y - \ddot{Z} - H$. The atoms $X$, $Y$, and $Z$ can be of any kind, the only essential restriction being that the hydrogen, H, must be joined to an atom $Z$, which has an unshared pair of electrons and is linked by a single bond to a doubly bound atom $Y$. Thus, thiophenol, XII, and aniline, XIII, should be stronger acids than saturated aliphatic

mercaptans, RSH, and primary amines, $RNH_2$, respectively. Since the actual values of the ionization constants are not known, the correctness of these predictions can only be inferred from the chemical behaviors of the substances in question. In particular, thiophenol can be titrated with sodium hydroxide to a sharp end point when phenolphthalein is used as an indicator, but an aliphatic mercaptan cannot.[12] No corresponding data seem to be available, however, for the amino compounds. Similarly in diphenylamine, XIV, with an increased number of possible quinoid structures, and in pyrrole, XV, indole, XVI, and carbazole, XVII, the acid strengths should be still greater, as they do indeed appear to be.

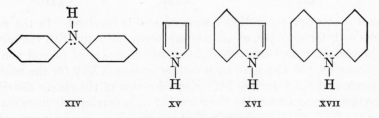

[11] F. C. Nachod, *Z. physik. Chem.*, **A182**, 193 (1938).
[12] P. Klason and T. Carlson, *Ber.*, **39**, 738 (1906).

In a carboxylic acid, XVIII, resonance of the present type may make a considerable contribution to the relatively great acid strength, although the closeness of the large carbonyl group moment makes a decision difficult. Both the electrostatic and the resonance factors operate here to increase the acidity, and so we cannot be sure how much

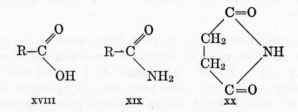

of the observed effect must be attributed to each cause. The same situation is encountered also in the amide of a carboxylic acid, XIX, and in the imide of a dicarboxylic acid, XX.

A different type of example in which the electrostatic and resonance factors produce effects in the same direction is provided by the nitrophenols. These substances are more acidic than the simple phenols, as could have been predicted from the fact that nitro groups, like chlorine atoms, seem always to increase the acidities of any compounds in which they are present. In general, this effect is due at least partly to the purely electrostatic interactions of the large nitro group moments. Here, however, the fact that the *ortho* and *para* nitrophenols, XXI and XXIII, respectively, are stronger acids than their *meta* isomer, XXII,

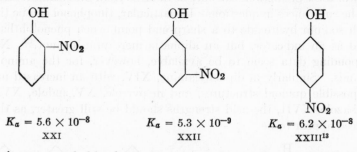

makes it seem probable that resonance also is involved. In the *para* compound, for example, resonance can occur not only with the structures analogous to those contributing to the states of phenol and of nitrobenzene, but also with such further ones as XXIV for the neutral molecule and XXV for the ion. Consideration of the charge distributions makes it apparent that the second of these is relatively more stable than the first, and consequently that the resonance should increase the

[13] G. W. Wheland and R. M. Brownell, unpublished work.

acid strength.   In the *ortho* isomer, the corresponding *ortho* quinoid
structures, XXVI and XXVII, lead similarly to an increase in acid

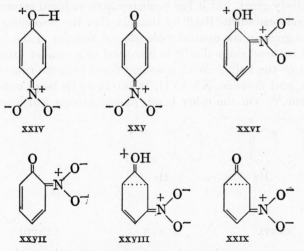

strength.   In the *meta* isomer, on the other hand, the *meta* quinoid
structures, XXVIII and XXIX, have formal bonds and so are too
unstable to have great effect.   Further evidence confirming this interpretation will be given in Section 7·4.

Resonance can frequently exert an appreciable effect upon the acid
strength even of a substance which possesses no enolic or similar grouping.   In the neutral molecule of cyclopentadiene, XXX, for example,
there is only the small stabilization due to the simple conjugated system,
whereas, in the corresponding negative ion, the much more effective
resonance among the five equivalent structures, XXXI–XXXV, can

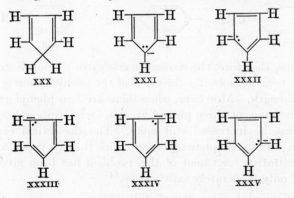

occur in addition.   It is only reasonable, then, that this substance
should be much more strongly acidic than a saturated hydrocarbon like

cyclopentane, although, of course, it is still an extremely weak acid when compared with, say, a phenol.    In indene, XXXVI, the acidity is also comparatively great, but it has probably been reduced somewhat from that of cyclopentadiene itself by the fact that the resonance energy is already so great in the neutral molecule (on account of the presence of the fused benzene ring) that it is increased to a smaller extent by the formation of the ion.[14]    With a second fused benzene ring, this trend continues, and fluorene, XXXVII, is known to be more weakly acidic than indene.[15]    On the other hand, phenyl groups which are present

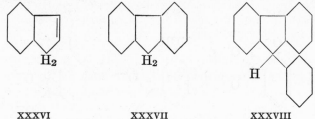

| XXXVI | XXXVII | XXXVIII |

as substituents upon the carbon atom carrying the acidic hydrogen atom have the opposite effect and increase the acid strength.    Thus, phenylfluorene, XXXVIII, is an acid of about the same strength as indene, and the strengths of triphenylmethane, diphenylmethane, toluene, and methane decrease in the order named.[15]    The reason for this effect of phenyl groups becomes apparent from a consideration of the resonating structures in toluene.    For the un-ionized molecule there are only the two Kekulé structures to be considered (structures with formal bonds being neglected), while for the ion there are, in addition to the Kekulé structures, also the three quinoid structures XXXIX, XL, and

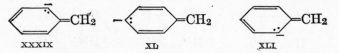

| XXXIX | XL | XLI |

XLI.    Since, therefore, the resonance energy of the ion is greater than that of the neutral molecule, the effect of the phenyl group is to increase the acid strength.    Moreover, when there are two phenyl groups, as in diphenylmethane, or three phenyl groups, as in triphenylmethane, the acidity must be increased still more.    The theoretical expectations, accordingly, are in complete agreement with the experimental facts.    A more quantitative treatment of this problem has been given, but the results are only moderately satisfactory.[14]

[14] G. W. Wheland, *J. Chem. Phys.*, **2**, 474 (1934).
[15] J. B. Conant and G. W. Wheland, *J. Am. Chem. Soc.*, **54**, 1212 (1932).    W. K. McEwen, *ibid.*, **58**, 1124 (1936).

On the basis of the above discussion, it might be expected that cyclo-heptatriene should be more acidic than even cyclopentadiene, since here the ion can resonate among *seven* equivalent structures.  Although no numeri-cal data are available, the chemical properties of the two substances show that the expectation is *not* realized and that, in fact, cycloheptatriene is con-siderably the weaker acid of the two.   There are probably two reasons for this discrepancy.   In the first place, the seven-membered ring probably is not completely planar, and so the seven structures for the ion are not actu-ally equivalent after all.    (See the analogous discussion of cyclooctatetraene in Section 4·2.)   Moreover, theoretical calculations have shown that, even if the ion were planar, the resonance should be much less effective here than with cyclopentadiene.   The reason for this surprising result cannot be ex-plained in non-mathematical language.[14,16]

In *p,p',p''*-trinitrotriphenylmethane, XLII, as in the nitrophenols, the nitro groups increase the acid strength both by their electrostatic interactions and also by virtue of the fact that they make possible, *in the ion alone*, resonance with such additional structures as XLIII.    The

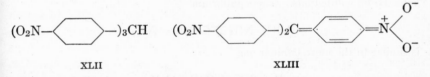

XLII                                    XLIII

effect here is so great that, whereas triphenylmethane has been assigned[15] an ionization constant smaller than $10^{-33}$, the alkali metal salts of its trinitro derivative are not completely solvolyzed even in aqueous alcoholic solution.[17]   It is, of course, difficult to assess the relative im-portance of the electrostatic and resonance factors, but evidence that the latter plays an important, even though not a decisive, role will be given in Section 7·4.

The relatively acidic nature of acetylene and of its monosubstitution products is apparently not a resonance effect but is due to some other cause.   The explanation is probably to be found in the fact that the carbon atom which carries the acidic hydrogen is linked by a triple bond to its adjacent carbon atom.   In fact, it can be shown on theoretical grounds that, when an atom is joined to another by a multiple bond, it may be expected to hold its remaining electrons more firmly than usual. Thus, as far as the electrons taking part in a carbon-hydrogen bond in acetylene are concerned, the carbon atom is acting like an atom of a more electronegative element, such as nitrogen, say.   Consequently, acetylene is more acidic than ethane, just as ammonia is more acidic

[16] E. Hückel, *Z. Elektrochem.*, **43**, 752 (1937).
[17] V. v. Richter, *Ber.*, **21**, 2475 (1888).

than methane. A similar, but smaller, effect should operate also in ethylenic compounds, so that a hydrogen atom joined to a doubly bonded carbon atom should show an intermediate acidity. This prediction is borne out by the fact that benzene is apparently a stronger acid than a paraffin hydrocarbon,[15] but, of course, a much weaker one than acetylene.

There is reason to believe that at least part of the relatively great acidity of phenol and related compounds is due to an effect of the kind just discussed in connection with acetylene and benzene. In phenol, for example, the oxygen atom must have given up a larger than usual share of its electrons to the carbon atom to which it is joined, merely as a result of the increased electronegativity of the latter. Consequently, for this additional reason also, the oxygen atom should be more positive, and the acid strength should be greater, in phenol than in a saturated alcohol. There is no way of estimating whether this additional effect is less or more important than the effect of the resonance. That it is by no means negligible is strongly suggested, however, by the following considerations,[18] which are taken from the field of the organic boron compounds. The equilibrium

$$R_3B + NH_3 \rightleftharpoons \overset{-}{R_3B} - \overset{+}{NH_3}$$

is similar to the more familiar one

$$\overset{+}{H} + NH_3 \rightleftharpoons H - \overset{+}{NH_3}$$

because, in each reaction, a new valence bond is formed with the aid of the unshared pair of electrons originally possessed by the ammonia. In order to call attention to similarities of this sort, Lewis has proposed that the terms " acid " and " base " be generalized so that an acid becomes any substance with a vacant place into which a pair of electrons can be placed, and a base becomes any substance with an unshared pair of electrons which can be put into such a vacant place.[19] It is of interest now to consider the acid strength of the substance $R_3B$, in this generalized sense, in relation to the nature of the group R. The facts are that these acids follow the same regularities as the hydroxy compounds, and, in particular, that phenyl groups lead to stronger acids than alkyl groups. For example, the addition compound of ammonia with trimethyl boron is about 90 per cent dissociated in the vapor phase at 25–30°,[20] whereas the corresponding addition compound with triphenyl boron is not noticeably dissociated at temperatures much below its melting point of 212°.[21]

Although a direct comparison of the dissociation constants of these two

---

[18] H. C. Brown, private communication.

[19] G. N. Lewis, *Valence and the Structure of Atoms and Molecules*, Chemical Catalog Company, New York, 1923, pp. 141 f.; *J. Franklin Inst.*, **226**, 293 (1938).

[20] A. Stock and F. Zeidler, *Ber.*, **54**, 531 (1921).

[21] E. Krause, *Ber.*, **57**, 813 (1924).

substances is impossible on account of lack of data, the greater acidity of the triphenyl compound seems beyond question. However, there is no obvious way in which this fact can be related to resonance, because no structures analogous to II or IV, above, can be drawn; the boron atom just does not have the necessary electrons. Consequently, it appears necessary to suppose that the much greater acidity of triphenyl boron, as compared with trimethyl boron, must be a result only of the greater electronegativity of the aromatic carbon atoms. If so, then the same effect should increase also the acid strength of phenol and its analogs to a considerable, but indeterminate, extent. The exact extent to which the resonance is responsible for the increased acid strengths of these latter substances is therefore uncertain. Evidence supporting the belief that resonance is a significant factor will be given, however, in Section 7·4.

**7·3 Base Strengths.** The same two factors which influence acid strengths, namely, the electrostatic interaction and the resonance, give rise also to characteristic variations in base strength as well. An example of a molecule in which only the resonance effect appears to be important is provided by aniline. This substance, with an ionization constant[22] of $3.8 \times 10^{-10}$, is much more weakly basic than any of the comparable aliphatic amines, which have ionization constants in the range $10^{-3}$ to $10^{-5}$. An explanation is to be found in the fact that the resonance energy here is greater in the neutral molecule than in the corresponding positive ion. Aniline can resonate not only with the Kekulé (and Dewar) structures, but also with such *ortho* and *para* quinoid structures as I. The anilinium ion, however, can receive no contributions from structures analogous to these latter, because the

I

unshared pair of electrons, which is on the nitrogen atom in the conventional structure of aniline itself, has been used up in forming the new nitrogen-hydrogen bond and so cannot be placed upon the *ortho* or *para* carbon atoms as in I. The effect of the resonance, therefore, is to stabilize the molecule relative to the ion. Reference to Table 3·6 shows that the effect should be of the order of something like 10 kcal per mole, a value which seems entirely reasonable when it is considered that $\Delta F°$ of ionization of aniline is greater than that of, say, ethylamine by 8 kcal per mole.

[22] N. F. Hall and M. R. Sprinkle, *J. Am. Chem. Soc.*, **54**, 3469 (1932).

As with the acid strength of phenol, the effect of the resonance here can be referred also to a change in the distribution of electric charge. Thus, the contribution of the structure I to the neutral molecule increases the positive charge (or decreases the negative charge) on the nitrogen atom, and so makes it more difficult for a proton to come up.

A useful, alternative way of stating the value of the basic ionization constant $K_b$ of an amine B is in terms of the acid ionization constant $K_a$ of the conjugate acid[23] BH+. Thus

$$K_a = \frac{[B][H^+]}{[BH^+]} = \frac{[B][H^+][OH^-]}{[BH^+][OH^-]} = \frac{K_w}{K_b} \tag{1}$$

where $K_w = [H^+][OH^-]$ is the ion product of water, which has a value of approximately $10^{-14}$ at ordinary temperatures. Moreover, in place of the constants $K_a$ and $K_b$, themselves, we shall frequently find it convenient to employ the quantities $pK_a$ and $pK_b$, respectively, which are defined by the equations

$$pK_a = -\log K_a \cong 14 - pK_b \tag{2}$$

and

$$pK_b = -\log K_b \cong 14 - pK_a \tag{3}$$

For example, Hall and Sprinkle[22] reported that the $pK_a$ of aniline is 4.58. This means that the ionization constants are $K_a = 10^{-4.58} = 2.63 \times 10^{-5}$, and $K_b \cong 10^{-14}/2.63 \times 10^{-5} = 3.8 \times 10^{-10}$. It is important to bear in mind that the stronger an amine is as a base, the smaller are the values of $K_a$ and $pK_b$, and the larger are the values of $K_b$ and $pK_a$.

Pyrrole, II, is like aniline in being a very weak base, because resonance with such structures as III occurs in the neutral molecule but is impossible in the positive ion. With diphenylamine, IV, triphenylamine, V,

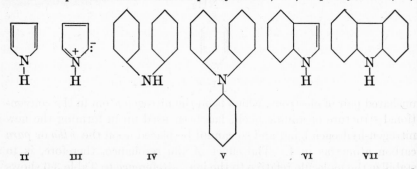

II          III          IV          V          VI          VII

indole, VI, and carbazole, VII, similarly, the base strengths are reduced by the decreased possibilities for resonance in the ion.

The weakly basic nature of pyridine[24] $(K_b = 1.7 \times 10^{-9})$ on the

[23] J. N. Brönsted, *Rec. trav. chim.*, **42**, 718 (1923). T. M. Lowry, *Chemistry & Industry*, **42**, 43 (1923).

[24] F. L. Hahn and R. Klockmann, *Z. physik. Chem.*, **A146**, 373 (1930).

other hand, cannot be explained in this manner and is presumably due to the fact that in each of the Kekulé-like structures, VIII, the nitrogen is doubly bonded to one of the two adjacent carbon atoms. The situa-

VIII

tion is therefore analogous to that discussed in the preceding section in connection with the acid strengths of acetylene and of benzene. The relation between the two problems is easily seen if it is borne in mind that, since pyridine is a relatively weak base, the pyridinium ion, which has a structure very analogous to that of benzene, must be a relatively strong acid. (See equations 1–3.)

Just as we found it necessary to consider the possibility that the strength of phenol as an acid might be partly due to the greater electronegativity of the aromatic carbon atoms, so also we should consider here the possibility that the weakness of aniline as a base might be partly due to the same cause. Indeed, if the nitrogen atom in aniline has lost a greater than usual share of its electrons to the carbon atom to which it is joined, it must have a smaller than usual net negative charge, so that its attraction for a proton has been decreased, in comparison with the nitrogen atom in a saturated amine. However, evidence will be presented in Section 7·4 to show that the resonance is nevertheless an important factor.

The resonance effect in some substances *increases* the base strength. Guanidine, for example, is a strong base with a $pK_a$ of 13.5,[25] presumably because the resonance among the three equivalent structures, IX, X, and XI, in the ion is much more effective than that between the corresponding non-equivalent structures, XII, XIII, and XIV, in the neutral molecule. The electrostatic effect due to the carbon-nitrogen dipoles should tend to *decrease* the base strength; the observed increase,

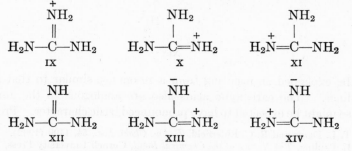

[25] N. F. Hall, *J. Am. Chem. Soc.*, **52**, 5115 (1930).

therefore, shows that the resonance effect must be quite large. The base strengths of the substituted guanidines show interesting regularities. Like the parent substance, the N-alkyl, the N,N-dialkyl, and the N,N′,N″-trialkyl derivatives are reported[26] to be strong bases, whereas the N,N′-dialkylguanidines are much weaker bases and have $pK_a$'s of about 10.3. An ingenious explanation of these facts has been given by Pauling,[27] but the problem might repay further experimental investigation.

In the amidines, the two principal structures in the ion, XV and XVI, are equivalent, whereas those in the neutral molecule, XVII and XVIII, are not. The base strength, accordingly, is increased by the resonance.

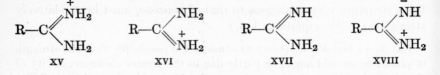

Although the electrostatic interactions again operate in the opposite direction, the substances are fairly strong bases. The $pK_a$ of acetamidine (structure XVII or XVIII with R = CH₃) has been reported to be 12.41.[5] The effect of alkyl substituents appears not to have been investigated. An interesting analog of the amidines is given by the substance XIX, which has a $pK_a$ of 12.13; the relatively great base strength

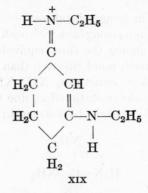

can be explained as resulting from a resonance similar to that in the amidines.[5] The carboxylic acids also are analogous to the amidines and so might be expected to have pronounced basic character. Probably

[26] T. L. Davis and R. C. Elderfield, *J. Am. Chem. Soc.*, **54**, 1499 (1932).

[27] L. Pauling, *The Nature of the Chemical Bond*, Cornell University Press, Ithaca, N. Y., 1st ed., 1939, pp. 198 f.; 2nd ed., 1940, pp. 213 f.

as a result of the electrostatic effect, however, these substances are slightly weaker bases than simple ketones.[28]

In urea and in the amides of carboxylic acids, the situations are similar to those encountered in guanidine and in the amidines, respectively. In these substances, however, the resonating structures, XX–XXIX, are completely equivalent in neither the ions nor the neutral molecules; consequently, the resonance effects are of less importance, and the base

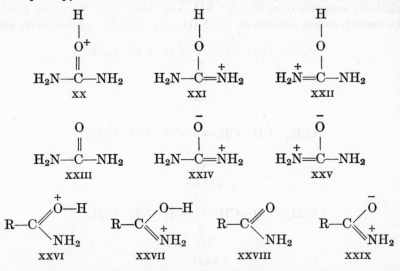

strengths of the substances are smaller. It is to be noted that in these positive ions the protons are considered to be attached to oxygen, and not to nitrogen as might perhaps have been anticipated in view of the fact that amines are stronger bases in general than ketones. This assumption is made because the resonance *increases* the ease of attachment of a proton to oxygen in these substances and *decreases* that to nitrogen. In the amides, for example, the structures XXVI and XXVII are more nearly of the same energy than are XXVIII and XXIX, and so the resonance favors the ion; the structure XXX for the other possible ion, however, has no possibility for resonance with a structure

XXX

analogous to XXVII or XXIX, and so here the resonance favors the neutral molecule.

[28] L. P. Hammett, page 271 of reference 3.

When a carboxylic acid, a urea, or an amide acts as a base, the proton taken up, as we have just seen, is probably attached to an oxygen atom. A number of further examples are known of the formation of " oxonium salts " of greater or less stability.   The halochromic salts formed by $\alpha,\beta$-unsaturated ketones, for example, are more stable than the corresponding derivatives of saturated ketones.   Thus, in dibenzalacetone, resonance occurs among the normal structure, XXXI, and several relatively unstable ones like XXXII.   In the ion, on the other hand, the corresponding structures, XXXIII and XXXIV, respectively, are

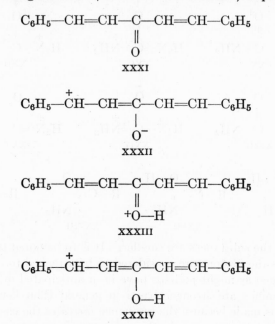

$$C_6H_5-CH=CH-C-CH=CH-C_6H_5$$
$$\overset{\|}{O}$$
XXXI

$$C_6H_5-\overset{+}{C}H-CH=C-CH=CH-C_6H_5$$
$$\overset{|}{O^-}$$
XXXII

$$C_6H_5-CH=CH-C-CH=CH-C_6H_5$$
$$\overset{\|}{^+O-H}$$
XXXIII

$$C_6H_5-\overset{+}{C}H-CH=C-CH=CH-C_6H_5$$
$$\overset{|}{O-H}$$
XXXIV

more nearly of the same stability since there is no separation of charge in either.   The resonance, therefore, is more effective in the ion, and so the base strength is increased.   An extreme example of this effect is provided by dimethyl-$\gamma$-pyrone, XXXV.   In this substance, the positive ion is stabilized to a particularly great extent by resonance between

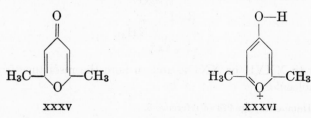

XXXV XXXVI

the equivalent Kekulé-like structures, XXXVI and XXXVII, as well as with such structures as XXXVIII, which are analogous to XXXIV.

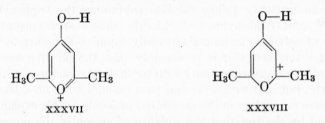

As a result, the substance is a particularly strong base for an oxygen compound. (In *International Critical Tables*[7] the ionization constant of this substance is given as $K_b = 6 \times 10^{-9}$. However, in the original paper from which this value was taken,[29] the author states that the pyrone is a much weaker base than aniline and has an ionization constant of $K_b = 3 \times 10^{-14}$.)

With flavone, XXXIX, the situation is entirely similar, in consequence of the γ-pyrone ring which the molecule contains. Pelargonidin, XL, is an example of a somewhat different type, but its corresponding positive ion, XLI, also is of the oxonium type and is stabilized by the presence of an oxygen-containing ring with aromatic character.

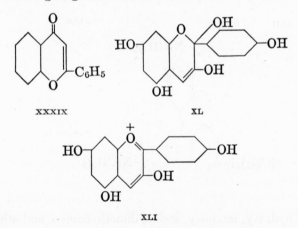

Just as hydrocarbons can be regarded as extremely weak acids, so alcohols can be regarded as extremely weak bases, not only in the sense that such substances are capable of forming oxonium salts of the type $(ROH_2)^+X^-$, but also in the sense that positive ions, $R^+$, can be derived from them by the removal of hydroxide ions. The simple aliphatic

[29] P. Walden, *Ber.*, **34**, 4185 (1901).

alcohols do not behave as bases in this way, but the triarylcarbinols do. Triphenylcarbinol, for example, dissolves in concentrated sulfuric acid to give an intensely yellow solution containing the triphenylmethyl cation;[30] and triphenylmethyl chloride ionizes spontaneously in a number of solvents, including especially liquid sulfur dioxide.[31]   The reason for this behavior is presumably that the positive ion here is stabilized by resonance not only with the Kekulé structures of each ring separately, but also with *ortho* and *para* quinoid structures, like XLII, which have no analogs in the un-ionized molecule.   This explanation is supported by the fact that the stability of an ion of the present type decreases as the number of aromatic rings decreases,[32] so that benzhydrol and benzyl alcohol appear to behave as progressively weaker bases.

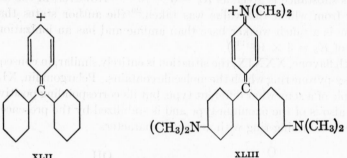

XLII                    XLIII

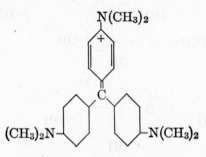

XLIV

Moreover, hydroxy, methoxy, amino, dimethylamino, and other similar groups greatly increase the stabilities of the ions when present as substituents in the *para* positions of the benzene rings.   This effect is

[30] A. Hantzsch, *Z. physik. Chem.*, **61**, 257 (1907).   L. P. Hammett and A. J. Deyrup, *J. Am. Chem. Soc.*, **55**, 1900 (1933).

[31] K. Ziegler and E. Boye, *Ann.*, **458**, 229 (1927).   K. Ziegler and H. Wollschitt, *ibid.*, **479**, 90 (1930).

[32] For data regarding the conductivities of the corresponding chlorides in liquid sulfur dioxide, see F. Straus and A. Dützmann, *J. prakt. Chem.*, [2] **103**, 1 (1921).

probably due to the possibility of resonance in the ion with a number of still further structures, such as XLIII for crystal violet, for example. These structures contain more bonds, and so are more stable, than structures like XLIV, analogous to XLII for the triphenylmethyl cation itself. Their contributions to the state of the ion are, therefore, large, and they are particularly effective in increasing the base strength of the carbinol.

**7·4  Steric Inhibition of Resonance in Acids and Bases.** It was pointed out in Section 7·2 that the relatively great acidities of *ortho* and *para* nitrophenol are due partly to resonance with quinoid structures. It is evident, then, that the acid strengths should be reduced if the resonance with these structures could be prevented in some way. This can be done, as was shown in Section 5·5, by the placing of methyl groups in the two positions *ortho* to the nitro group (in the *para* isomer only, of course). Methyl groups themselves, however, exert direct effects upon the acidities of phenols, and so a rather detailed study of the problem is necessary.[13]  Since *m*-2-xylenol, I, is a weaker acid than *m*-5-xylenol, II, which in turn is a weaker acid than phenol itself, III, it follows that the methyl groups, even in the absence of any other fac-

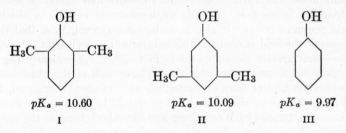

$pK_a = 10.60$        $pK_a = 10.09$        $pK_a = 9.97$

I        II        III

tors, decrease the acidity of the compound, and are more effective when *ortho*, than when *meta*, to the hydroxyl group. On the other hand, 2-nitro-*m*-5-xylenol, V, is a weaker acid than 5-nitro-*m*-2-xylenol, IV. The order here is the opposite of that observed in the simple xylenols

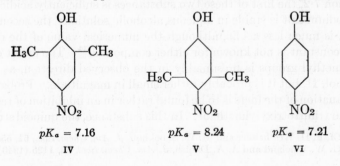

$pK_a = 7.16$        $pK_a = 8.24$        $pK_a = 7.21$

IV        V        VI

and so can hardly be due to any direct interaction of the methyl groups. The explanation is presumably that the nitro group in V can exert only its electrostatic, and not its resonance, effect, whereas that in IV can exert both effects. If the data are taken at their face value, it would appear that the resonance is responsible for between one-third and one-half of the total effect.

It is interesting that 5-nitro-$m$-2-xylenol, IV, is apparently a slightly stronger acid than $p$-nitrophenol, VI, although the opposite order might have been expected from analogy with $m$-2-xylenol and phenol. A possible explanation of this fact is as follows.[33] The comparatively great acidity of all the nitrophenols must be due partly to the direct electrostatic interaction between the nitro group moments and the ionizable protons. Coulomb's law shows that this interaction is increased in magnitude if the dielectric constant of the medium is lowered. Now the methyl groups in the nitroxylenol increase the size of the molecule, so that more of the electrostatic lines of force between the nitro group and the proton must pass through the molecule, and less must pass through the solvent, than is true in $p$-nitrophenol. Since the volume occupied by the molecule must be a region of low dielectric constant (possibly about 2) whereas the aqueous solvent has a much higher dielectric constant (about 80), it follows that the methyl groups in the nitroxylenol lower the *effective* dielectric constant and therefore increase the electrostatic interaction. If this explanation is correct, a similar effect should presumably operate also in 2-nitro-$m$-5-xylenol, V, so that the actual decrease of the acid strength of this substance by the inhibition of resonance is somewhat greater than appears at first sight; consequently the effect of the resonance alone in increasing the acid strength of the nitrophenols may be somewhat greater than estimated above. It should be noted, however, that the shielding by the methyl groups should be less effective here than in the examples treated by Westheimer and Shookhoff, because the electrostatic interaction in question is here of the dipole-ion, and not of the ion-ion, type.

A similar example, for which the data are less complete, is given by a comparison of 4,4′,4″-trinitrotriphenylmethane and 3,3′,3″,5,5′,5″-hexamethyl-4,4′,4″-trinitrotriphenylmethane. As was mentioned in Section 7·2, the first of these two substances is sufficiently acidic so that its sodium salt is stable in aqueous alcoholic solution; the second, however, is much less acidic, although the numerical value of the dissociation constant is not known for either compound.[34] The direct effect of the methyl groups is presumably in the observed direction, as in $m$-5-xylenol, II, but it is probably rather small in magnitude. Probably, the explanation of the facts is to be found rather in an inhibition of resonance in the trinitrotrixylylmethane. In this substance, the quinoid structures

[33] Cf. F. H. Westheimer and M. W. Shookhoff, *J. Am. Chem. Soc.*, **61**, 555 (1939).
[34] G. W. Wheland and A. A. Danish, *J. Am. Chem. Soc.*, **62**, 1125 (1940).

like VII are rendered unstable by the twisting of each nitro group out
of the plane of the benzene ring to which it is joined; these structures,

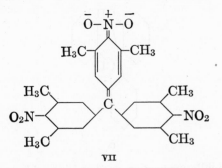

VII

therefore, can make only small contributions to the state of the ion, and
so they can increase its stability to only a small extent.  The electrostatic effect of the nitro groups remains, however, so that the trinitrotrixylylmethane is still a much stronger acid than trixylylmethane itself.

In tri-*o*-tolylmethane, the hydrogen atoms of the side-chain methyl
groups have been found to be more acidic than the one attached to the
central carbon atom.[35]  This fact is somewhat surprising, since triphenylmethane is known to be much more acidic than toluene.[15]  A
possible explanation is that, in the ion of the tritolyl compound, the
resonance with structures like VIII is inhibited by the bulky methyl
groups, which prevent the achievement of the completely planar con-

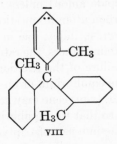

VIII

figuration.  As a matter of fact, such a configuration is impossible also
in the corresponding ion formed from triphenylmethane itself, because
even the hydrogen atoms in the ortho positions are large enough to
interfere with each other.  However, the methyl groups must lead to
considerably greater departures from planarity and, therefore, to an
appreciably decreased acid strength.

Still a further example of a slightly different kind of steric inhibition

[35] P. D. Bartlett and J. E. Jones, *J. Am. Chem. Soc.*, **64**, 1837 (1942).

of resonance is possibly given by the hydrocarbon triptycene, IX.[36]
From analogy with triphenylmethane, this substance might be expected

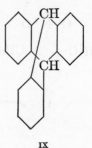

IX

to have weakly acidic properties, so that it should react with phenyl-*i*-propyl potassium in accordance with the equation

$$C_{20}H_{14} + C_6H_5C(CH_3)_2K \longrightarrow C_{20}H_{13}K + C_6H_5CH(CH_3)_2$$
triptycene

Actually, however, no such reaction occurs here even in twenty-one hours, although the corresponding reaction with triphenylmethane is complete almost instantaneously.   The explanation of this difference in behavior may be merely that the reaction requires a Walden inversion about the carbon atom at which substitution occurs.   This proposal would mean that perhaps the hydrogen atom which is replaced cannot leave the triptycene molecule (either as a solvated proton or in combination with the phenyl-*i*-propide anion) unless the potassium cation has already approached the carbon atom in question from the opposite side. Such an inversion is, of course, impossible in consequence of the ring structure.   Under these circumstances, the rate of the reaction would be practically zero, and the failure of the reaction to occur sheds no light either on the position of the equilibrium or on the acidity of the hydrocarbon.   On the other hand, triptycene may actually be a much weaker acid than *i*-propylbenzene, so that the equilibrium in the above reaction is far to the left.   The potassium salt of triptycene could then never be formed in the above manner, regardless of rates.   If this second possibility is correct, the fact that triptycene is a so much weaker acid than the analogous triphenylmethane could be accounted for as the result of an inhibition of resonance.   On account of the presence of the rings, the triptycene negative ion would be held rigidly in a configuration which is even farther from the completely planar one than that of the corresponding tri-*o*-tolylmethide negative ion.   As a result, the former ion cannot

[36] P. D. Bartlett, M. J. Ryan, and S. G. Cohen, *J. Am. Chem. Soc.*, **64**, 2649 (1942).

be stabilized by the resonance to any appreciable extent, and consequently the hydrocarbon has no apparent acid character. It seems necessary to suppose that this second factor is important, whether the rates of reaction are fast or slow.

A few examples have been reported in which the base strength of an amine is increased by an inhibition of resonance. Dimethyl picramide, X, for example, has a $pK_a$ of $-4.69$, as compared with $-9.29$ for unsubstituted picramide.[37] The former substance is therefore a stronger base by a factor of about $4 \times 10^4$ in the ionization constant. Since the corresponding factor for dimethylaniline and aniline[22] is only about 3, it seems apparent that in dimethylpicramide the base strength must be greatly increased by an inhibition of the resonance with such structures as XI. This explanation is a reasonable one, since the dimethylamino group is large enough to interfere sterically with the *ortho* nitro groups, whereas the simple amino group is not.

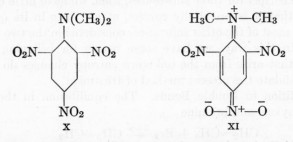

Some further, much less striking, examples are given in Table 7·1. The calculated values of $pK_a$ for the dimethyl- and diethyltoluidines were obtained with the not unreasonable assumption that, if it were not for an in-

TABLE 7·1

INHIBITION OF RESONANCE AND BASE STRENGTH OF AROMATIC AMINES

| | $pK_a$ | |
|---|---|---|
| Substance | Calcd | Obs[a] |
| Aniline | — | 4.58 |
| *o*-Toluidine | — | 4.39 |
| *p*-Toluidine | — | 5.07 |
| Dimethylaniline | — | 5.06 |
| Dimethyl-*o*-toluidine | 4.87 | 5.86 |
| Dimethyl-*p*-toluidine | 5.55 | 5.50 |
| Diethylaniline | — | 6.56 |
| Diethyl-*o*-toluidine | 6.37 | 7.18 |
| Diethyl-*p*-toluidine | 7.05 | 7.09 |

[a] N. F. Hall and M. R. Sprinkle, reference 22.

[37] L. P. Hammett and M. A. Paul, *J. Am. Chem. Soc.*, **56**, 827 (1934).

hibition of resonance, the effects of the *ortho* and *para* methyl groups upon the $pK_a$'s would be just the same as in the corresponding simple toluidines. This assumption is seen to be in quite satisfactory accord with the facts for the *p*-toluidines but to lead to too small values of $pK_a$ for the *o*-toluidines. It appears that in these latter substances the inhibition of the resonance increases the base strengths by a factor of about 6 to 10 in the ionization constant.    The effect is not large enough, however, to be of completely certain significance, especially since the *ortho* methyl groups in the *o*-toluidines are close to the amino nitrogen atoms, and so might be expected to produce abnormalities in base strength regardless of any inhibition of resonance.

The above examples of steric effects are of interest not only for their own sakes, but also for the light which they shed upon the effects of resonance upon acid and base strengths in general.    It seems difficult, for example, to explain the data for the xylenols, nitroxylenols, and so on, on any other basis than an inhibition of resonance.    If this interpretation is correct for these substances, then, we have little choice but to assume that it is essentially correct, at any rate in its qualitative aspects, for most of the other substances considered in the two preceding sections.    In this way, we have some reason for believing that the difficulties that arise from the unknown entropy changes do not completely invalidate the present method of treatment.

**7·5  Addition to Double Bonds.**  The equilibrium in the reaction between ethylene and bromine

$$CH_2\!\!=\!\!CH_2 + Br_2 \;\rightleftarrows\; \underset{\underset{Br}{|}}{CH_2}\!\!-\!\!\underset{\underset{Br}{|}}{CH_2}$$

is greatly in favor of the addition product, ethylene bromide.    On the other hand, bromine does not add at all to tetraphenylethylene, I. Although this failure to add may be due merely to an unexpectedly slow rate of reaction, it appears that here the equilibrium between the ethylene and its bromide, II, has probably been considerably displaced toward the ethylene.    If the possibility of resonance were ignored, the

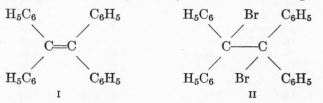

difference in behavior between these two unsaturated substances could not be related to a difference in the natures of the bonds broken and formed in the reactions, because the two systems would then be identical in that regard. The explanation may lie, therefore, in the fact that tetraphenylethylene is stabilized to an appreciable extent by the conjugation of the four phenyl groups with the ethylenic linkage. This stabilization would be lost if addition occurred, because then the central double bond would have been destroyed and so the conjugation would no longer exist. In ethylene itself, no such resonance effect is involved, since there is no conjugation in either the unsaturated compound or its addition product. The correctness of the above interpretation is supported by the fact that hydrogen, $H_2$, and chlorine, $Cl_2$, which have greater intrinsic tendencies than bromine to add to double bonds, react even with tetraphenylethylene in the usual manners to give tetraphenylethane and tetraphenylethylene chloride, respectively. An alternative explanation, which also seems to be in agreement with the facts, is that the addition of bromine may be prevented by the steric repulsions which are exerted by the bulky phenyl groups. The fact that the atoms of hydrogen and chlorine are smaller than those of bromine is then partly responsible for the ability of hydrogen and chlorine to react. Probably both the resonance and steric factors are involved to some extent.

In the reaction of an alkali metal with an olefine, the situation is the exact reverse of that discussed in the preceding paragraph. Sodium adds readily to tetraphenylethylene to form a disodium salt, but it does not add to ethylene at all. The reason for this difference in behavior is presumably that the resonance in the negative ion of the salt derived from the tetraphenyl compound can occur with structures like III and

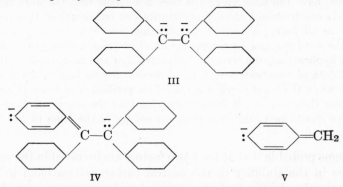

IV; the second of these is analogous to structure V for the benzyl anion. (See Section 7·2.) Moreover, this resonance in the ion should be more important than that resulting from the conjugation in the original tetraphenylethylene, because the additional structures (IV and the like) have neither formal bonds nor separated charges of opposite sign, and so are relatively stable. Thus, the resonance, which does not occur in either ethylene itself or its corresponding ion, facilitates the addition in the tetraphenyl compound and so displaces the equilibrium in the observed direction.

**7·6   Free Radicals.**   The energy of dissociation of ethane into methyl radicals is apparently about 80–85 kcal per mole,[38] whereas that of hexaphenylethane into triphenylmethyl radicals is only about 11.5 kcal per mole.[39]   These two values are not strictly comparable with each other, because the first refers to the gas phase and the latter to solution; however, the difference between them must be real because it is much too large to be due merely to solvent effects.   Evidently, therefore, the six phenyl groups in hexaphenylethane have in some way greatly reduced the strength of the central carbon-carbon bond.   In consequence of this weakening of the bond, the substance is appreciably dissociated into radicals in solution at ordinary temperatures, whereas ethane itself shows no detectable dissociation except at extremely high temperatures.

Attention should be called here to the fact that the value of 58.6 kcal per mole, which was given in Table 3·7 as the energy of a carbon-carbon single bond, is not exactly the same thing as the energy required to break such a bond.   This is because the bond energies, having been derived from heats of combustion of normal substances, refer only to the *average* energies of *all* the bonds formed by each atom, and may not be correct for any individual bond.   The difficulty can perhaps be made clearer by a consideration of the simpler problem of the energies of the carbon-hydrogen bonds in methane.   Although all these bonds are equivalent to each other and so, in one sense, have the same energy, it does not follow that the work required to remove one hydrogen atom is necessarily just one-fourth of that required to remove all four.   A further complication, which makes impossible the use of the bond energies for the prediction of energies of dissociation, is that, in such applications, the errors of uncertain sign and magnitude in the numerical data of equations 3–6, 8–15 of Section 3·4 no longer cancel out, as they do when the bond energies are used for prediction of heats of combustion.   For these reasons, it is not surprising that the energy of dissociation of ethane should be so different from the energy of the bond broken in the dissociation.

It seems probable that at least two factors are involved in the marked decrease in the stability of the central carbon-carbon bond in hexaphenylethane.   In the first place, the phenyl groups are quite bulky, and they possibly interfere with each other in such a way that the two

---

[38] H. G. Andersen, G. B. Kistiakowsky, and E. R. Van Artsdalen, *J. Chem. Phys.*, **10**, 305 (1942).   H. G. Andersen and G. B. Kistiakowsky, *ibid.*, **11**, 6 (1943). D. P. Stevenson, *ibid.*, **10**, 291 (1942).

[39] K. Ziegler and L. Ewald, *Ann.*, **473**, 163 (1929).   E. Müller and I. Müller-Rodloff, *ibid.*, **521**, 89 (1936).   R. Preckel and P. W. Selwood, *J. Am. Chem. Soc.*, **63**, 3397 (1941).

triphenylmethyl radicals cannot come close enough together for a strong bond to be formed between them.   This suggestion receives some support from the fact that the central bond in hexa*methyl*ethane has been found[40] to be slightly longer, and so presumably somewhat weaker, than usual; consequently, it appears that in this substance an analogous steric interaction actually produces the postulated effect.   More direct evidence pointing in the same direction has been provided by the fact that the heat of hydrogenation of hexaphenylethane, to give two molecules of triphenylmethane, is greater by 27 kcal per mole than that of ethane, to give two molecules of methane.[41]   In neither hydrogenation is there any significant change in the possibilities for resonance, and so the most reasonable explanation of the difference in the heats of the reactions is the steric one.   A similar study of the reactions with oxygen to form peroxides has led to the conclusion that the central bond in hexaphenylethane has been weakened to the extent of about 35 kcal per mole;[41] this value is probably less reliable, however, than the one of 27 kcal per mole, which was obtained from the heats of hydrogenation. (As with the heats of dissociation, the heats of hydrogenation and oxidation of ethane are not exactly comparable with those of hexaphenylethane, because the former refer to the gas phase and the latter to solution; again, however, the observed effects are so large that they must surely be real.)

The second factor weakening the bond in hexaphenylethane is a resonance effect.   In the undissociated molecule, resonance occurs among the various Kekulé (and Dewar) structures of all the benzene rings separately, but there is no conjugation between the rings.   The total resonance energy is therefore just six times that of benzene itself.   In the triphenylmethyl radical, however, resonance occurs in addition with such *ortho* and *para* quinoid structures as I.   The resonance energy per

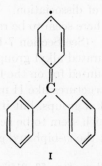

I

[40] S. H. Bauer and J. Y. Beach, *J. Am. Chem. Soc.*, **64**, 1142 (1942).   See also the table in the Appendix.

[41] H. E. Bent and G. R. Cuthbertson, *J. Am. Chem. Soc.*, **58**, 170 (1936).

radical is, accordingly, greater than three times that of benzene, and so the resonance facilitates the dissociation.

An idea of the order of magnitude of the resonance effect can be obtained with the use of the approximate method of calculation described in Section 3·5. Equation 1 of that section, in fact, gives a resonance energy of 216 kcal per mole for hexaphenylethane and of 288 kcal for two moles of the triphenylmethyl radical (when $A$ is set equal to 12). The difference of 72 kcal per mole between these two quantities is then an approximate measure of the extent to which the resonance weakens the central carbon-carbon bond in the ethane. This figure is presumably an upper limit since, in order for the resonance in the radical to be completely effective, the radical would have to be planar, on account of the various quinoid structures of the type of I. As was mentioned above, however, in connection with the triphenylmethyl anion, complete planarity is impossible because it would require that the *ortho* hydrogen atoms of the different phenyl groups lie unreasonably close together. Consequently, there must be some twisting about the bonds linking the phenyl groups to the methyl carbon atom, and the resonance energy must be somewhat reduced in magnitude. It is significant, however, that the calculated resonance effect, when combined with the steric effect, is of at any rate the correct order of magnitude to account for the observed weakening of the bond.

Calculations of the above simple type for any of the remaining hexaarylethanes lead always to identical answers, namely, that the resonance favors dissociation by 72 kcal per mole of ethane (or by a somewhat smaller amount when the lack of planarity is considered). More elaborate calculations, however, distinguish among the various aryl groups, as is shown in Table 7·2. It is interesting that the order of increasing calculated resonance effect is usually the same as that of increasing observed degree of dissociation. This agreement is possibly fortuitous, however, since there seem to be rather wide variations in the entropies of dissociation.[42] (See Section 7·1.) Moreover, the surprisingly large effects that saturated alkyl groups exert upon the extent of dissociation cannot be accounted for on the basis of resonance.[43] (Hyperconjugation involving structures like II might be used to explain the effects of *ortho* and *para* alkyl groups, but it cannot be of much importance with *meta* groups, which seem to be actually the most effective of all.) The further fact that the *m*-biphenyl group promotes dissociation

[42] C. B. Wooster, *J. Am. Chem. Soc.*, **58**, 2156 (1936). R. Preckel and P. W. Selwood, *ibid.*, **63**, 3397 (1941).

[43] C. S. Marvel, M. B. Mueller, C. M. Himel, and J. F. Kaplan, *J. Am. Chem. Soc.*, **61**, 2771 (1939).

## TABLE 7·2

### FREE RADICAL RESONANCE ENERGIES OF PHENYL-SUBSTITUTED ETHANES

| Ethane[a] | Calculated Free Radical Resonance Energy[b] | | |
|---|---|---|---|
| | I[c] | II[d] | III[e] |
| Diphenylethane | 24 | 37 | 30 |
| Di-*m*-biphenylethane | 24 | 37 | 30 |
| Di-*β*-naphthylethane | 24 | 45 | 33 |
| Di-*p*-biphenylethane | 24 | 47 | 33 |
| Di-*α*-naphthylethane | 24 | 54 | 37 |
| Difluoryl | 48 | 58 | 59 |
| Tetraphenylethane | 48 | 61 | 52 |
| Diphenyldifluoryl | 48 | 78 | 75 |
| Hexaphenylethane | 72 | 80 | 70 |
| Tetraphenyldi-*p*-biphenylethane | 72 | 84 | 71 |
| Hexa-*m*-biphenylethane | 72 | 80 | 70 |
| Tetraphenyldi-*α*-naphthylethane | 72 | 89 | 77 |
| Hexa-*p*-biphenylethane | 72 | 93 | 74 |

[a] The ethanes are listed in the approximate order of increasing dissociation. Cf. W. E. Bachmann in H. Gilman, *Organic Chemistry*, John Wiley & Sons, New York, 1st ed., 1938, vol. I, p. 504; 2nd ed., 1943, vol. I, pp. 587 ff.

[b] The "free radical resonance energy" is defined as the resonance energy of two moles of the radical (in kilocalories per mole) minus that of one mole of the ethane. It is, therefore, a measure of the extent to which the resonance favors dissociation into radicals.

[c] Calculated from equation 1 of Section 3·5, with $A = 12$.

[d] Calculated by the valence-bond method, with the integral $J$ set equal to $-36$ kcal per mole. See G. W. Wheland, *J. Am. Chem. Soc.*, **63**, 2025 (1941).

[e] Calculated by the corrected molecular orbital method with the parameter $\beta$ set equal to $-38$ kcal per mole. See G. W. Wheland, note *d*. In the values given here for di-*β*-naphthylethane and for di-*α*-naphthylethane, small numerical errors appearing in Table II of the original paper have been corrected.

to a considerably greater extent than the simple phenyl group is also difficult to understand.[44] It seems evident, therefore, that although

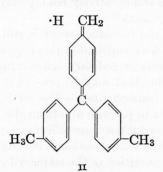

II

resonance is probably the major factor responsible for the stability of the triarylmethyl radicals, some additional factors as well must play impor-

[44] C. S. Marvel, E. Ginsberg, and M. B. Mueller, *J. Am. Chem. Soc.*, **61**, 77 (1939).

tant roles in determining the relatively small differences among the various hexaarylethanes. The steric effect, for example, must vary within rather wide limits, and possibly still other factors, which are not as yet understood, would have to be considered in a completely satisfactory theory.

The tetraarylethanes, on the whole, are much less highly dissociated into radicals than are the hexaarylethanes. This difference could have been expected on the resonance theory, since the gain in resonance energy on dissociation decreases rapidly as the number of aryl groups decreases. Indeed, equation 1 of Section 3·5 leads to the result that the resonance effect facilitates the dissociation of a tetraaryl compound by only 48 kcal per mole, as compared with 72 kcal per mole for a hexaaryl compound; and the more elaborate calculations reported in Table 7·2 lead to similar conclusions. Moreover, the steric factor also should in general become less important as the number of aryl groups decreases. Consequently, appreciable dissociation is possible only when the steric effects are exceptionally large, as, for example, in tetraphenyldi-$t$-butylethane,[45] tetra-$p$-biphenyldi-$t$-butylethane,[46] and decaphenylbutane.[47] (This last compound, although it contains ten phenyl groups altogether, belongs to the class of tetraarylethanes and, for our present purposes, might better be called tetraphenyldi(triphenylmethyl)ethane. This is because the triphenylmethyl groups do not increase the possibilities for resonance any more in the radical than in the undissociated molecule.) In these various substances, the $t$-butyl and triphenylmethyl groups, which are certainly very bulky, probably serve to lengthen, and so to weaken, the central carbon-carbon bond. The fact that tetramesitylethane and several analogous tetraarylethanes also appear to dissociate into radicals comparatively readily may also be due to steric interactions of the same sort.[48]

In diphenylethane, the resonance effect is still less important, as is shown in Table 7·2. No compound of this type is known to dissociate appreciably into radicals at ordinary temperatures, regardless of the sizes of any substituents that may be present upon either the ethane carbon atoms or the benzene rings. The steric effect is apparently, therefore, not sufficient to produce a measureable dissociation unless it is augmented by a powerful resonance effect.

The dissociation of the tetraarylethanes into diphenylmethyl radicals is paralleled by the dissociation of the tetraarylhydrazines into radicals

[45] J. B. Conant and N. M. Bigelow, *J. Am. Chem. Soc.*, **50**, 2041 (1928).

[46] J. B. Conant and R. F. Schultz, *J. Am. Chem. Soc.*, **55**, 2098 (1933).

[47] W. Schlenk and H. Mark, *Ber.*, **55**, 2285 (1922).

[48] W. T. Nauta and P. J. Wuis, *Rec. trav. chim.*, **57**, 41 (1938). See also J. Coops, W. T. Nauta, M. J. E. Ernsting, and A. C. Faber, *ibid.*, **59**, 1109 (1940).

containing "divalent nitrogen," thus

$$(C_6H_5)_2N—N(C_6H_5)_2 \rightleftarrows 2(C_6H_5)_2N$$

(On account of resonance with quinoid structures in which the odd electrons are on *ortho* or *para* carbon atoms, these radicals could, of course, be described equally well as containing trivalent carbon.) The reason for the greater dissociation of compounds of this latter type even in the absence of especially large steric interactions, is presumably that less work is required to break a nitrogen-nitrogen than a carbon-carbon bond, so that a given stabilization of the radical by resonance produces a greater net effect. The hexaaryltetrazanes dissociate similarly into triarylhydrazyls, thus

$$(C_6H_5)_2N—N\underset{\underset{C_6H_5}{|}}{}—\underset{\underset{C_6H_5}{|}}{N}—N(C_6H_5)_2 \rightleftarrows 2(C_6H_5)_2N—\underset{\underset{C_6H_5}{|}}{N}$$

Again, the relative stabilities of the radicals can be related to their greater possibilities for resonance. For one group of related compounds, dipole moment measurements are available,[49] which shed light upon the nature of the electronic changes accompanying dissociation. Hydrazine, III, phenylhydrazine, IV, 1,1-diphenylhydrazine, V, and 1,2-diphenyl-hydrazine, VI, all have dipole moments in the range 1.53–1.87$D$. Consequently, 1,1,2-triphenylhydrazine, VII, might be expected to have a

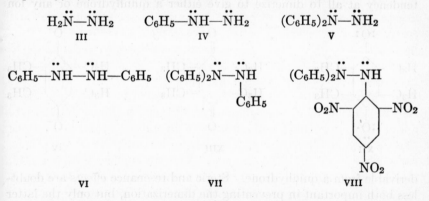

moment of about the same magnitude, as might also 1-picryl-2,2-diphenylhydrazine, VIII, if resonance interactions were ignored, since then the three nitro group moments in the 2,4,6 positions should cancel each other out. For VII, no measurements have been made, but there is no

[49] J. Turkevich, P. F. Oesper, and C. P. Smyth, *J. Am. Chem. Soc.*, **64**, 1179 (1942).

reason to expect that the prediction is not essentially correct. For VIII, however, the observed moment is actually $3.59D$, which is about $2D$ greater than anticipated. The explanation is presumably that resonance occurs with structures like IX. (Compare the discussion of $p$-nitroaniline in Section 5·4.) In the 1-picryl-2,2-diphenylhydrazyl radical, X, the moment is increased still further to $4.92D$. Structures like XI thus appear to make larger contributions to the state of the radical than do those like IX to the state of the hydrazine.

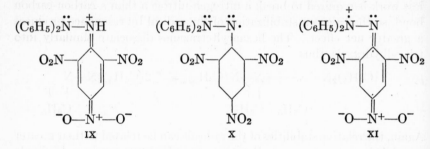

A further type of free radical, which has received a great deal of attention in recent years,[50] is illustrated by the semiquinone XII. This substance exhibits considerable stability.[51] It shows a relatively small tendency to disproportionate into a mixture of duroquinone, XIII, and the doubly charged durohydroquinone ion, XIV; and it shows no tendency at all to dimerize to give either a quinhydrone or any ion

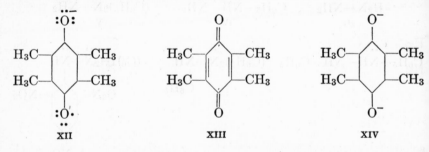

derivable from a quinhydrone. Steric and resonance effects are doubtless both important in preventing the dimerization, but only the latter effect can account for the failure of the substance to disproportionate.

[50] For general discussions, see L. Michaelis, *Chem. Rev.*, **16**, 243 (1935). L. Michaelis and M. P. Schubert, *ibid.*, **22**, 437 (1938). Experimental papers by Michaelis and co-workers, which are too numerous to list here, are to be found in the *Journal of the American Chemical Society.* (See also references 51, 52, and 53.)

[51] L. Michaelis, M. P. Schubert, R. K. Reber, J. A. Kuck, and S. Granick, *J. Am. Chem. Soc.*, **60**, 1678 (1938).

This interpretation is supported by the further fact that the semiquinone is stable only in rather strongly alkaline solution, in which it can exist as the ion XII. On account of the possibility of resonance between the two equivalent structures, XII and XV (together with several others in which the unpaired electron is on a carbon atom of the ring), the stabilization by resonance should therefore be relatively great. In neutral solution, however, the semiquinone would presumably acquire a proton; it could then resonate only among such non-equivalent, electrically neutral structures as XVI and XVII, and so should be much less stabilized. It disproportionates, therefore, practically completely into

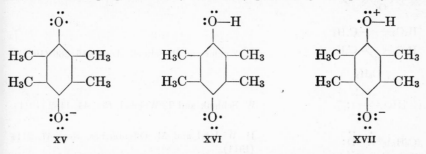

duroquinone, XIII, and durohydroquinone, XVIII. We might expect that the present semiquinone should become stable again in strongly acid solution, as a result of the equivalence of the structures XIX and XX. This question does not seem to have been investigated, but the

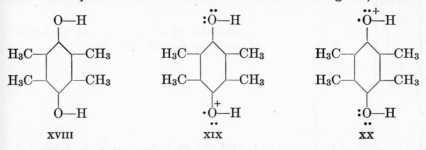

somewhat analogous semiquinone that is obtained by the oxidation of $p,p'$-dihydroxydiphenylamine, XXI, is reported to be more stable in either alkaline or acid solution than it is in neutral solution.[52]

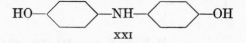

An interesting example of steric inhibition of resonance is apparently

[52] G. Schwarzenbach and L. Michaelis, *J. Am. Chem. Soc.*, **60**, 1667 (1938).

## TABLE 7·3

### SOME IMPORTANT TYPES OF FREE RADICAL OF LONG LIFE

| Characteristic Structure | Reference[a] |
|---|---|
| $(C_6H_5)_3C\cdot$ | M. Gomberg, *Ber.*, **33**, 3150 (1900); *J. Am. Chem. Soc.*, **22**, 757 (1900). |
| 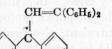 | K. Ziegler and C. Ochs, *Ber.*, **55**, 2257 (1922). |
| 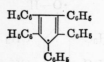 | K. Ziegler and B. Schnell, *Ann.*, **445**, 266 (1925). |
| $[(C_6H_5)_2\overset{\cdot}{C}—\overset{..}{\underset{..}{O}}:]^-$ | W. Schlenk and T. Weickel, *Ber.* **44**, 1182 (1911). |
| $(C_6H_5)_2{}^+\overset{\cdot}{N}—\overset{..}{\underset{..}{O}}:{}^-$ | H. Wieland and M. Offenbächer, *Ber.*, **47**, 2111 (1914). |
| $[(C_6H_5)_3N\cdot]^+$ | E. Weitz and H. W. Schwechten, *Ber.*, **59**, 2307 (1926). |
| 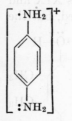 | L. Michaelis, M. P. Schubert, and S. Granick, *J. Am. Chem. Soc.*, **61**, 1981 (1939). |
| 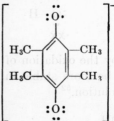 | L. Michaelis, M. P. Schubert, R. K. Reber, J. A. Kuck, and S. Granick, *J. Am. Chem. Soc.*, **60**, 1678 (1938). |
| $(C_6H_5)_2\overset{..}{N}\cdot$ | H. Wieland, *Ann.*, **381**, 200 (1911). |
| $(C_6H_5)_2\overset{..}{N}—\overset{..}{N}—C_6H_5$ | S. Goldschmidt, *Ber.*, **53**, 44 (1920). |

TABLE 7·3 (*Continued*)

Characteristic Structure                                    References[a]

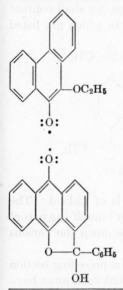

S. Goldschmidt, A. Vogt, and M. A. Bredig, *Ann.*, **445**, 123 (1925).

L. F. Fieser and W. Y. Young, *J. Am. Chem. Soc.*, **54**, 4095 (1932).

---

[a] These references are, of course, not intended to be complete. For further references and for a more detailed discussion of free radicals of long life, see W. E. Bachmann in H. Gilman, *Organic Chemistry*, John Wiley & Sons, New York, 1st ed., 1938, vol. I, Chapter 5; 2nd ed., 1943, vol. I, Chapter 6.

given by a comparison of the semiquinone, XXII, with its lower homologs, XXIII, XXIV, and XXV.[53] Since these last three radicals are all relatively stable, it appears that methyl groups as such have no adverse

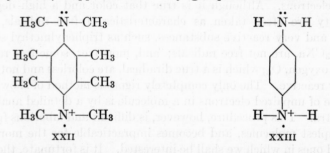

effect. The radical XXII, however, is so unstable that it is not formed at all. The explanation is apparently that, in this substance, the planarity necessary for the quinoid structure, and hence for the resonance, is impossible.

[53] L. Michaelis, M. P. Schubert, and S. Granick, *J. Am. Chem. Soc.*, **61**, 1981 (1939).

The foregoing discussion by no means exhausts the known types of free radical. Since nothing essentially new is to be learned, however, from a detailed consideration of the remaining types, we shall content ourselves here with calling attention to Table 7·3, in which are listed

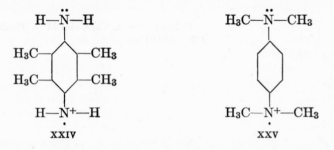

examples of a number of the most important kinds of radical. The reader should now be able without difficulty to see for himself the nature of the steric interactions that operate, and to write down the various structures that are involved in the resonance.

**7·7 Diradicals.** The free radicals discussed in the preceding section contain odd numbers of electrons per molecule, so that each must have (at least) one unpaired electron. (See Section 1·4.) It is of interest now to consider the question whether a molecule with an even number of electrons can have two of them unpaired and so be a diradical. This question cannot be answered experimentally on the basis of chemical evidence alone, because there is no necessary correlation between the chemical properties of a substance and the presence or absence of unpaired electrons. Although it is true that color and a high degree of reactivity are often taken as characteristics of free radicals, many colored and very reactive substances, such as triphenylmethyl sodium, $(C_6H_5)_3CNa$, are not free radicals; and, moreover, some free radicals, such as oxygen, $O_2$, which is a true diradical, are colorless and not exceptionally reactive. The only completely rigorous method of showing the presence of unpaired electrons in a molecule is by a detailed analysis of its spectra. This procedure, however, is difficult and laborious for even the simplest molecules, and becomes impracticable for the more complicated ones in which we shall be interested. It is fortunate, therefore, that an alternative method is available, which provides trustworthy information, except under certain special circumstances[54] that are not very likely to be encountered in complex organic molecules. This second method is based upon the fact that molecules without unpaired

---

[54] J. H. Van Vleck, *The Theory of Electric and Magnetic Susceptibilities*, Oxford University Press, Oxford, 1932, pp. 272 ff.

electrons are almost invariably *diamagnetic,* whereas those with unpaired electrons are normally *paramagnetic.* A measurement of the *magnetic susceptibility* of a substance thus shows with almost complete certainty whether unpaired electrons are present or not. Moreover, the actual number of unpaired electrons can be determined from the numerical value of the magnetic susceptibility, so that, for example, the degree of dissociation of a molecule like hexaphenylethane can be measured magnetically.[42,43,44]

A substance is said to be diamagnetic if it is repelled by an inhomogeneous magnetic field, and paramagnetic if it is attracted by such a field. Moreover, it will be sufficient for our purposes to define the magnetic susceptibility simply as a quantitative measure of the force by which the substance in question is attracted by the inhomogeneous field. A positive value of the susceptibility corresponds to paramagnetism, whereas a negative value corresponds to diamagnetism.[54]

In the way sketched briefly above, it has been found that certain molecules with even numbers of electrons do indeed exist as diradicals, but that many others, which had previously been considered diradicals on account of their color and chemical behavior, are actually normal molecules with no unpaired electrons. The situation can be conveniently summarized by the following rule: A molecule is a diradical if, and only if, no structures of the conventional type can be written for it without formal bonds. For example, *m,m′*-dibenzhydrylbiphenyl, I, is a diradical, but its *p,p′* isomer is not. The latter substance is indeed most satisfactorily represented by the quinoid structure II, in which all electrons are paired.

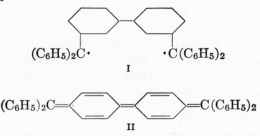

Even though it is diamagnetic, *p,p′*-dibenzhydrylbiphenyl, II, has been reported[55] to catalyze the *ortho-para* hydrogen interconversion. Since in general only paramagnetic substances have such catalytic effect, the substance thus behaves in this regard as if it exists partly in a diradical form. In an attempt to explain this discrepancy, it has been suggested[55] that the

[55] G. M. Schwab and N. Agliardi, *Ber.,* **73,** 95 (1940).

molecule might be represented by either one of the two equivalent structures, III and IV. According to this explanation, the two electrons, although they are thus paired with each other, are so far apart in space that each can act as if alone and unpaired in catalyzing the interconversion. The situation

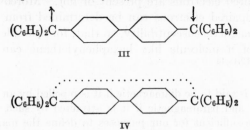

III

IV

would thus be somewhat analogous to that in, say, *p*-dinitrobenzene, where localized *electric* dipoles exist even though the molecule as a whole is nonpolar. This suggestion, however, cannot possibly be correct, because the molecule must actually resonate among a large number of structures. Although structures like III or IV must certainly make contributions, they are less stable, on account of their formal bonds, and so are of less importance than II. In any event, no significance can be attached to the statement that there are odd electrons upon *any* two *specified* atoms. A more complete analysis, which cannot be given here, shows that the suggested explanation (to the extent that it has any meaning at all) is equivalent to the supposition that the difference in energy between the forms with no, and with two, unpaired electrons is small compared with the energy of interaction between the molecule and the *ortho* or *para* hydrogen. If such were correct, however, the substance should be paramagnetic, because then a large fraction of the molecules would exist in the diradical form even at ordinary temperatures. The correct explanation of the facts is not known at present.

There are two kinds of apparent exception to the above rule regarding the occurrence of diradicals. In the first place, porphyrindine is paramagnetic, although the structure V, without formal bonds, can be written for it.[56] The paramagnetism increases with temperature, however, and so there is apparently something analogous to a tautomeric equilibrium between the diamagnetic form, V, and an isomeric (or electromeric)

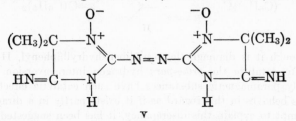

V

[56] E. Müller and I. Müller-Rodloff, *Ann.*, **521**, 81 (1936).

paramagnetic form, VI. From the temperature coefficient of the magnetic susceptibility, it has been concluded that the form V is more stable than VI by about 0.5 kcal per mole. The ground state of the molecule is therefore actually diamagnetic in agreement with the rule.

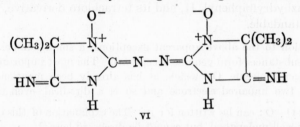

VI

The second type of molecule which appears to violate the rule is illustrated by the tetrachlorodibenzhydrylbiphenyl, VII, which exists as a diradical.[57] Here, however, the quinoid structure, VIII, although it can be written on paper, does not represent a possible state of the mole-

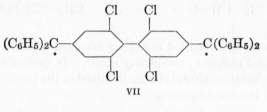

VII

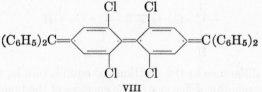

VIII

cule, because it requires that the two central phenyl groups be coplanar. The existence of optically active biphenyls like 2,2′,4,4′,6,6′-hexachloro-3,3′-dicarboxybiphenyl, IX, for example, however, shows that the bulky substituents make such coplanarity impossible.[58] This example is of

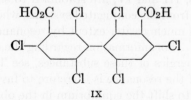

IX

[57] E. Müller and H. Neuhoff, *Ber.*, **72**, 2063 (1939).
[58] J. White and R. Adams, *J. Am. Chem. Soc.*, **54**, 2104 (1932).

particular interest since it provides evidence in support of the belief that, in the absence of steric interference, the molecules of biphenyl and related substances tend to assume the planar configuration.   Indeed, it is only on this basis that the striking difference in properties between $p,p'$-dibenzhydrylbiphenyl, II, and its tetrachloro derivative, VII, is at all understandable.

In addition to the above apparent exceptions, a small number of simple inorganic substances form genuine exceptions.   The most important of these is the oxygen molecule, $O_2$, which, as has already been mentioned several times, has two unpaired electrons and so is a diradical, even though the structure : O̤=O̤ : can be written for it.   The explanation of this exceptional behavior is well understood, but cannot be discussed here.[59]

**7·8 Tautomerism.**   In a simple keto-enol system, such as acetaldehyde, the equilibrium is greatly in favor of the keto form, I; and the enol form, II, is present only in minute traces, if at all.   In phenol, on

$$CH_3—CH{=}O \qquad\qquad CH_2{=}CH—OH$$
$$\text{I} \qquad\qquad\qquad\qquad \text{II}$$

the other hand, the situation is exactly reversed, and the substance is for all practical purposes, completely enolic.   In each of these extreme cases, the essential structural change involved in the tautomerism can be expressed by the same equation

$$\begin{array}{ccc} | & & \\ —C—C{=}O & \rightleftarrows & —C{=}C—OH \\ |\ \ | & & |\ \ \ | \\ H & & \end{array}$$

The striking difference in the positions of equilibrium is, therefore, not due to a corresponding difference in the energies of the bonds broken and formed, but must be a result of resonance.   In acetaldehyde, neither the keto nor the enol form is stabilized to any great extent by resonance, so that the observed position of the equilibrium expresses merely the greater intrinsic stability of the keto grouping.   In phenol, however, the two possible keto forms, III and IV, are stabilized to small extents by the resonance resulting from the conjugated systems, whereas the enol form, V, is stabilized to a much greater extent by resonance between the two Kekulé structures.   (For information regarding the order of magnitude of the resonance energies of these substances, see Tables 3·2, 3·3, and 3·6.)   The effect of the resonance is therefore to favor the enol form of this substance and to shift the equilibrium in the observed direction.

[59] J. E. Lennard-Jones, *Trans. Faraday Soc.*, **25**, 668 (1929).   G. W. Wheland, *ibid.*, **33**, 1499 (1937).

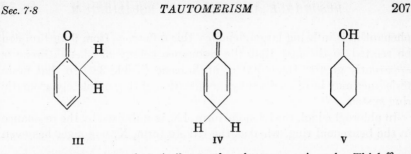

III            IV            V

An explanation somewhat similar to the above was given by Thiele[60] on the basis of his theory of partial valence. It has, of course, long been realized that the stability of the enol form of phenol must be due to the same factors which account for the stability of benzene itself.

In the various substituted phenols (such as the cresols, nitrophenols, and so on) and in 1- and 2-naphthol, 1- and 2-anthrol, and the like, the resonance stabilizes the fully aromatic ring systems in similar manners and so displaces the equilibria toward the enol forms. In 9-anthrol, VI, however, the keto form, VII, is the more stable of the two forms, al-

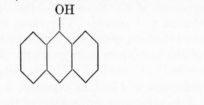

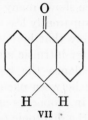

VI                      VII

though both can be isolated.[61] This difference from phenol presumably exists because the resonance energy of the anthrol form, VI, is only slightly greater than that of anthracene, which is less than three times that of benzene (Table 3·6); whereas in the anthrone form, VII, the resonance energy should be about the same as that of benzophenone, which is greater than twice that of benzene. Consequently, the gain in resonance energy in passing from the keto to the enol form is less here than in phenol, and so the keto form is relatively more stable. On the other hand, 9-phenanthrol, VIII, apparently resembles the remaining

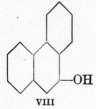

VIII

[60] J. Thiele, *Ann.*, **306**, 87 (1899).
[61] K. H. Meyer, *Ann.*, **379**, 37 (1911).

phenanthrols in being largely enolic; this difference from 9-anthrol can be related to the fact that the resonance energy of phenanthrene is apparently greater than that of anthracene (Table 3·6) so that more resistance may be offered to any modification of the completely aromatic ring system.

In phloroglucinol, the trienolic form, IX, is stabilized by the resonance in the benzenoid ring, whereas the triketo form, X, no longer has even

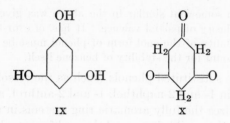

the small stabilization resulting from conjugation. Nevertheless, the substance shows many of the reactions of a triketone, and the equilibrium is apparently less one-sided than with phenol. The reason for this is probably that here, with *three* keto-enol groupings in the molecule, the greater intrinsic stability of the keto form is more nearly able to counterbalance the resonance effect. Resorcinol is intermediate in structure between phenol and phloroglucinol and, as expected, is intermediate in properties as well. This substance shows some of the reactions of the diketonic form, XII, but the equilibrium seems to be more in favor of the completely enolic form, XI, than is true with phloroglucinol.

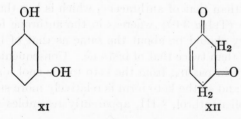

In acetylacetone, XIII and XIV, as in 9-anthrol, the keto-enol equilibrium is evenly enough balanced so that both forms can be isolated. In the gas phase, the equilibrium mixture contains 91–93 per

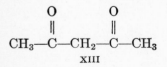

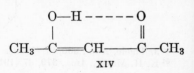

cent enol.[62] The stabilization of the enolic form, XIV, seems to be due here to at least two factors. In the first place, the hydrogen bond which is present between the two oxygen atoms in this, but not in the keto form, XIII, must have an energy of 5–10 kcal per mole. (See Section 2·8.) The energies of the bonds (including now the hydrogen bond) are therefore not so unfavorable for the enol form as in, say, acetaldehyde. In the second place, the resonance effect must displace the equilibrium further in the same direction. Whereas the keto form has no possibilities for resonance, the enol form is stabilized by resonance with the structures XV, XVI, and XVII. Structure XV is of the type en-

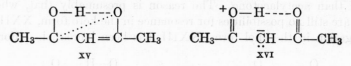

countered in conjugated systems in general. The role of conjugation in keto-enol tautomerism seems to have been discussed first by Thiele.[60] Structures analogous to XVI play a role in the phenols too, of course, but there they are of negligible importance in comparison with the Kekulé structures, which produce such a large stabilization. (Compare the discussion of divinyl ether in Section 3·2.) On the other hand, structures like XVII have no close analogs in any of the enols discussed heretofore.

In acetoacetic ester, XVIII and XIX, the conjugation is less able to stabilize the enol form, since, as was shown in Section 3·2, little or

no resonance energy results from the conjugation of an ethylenic linkage with a carbalkoxy group. The equilibrium is, accordingly, less favorable to the enol form than it is in acetylacetone, and the equilibrium mixture in the gas phase contains only 45.3–46.9 per cent enol. In malonic ester, XX and XXI, the amount of enol form present at equilib-

[62] Data for the equilibrium in the gas phase for this and other keto-enol systems are taken from J. B. Conant and A. F. Thompson, Jr., *J. Am. Chem. Soc.*, **54**, 4039 (1932).

rium is too small to be measured.   This decreased stability of the enol can be related to the fact that in the structure XXI, one of the two

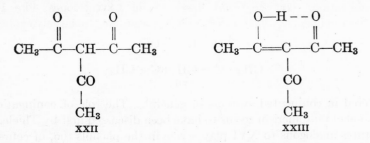

carbethoxy groups is no longer intact and has presumably therefore lost part of its large resonance energy.   (See Table 3·6.)

Triacetylmethane, XXII and XXIII, seems to be somewhat more enolic than acetylacetone.   The reason is presumably that, whereas there are still no possibilities for resonance in the keto form, XXII, the conjugation in the enol form, XXIII, has been increased.   (For this

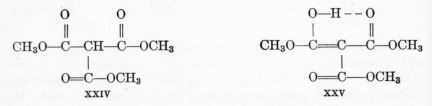

substance, the equilibrium has not been studied in the gas phase. Schwarzenbach and Lutz[10] consider that it is 100 per cent enolic in aqueous solution, whereas Nachod[11] has found acetylacetone to be only 19.6 per cent enolic in the same solvent.   On the other hand, it has been reported that in alcoholic solution, triacetylmethane is about 89 per cent enolic[63] and acetylacetone is about 83 per cent enolic.[62])   Even tricarbomethoxymethane, XXIV and XXV, in which the enol form necessarily contains a no longer intact carbomethoxy group, is 8–16 per cent enolic in the gas phase.

$$\underset{\text{XXIV}}{\underset{\underset{\displaystyle O\!=\!\!C\!\!-\!\!OCH_3}{|}}{CH_3O\!\!-\!\!\overset{\displaystyle O}{\overset{\|}{C}}\!\!-\!\!CH\!\!-\!\!\overset{\displaystyle O}{\overset{\|}{C}}\!\!-\!\!OCH_3}} \qquad \underset{\text{XXV}}{\underset{\underset{\displaystyle O\!=\!\!C\!\!-\!\!OCH_3}{|}}{CH_3O\!\!-\!\!\overset{\displaystyle O\!\!-\!\!H\!-\!-\!O}{\overset{|}{C}}\!\!=\!\!\overset{|}{C}\!\!-\!\!\overset{\displaystyle}{\overset{\|}{C}}\!\!-\!\!OCH_3}}$$

In the keto-enol systems of the type of acetylacetone, acetoacetic ester, and so on, the entropy of enolization seems to be very small,[62] so that the

[63] F. Seidel, W. Thier, A. Uber, and J. Dittmer, *Ber.*, **69**, 650 (1936).

neglect of $\Delta\Delta S°$ is apparently justified.   (See Section 7·1.)   It is not known, however, whether this same fortunate circumstance obtains also in the other tautomeric systems discussed in this section.

Acyclic 1,2-diketones, like diacetyl, XXVI, exist largely in the keto form, probably because their corresponding enol forms, XXVII, are

prevented by steric requirements from having hydrogen bonds between the oxygen atoms, and because the conjugation is not increased in extent by enolization.   On the other hand, cyclic 1,2-diketones, like 1,2-cyclohexanedione, XXVIII and XXIX, for example, are largely enolic.[64]

It has been suggested[65] that the reason for the difference between the acyclic and cyclic compounds is that the former are free, whereas the latter are not free, to assume the stable *trans* arrangement of the carbonyl groups.[66]   Thus, in the cyclic 1,2-diketones, the electrostatic repulsions of the carbonyl group moments must be very large in the keto form, XXVIII, but are considerably smaller in the enol form, XXIX. This explanation may be partly correct, but it should be noted that there seems to be a definite tendency, which is as yet unexplained, for a double bond to take up a position *in* a ring, even in the absence of large dipole interactions.   For example, cyclopentanone, cyclohexanone, and cyclo-heptanone react with acetic anhydride to form enol acetates, whereas acetone does not.[67]   Furthermore, 1,3-cyclohexanedione, XXX and XXXI, seems to be largely enolic[68] even though there is no possibility

[64] For a discussion of these so-called diosphenols, see O. Wallach, *Ann.*, **437**, 148 (1924).

[65] G. W. Wheland, *J. Chem. Phys.*, **1**, 731 (1933).

[66] Cf. J. E. LuValle and V. Schomaker, *J. Am. Chem. Soc.*, **61**, 3520 (1939).

[67] C. Mannich and V. H. Hâncu, *Ber.*, **41**, 564 (1908).

[68] Cf. W. Dieckmann, *Ber.*, **53**, 1772 (1920).

for the formation of a hydrogen bond in the enol, XXXI; here, however, the dipole effect is presumably still large.

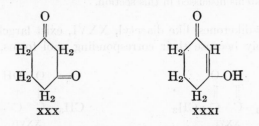

XXX                                                    XXXI

Keto-enol tautomerism is known to occur also in substances in which the two carbonyl groups involved are farther apart than in those considered hitherto. For example, glutaconic dialdehyde, XXXII and XXXIII, seems to be largely enolic. As with the 1,3-diketones like

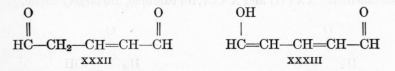

XXXII                                    XXXIII

acetylacetone, the enolization results in an increase in the length of the conjugated system and hence in the resonance energy. It seems unlikely, however, that a very strong hydrogen bond could be formed here between the two oxygen atoms, because the necessary eight-membered ring is not commonly encountered. The stability of the enol is probably due largely to the fact that, in general, aldehydic carbonyl groups seem to be enolized with relative ease.

Lactam-lactim tautomerism of the sort

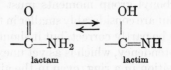

is analogous to the keto-enol tautomerism just considered. The equilibrium is commonly considered to lie far toward the lactam form, but it frequently seems to be displaced by a resonance effect in the direction of the lactim form. Some typical examples are isatin, XXXIV and XXXV, carbostyril, XXXVI and XXXVII, and cyanuric acid, XXXVIII and XXXIX. In each of these, the possibilities for resonance are greater in the lactim than in the lactam form, and, as a result, the equilibrium should be less one sided. In none of these substances, however, is the exact position of the equilibrium known; the statement that it is less unfavorable than usual to the lactim form is based upon various kinds of chemical evidence.[69]

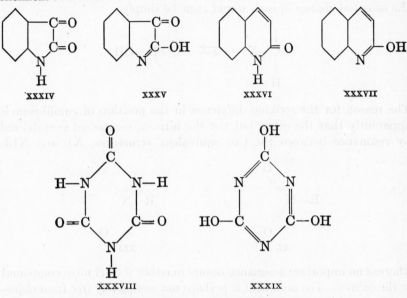

XXXIV　　　　　XXXV　　　　　XXXVI　　　　　XXXVII

XXXVIII　　　　　　　　　　XXXIX

Primary and secondary nitroso compounds are in general unstable and rearrange to the corresponding oximes, thus

$$\underset{\underset{\text{H}}{|}}{\overset{\overset{\text{R}}{|}}{R'-C-N=O}} \longrightarrow \overset{\overset{\text{R}}{|}}{R'-C=N-OH} \qquad (R, R' = H, \text{alkyl, or aryl})$$

On the other hand, primary and secondary nitro compounds are the stable forms, and the aci nitro compounds, although their existence can be shown, and although they can occasionally be isolated, are ordinarily present at equilibrium only in traces,[70] thus

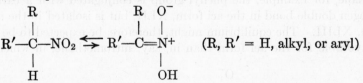

$$\underset{\underset{\text{H}}{|}}{\overset{\overset{\text{R}}{|}}{R'-C-NO_2}} \rightleftarrows \underset{\underset{\text{OH}}{|}}{\overset{\overset{\text{R} \quad O^-}{| \quad |}}{R'-C=N^+}} \qquad (R, R' = H, \text{alkyl, or aryl})$$

[69] See W. Hückel, *Theoretische Grundlagen der organischen Chemie*, Akademische Verlagsgesellschaft, Leipzig, 1st ed., 1931, vol. I, pp. 190 ff.; 2nd ed., 1934, vol. I, pp. 192 ff. for a discussion of the tautomerism in these substances.

[70] See D. Turnbull and S. H. Maron, *J. Am. Chem. Soc.*, **65**, 212 (1943) for numerical values of the equilibrium constants for a few simple aliphatic nitro compounds.

As far as the natures of the bonds broken and formed are concerned, these two equilibria would be identical if resonance were ignored, since the essential change in each would then be simply

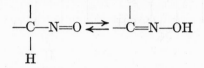

The reason for the striking difference in the position of equilibrium is apparently that the nitro, but not the nitroso, compound is stabilized by resonance between the two equivalent structures, XL and XLI,

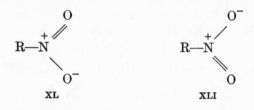

whereas no important resonance occurs in either the aci nitro compound or the oxime.   The argument is perhaps not completely free from objection because the presence of the formal positive charge on the nitrogen atom of the nitro compound makes the two situations not exactly comparable.   There is no way, unfortunately, of predicting the magnitude, or even the direction, of the effect produced upon the equilibrium by that formal charge.   However, since the structures between which the resonance occurs in the nitro compound are equivalent to each other, it seems certain that the resonance energy must be large and, in fact, must be the dominating factor.

In some substances, the nitro-aci-nitro equilibrium is affected by resonance with still further structures in such a way that it is shifted back again part of the way toward the aci form.   In phenylnitromethane, for example, the phenyl group is conjugated with a carbon-nitrogen double bond in the aci form, XLII, but is isolated in the nitro form, XLIII.   The equilibrium might, therefore, be expected to be less unfavorable for the aci form than in, say, nitromethane, in which no

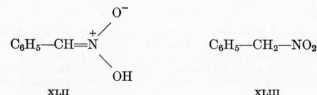

such conjugation is possible.    The actual position of equilibrium is not
known for the former substance, but the fact that its aci form can be
isolated,[71] whereas that of the latter cannot, suggests that the expectation is in accord with the facts.    In *p*-nitrophenylnitromethane, XLIV
and XLV, the effect of the conjugation appears to be still greater, since

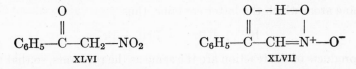

$$p\text{-}O_2N\text{—}C_6H_4\text{—}CH_2\text{—}NO_2$$

$$p\text{-}O_2N\text{—}C_6H_4\text{—}CH{=}\overset{+}{N}\overset{O^-}{\underset{OH}{}}$$

XLIV                              XLV

the equilibrium mixture contains measurable amounts of the aci form,
XLV, varying from 0.18 per cent in ethyl alcoholic solution to 16 per
cent in pyridine solution.[72]    In ω-nitroacetophenone, XLVI and XLVII,
similarly, the conjugation favors the aci form, which is present to the
extent of 10.3 per cent in toluene and of 2.7 per cent in 67 per cent
aqueous methyl alcohol.[72]    Since the equilibrium in this last example
is shifted *away* from the aci form in hydroxylic solvents, it appears that

$$\overset{O}{\overset{\|}{C_6H_5\text{—}C\text{—}CH_2\text{—}NO_2}}$$

$$\overset{O\text{-}\text{-}H\text{—}O}{\overset{\|\qquad|}{C_6H_5\text{—}C\text{—}CH{=}N^+\text{—}O^-}}$$

XLVI                              XLVII

a hydrogen bond between the carbonyl and nitro oxygen atoms, as in
XLVII, must be responsible for at least a part of the observed effect.[73]

[71] A. Hantzsch and O. W. Schultze, *Ber.*, **29**, 699, 2251 (1896).
[72] K. H. Meyer and P. Wertheimer, *Ber.*, **47**, 2374 (1914).
[73] N. V. Sidgwick, T. W. J. Taylor, and W. Baker, *The Organic Chemistry of Nitro-gen*, Oxford University Press, Oxford, 1937, p. 233.

# Chapter 8

## RESONANCE AND CHEMICAL REACTION

**8·1  The Activated Complex and the Rates of Reaction.**  As was pointed out in Chapter 1, the theory of resonance can be considered an outgrowth of the theories of intermediate stages and of mesomerism. Since these earlier theories were concerned largely with the relative speeds of chemical reactions, it is to be expected that the more modern point of view also should be applicable to this important problem. Such has indeed proved to be the case, as we shall see in the following sections of the present chapter.  It will be advantageous, however, for us first to consider in some detail the more fundamental question of the actual nature of the reaction process.

It will be convenient to discuss a rather simple reaction, in which a bromide ion collides with an alkyl bromide molecule and replaces the bromine atom which the latter contains, thus

$$Br^- + RBr \longrightarrow BrR + Br^-$$

The products of the reaction are the same as the reactants, so that there is no net change, but the course of the reaction can be followed experimentally by observation of the racemization of an optically active alkyl bromide or by the use of radioactive bromide ion.[1]  If we represent the bromine atoms as Br and Br*, we can write the two independent structures, I and II, for the system.  For our present purposes, we may ignore the distinction between real and formal bonds, because

$$Br^{*-} \qquad R{-}Br \qquad\qquad Br^*{-}R \qquad Br^-$$

I             II

we shall wish to consider the distances between the atoms as capable of continuous variation within wide limits.  The structure I can be taken as that of the original reactants when the ion $Br^{*-}$ is at a large distance from the molecule RBr, and the structure II can be taken as that of the final products when the ion $Br^-$ is at a large distance from the molecule RBr*.  The reaction itself, therefore, is to be regarded

---

[1] E. D. Hughes, F. Juliusburger, S. Masterman, B. Topley, and J. Weiss, *J. Chem. Soc.*, 1525 (1935).  E. D. Hughes, F. Juliusburger, A. D. Scott, B. Topley, and J. Weiss, *ibid.*, 1173 (1936).  W. A. Coudrey, E. D. Hughes, T. P. Nevell, and C. L. Wilson, *ibid.*, 209 (1938).

as a transition — we might perhaps say a rearrangement — between the two structures.

The course of the reaction can be visualized with the aid of Figure 8·1, in which the energies, $E$, of the two structures and of the system are plotted schematically against a parameter $r$. This parameter is defined by the equation

$$r = r_{CBr} - r_{CBr*}$$

where $r_{CBr}$ and $r_{CBr*}$ are the distances between the nucleus of the carbon atom at which the reaction occurs and the nuclei of the appropriate bromine atoms or ions. At the outset, when $r$ has a very large negative value, the structure I has a low energy, since the ion Br*$^-$ is at a

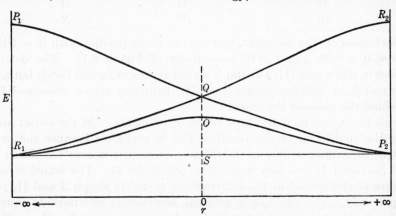

FIG. 8·1. Energies $E$ of the initial and final structures, and of their resonance hybrid, during the course of a chemical reaction.

great distance from the normal molecule RBr. As the ion approaches the molecule, however, the energy of this structure rises along the curve $R_1QR_2$. As far as the midpoint $Q$, the increase in energy is due largely to the mutual repulsion of the atoms which are not bonded to each other but are forced to come close together; from the midpoint on, it is due largely to the stretching of the bond between the radical R and the atom Br as the latter goes off to infinity. Conversely, the energy of structure II starts at a high value and decreases along the curve $P_1QP_2$ as the reaction proceeds. From the fact that the reactants and the products are identical, it follows that the curves $R_1QR_2$ and $P_1QP_2$ are symmetrical about the vertical broken line, and also that, at the point $Q$, the carbon atom at which the replacement occurs is equidistant from Br and Br*, so that $r = 0$. The fact that a Walden inversion is known to occur in the reaction[1] shows, furthermore, that the ion Br*$^-$ must have approached the molecule from the side opposite the atom Br; when $r = 0$, the three bonds which the central carbon atom forms with atoms other than Br and Br* are therefore in, or approximately in, a plane at right angles to a line passing through the carbon and the two bromine nuclei. In the course of the reaction, the molecule is therefore " turned inside out," like an umbrella in a high wind. The situation is shown graphically in structures III, IV, and V, in which the geometrical arrangements of the atoms are given for

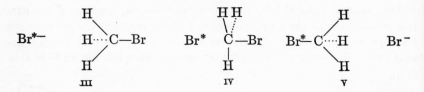

the beginning, the midpoint, and the end of the reaction with $R = CH_3$ ($r \ll 0$, $r = 0$, and $r \gg 0$, respectively of Figure 8·1). The dotted lines in structures III, IV, and V do not represent formal bonds but are intended to indicate merely that the hydrogen atoms concerned lie behind the plane of the paper.

So far, no account has been taken of resonance. At the outset and at the conclusion of the reaction, this is negligible because the two structures differ widely in distribution of electric charge (condition 2 of Section 1·4) and also in stability (condition 4). The actual structures of the system at the extremes are therefore simply I and II, respectively. The situation is different, however, at intermediate values of $r$, for then the charge distributions become more nearly alike. The stabilities of the structures also differ less widely and actually become equal when $r = 0$. Resonance is important, accordingly, when $r$ is small in magnitude. That is to say, the actual structure of the system is neither I nor II but something intermediate; in fact, it changes in a continuous manner from I to II as the reaction proceeds, and is just halfway between these structures when $r = 0$. Moreover, the energy of the system is lower, on account of the resonance, than would correspond to either of the two structures, and so it follows a curve $R_1OP_2$ that lies below the broken curve $R_1QP_2$ and becomes coincident with it at the extremes.

At the point $O$, at which the actual energy is highest, the system is, as we have just seen, a resonance hybrid receiving contributions from the structures I and II. It is commonly referred to as the *activated complex*, or as the *transition state*, for the reaction.[2] Its energy is

[2] The following treatment follows the discussions of H. Pelzer and E. Wigner, *Z. physik. Chem.*, **B15**, 445 (1932). H. Eyring, *J. Chem. Phys.*, **3**, 107 (1935). M. G. Evans and M. Polanyi, *Trans. Faraday Soc.*, **31**, 875 (1935).

greater than that of the reactants by the amount $SO$, which is known as the *energy of activation* $\Delta E^{\ddagger}$ of the reaction. Like an ordinary molecule, it can be considered to have other thermodynamic properties in addition to internal energy, so that we may speak of a *heat*, a *free energy,* and an *entropy* of activation, $\Delta H^{\ddagger}$, $\Delta F^{\ddagger}$, and $\Delta S^{\ddagger}$, respectively.

According to the theory of absolute reaction rates,[2] the velocity of the forward reaction is given by the equation

$$-\frac{d(\text{Br}^{*-})}{dt} = -\frac{d(\text{RBr})}{dt} = \frac{kT}{h}(\text{Br}^*\text{RBr}) \tag{1}$$

where $k$ is Boltzmann's constant, $T$ is the absolute temperature, $h$ is Planck's constant, Br*RBr stands for the activated complex, and the quantities in parentheses represent the concentrations of the substances in question. With the aid of the thermodynamic relations

$$K^{\ddagger} = \frac{[\text{Br}^*\text{RBr}]}{[\text{Br}^{*-}][\text{RBr}]} = \frac{(\text{Br}^*\text{RBr})}{(\text{Br}^{*-})(\text{RBr})}\frac{\gamma_{\text{Br}^*\text{RBr}}}{\gamma_{\text{Br}^*}\cdot\gamma_{\text{RBr}}} = e^{-\Delta F^{\ddagger}/RT} \tag{2}$$

where the quantities in the square brackets represent the activities of the appropriate substances, and the $\gamma$'s are the activity coefficients, equation 1 can be put into the form

$$-\frac{d(\text{Br}^{*-})}{dt} = \frac{kT}{h}K^{\ddagger}(\text{Br}^{*-})(\text{RBr})\frac{\gamma_{\text{Br}^*}\cdot\gamma_{\text{RBr}}}{\gamma_{\text{Br}^*\text{RBr}}}$$

$$= \frac{kT\gamma_{\text{Br}^*}\cdot\gamma_{\text{RBr}}}{h\gamma_{\text{Br}^*\text{RBr}}}(\text{Br}^{*-})(\text{RBr})e^{-\Delta F^{\ddagger}/RT} \tag{3}$$

The specific rate constant $k$ is therefore

$$k = \frac{kT\gamma_{\text{Br}^*}\cdot\gamma_{\text{RBr}}}{h\gamma_{\text{Br}^*\text{RBr}}}e^{-\Delta F^{\ddagger}/RT}$$

$$= \frac{kT\gamma_{\text{Br}^*}\cdot\gamma_{\text{RBr}}}{h\gamma_{\text{Br}^*\text{RBr}}}e^{\Delta S^{\ddagger}/R}\,e^{-\Delta H^{\ddagger}/RT} \tag{4}$$

From the foregoing very brief discussion, it is evident that the nature and properties of the activated complex are of the utmost importance in determining the rate of a chemical reaction. We shall, accordingly, center our attention upon it throughout the present chapter. We shall find that certain of the features encountered above in the discussion of the reaction between a bromide ion and an alkyl bromide molecule are common to all reactions, but that others are special and do not obtain generally. The activated complex is always a resonance hybrid among several structures, and the specific rate constant is always given by an equation analogous to equation 4. On the other hand, unless the reactants and products are identical, the points corresponding to $R_1$ and $P_2$ of Figure 8·1 need not lie at the same value of the energy, $E$; the points corresponding to $P_1$ and $R_2$ need not lie at the same value of $E$; and the activated complex need not receive equal contributions from the initial and final structures.

In the manner described above, the problem of reaction rates has been reduced to one of equilibria. The present situation differs from those considered in Chapter 7 only in that here the " reaction product " which is in equilibrium with the reactants is not an ordinary molecule capable of isolation, but is instead an activated complex. Just as before, therefore, we may feel that, as long as we restrict ourselves to qualitative comparisons of the rates of very similar reactions, we may safely ignore the distinctions both between concentration and activity, and between internal energy and free energy. This assumption is valid, of course, only if certain conditions are satisfied. First, the activity coefficients of all the corresponding reactants and of the activated complexes that are involved in the reactions to be compared (but now not necessarily those of the final products) must be respectively equal to each other; second, the entropies of activation of the reactions to be compared must similarly be equal; and finally, the changes in the pressure-volume products during activation must be equal, so that the distinction between the energy and the heat of activation may be ignored. The first and third of these conditions are probably satisfied with sufficient accuracy in all the cases in which we shall be interested, but the second is much more dubious.[3] In some reactions (for example, in the substitution reactions of aromatic systems) this second condition also seems to be generally satisfied, but in others (for example, in the side-chain reactions of the *ortho* substituted benzyl halides) it may be in more or less serious conflict with the facts. However, *to the extent that the above basic assumptions are actually valid*, we can predict that, of two similar reactions, the one involving the activated complex which is stabilized to the greater extent with respect to the reactants (by factors like electrostatic interactions or resonance) will proceed at the faster rate. In the subsequent sections, we shall see that such predictions are indeed in agreement with experiment in a considerable number of reactions. As might be expected, the theory does not always permit the interpretation of small differences in the rates of reaction, but it does often lead to an understanding of the larger and more striking differences. It seems probable, therefore, that the various

[3] See, for example, L. P. Hammett, *Physical Organic Chemistry*, McGraw-Hill Book Company, New York, 1940, Chapters IV and VII.

activity coefficients, entropies of activation, and pressure-volume products, although not strictly constant, are nevertheless nearly enough constant in many series of reactions to permit valid qualitative conclusions to be drawn. A *quantitative* theory of reaction rates is, however, still a goal for future achievement,[4] as indeed is also a completely unimpeachable qualitative one.

As in the discussion of equilibria, the difficulty in connection with changes in entropy does not enter if the reactions to be compared with each other differ only in electrostatic effects exerted by polar groups situated far from the reaction centers. (See Section 7·1.) Under such circumstances, the theoretical treatment refers directly to the free energy, and not to the internal energy, of activation, so that the entropy of activation does not matter. As before, however, structural changes near to the reaction centers often produce large and unpredictable effects which make a satisfactory discussion impossible. A further point of interest in the present connection is that Evans and Polanyi[5] have given theoretical reasons for supposing that the rate constant itself (or, what amounts to the same thing, the free energy of activation) is actually the quantity which is related directly to structure in series of related reactions. If this conclusion is correct, then the internal energy and entropy of activation are separately of little interest, and the present method of treatment is justified for qualitative discussions. Until this question has received further clarification, however, it would seem safer to consider that errors of uncertain magnitude and sign may always be introduced by unpredictable variations in (especially) the entropy of activation.

**8·2 Reactions of Resonating Molecules.** If a molecule resonates between two structures (or among more than two structures), we might naturally suppose that its chemical reactions would be those characteristic of, at any rate, all the structures which make important contributions. This expectation is frequently, but not always, borne out by the facts. Thus, ozonolysis of *o*-xylene[6] leads not only to glyoxal and methylglyoxal, the products to be expected from the structure I, but also to dimethylglyoxal, a product to be expected only from structure II. These three products (isolated in the form of their dioximes) are reported to occur in the molar ratio of 3.2 : 2 : 0.88, respectively, whereas a ratio of 3 : 2 : 1 would have been anticipated if the two triozonides related to the structures I and II had been formed in equal

[4] However, see F. H. Westheimer and M. W. Shookhoff, *J. Am. Chem. Soc.*, **62**, 269 (1940), for a semiquantitative theoretical interpretation of electrostatic effects upon the rates of certain hydrolytic reactions.

[5] M. G. Evans and M. Polanyi, *Trans. Faraday Soc.*, **32**, 1333 (1936).

[6] A. A. Levine and A. G. Cole, *J. Am. Chem. Soc.*, **54**, 338 (1932). J. P. Wibaut and P. W. Haayman, *Nature*, **144**, 290 (1939).

amount. On the other hand, 2,7-dihydroxynaphthalene couples with a diazonium salt at the 1 and 8 positions, in accordance with the Erlen-

          I                           II

meyer structure, III, but it cannot be made to couple at the 3 or 6 positions,[7] even though resonance occurs also with the further structures IV and V. (A further reaction, which also seems to involve only the

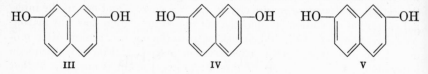

     III                        IV                     V

Erlenmeyer structure, but which is less conclusive, is the ozonolysis of naphthalene itself to give glyoxal and phthalaldehyde, $o\text{-}C_6H_4(CHO)_2$, but no $o$-benzoquinone.[8]) The reason for the difference between these two types of molecule should become apparent as we proceed. In the present section, however, we can discuss only the ozonolysis of $o$-xylene in any detail.

The actual mechanism of the ozonization reaction is not known, and, moreover, the exact detailed structures of the ozonides formed are also not established beyond dispute.[9] The following discussion will therefore involve certain assumptions, which have been made for the purpose of maximum simplicity in exposition, but which may not be correct. It seems unlikely, however, that the qualitative conclusions to which we shall come can be subject to any serious error on this account, since they could doubtless be derived equally well on the basis of any other reasonable set of assumptions.

The products of the ozonolysis of $o$-xylene are determined by the identity of the triozonides that are formed. The triozonide VI, for example, which is related to the structure I for the original $o$-xylene, can lead only to glyoxal and methylglyoxal, whereas the triozonide VII, which is related to the structure II, can give only glyoxal and dimethylglyoxal. Since all three molecules of ozone can hardly react simultaneously with the molecule of $o$-xylene, it is evident that a mono- and a diozonide must be formed as intermediates. Moreover, the ques-

[7] L. F. Fieser and W. C. Lothrop, *J. Am. Chem. Soc.*, **57**, 1459 (1935).

[8] C. Harries, *Ann.*, **343**, 311 (1905).

[9] For a recent discussion of the ozonization reaction and of the structure of the ozonides, see L. Long, Jr., *Chem. Rev.*, **27**, 437 (1940).

tion whether the triozonide that is formed will be VI or VII is settled
as soon as the mono-ozonide is formed.  We need consider, therefore,
only the primary reaction, in which the first molecule of ozone comes

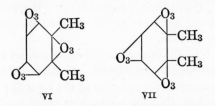

VI                        VII

up to attack the *o*-xylene.  It will be sufficient to discuss only the two
mono-ozonides VIII and IX, which would lead ultimately to the triozonides, VI and VII, respectively.  Other mono-ozonides in addition

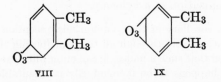

VIII                        IX

to these two are possible and probably play equally important roles in
the actual reaction; however, they add nothing essentially new to the
discussion, and do not affect the conclusions in any way.  In the formation of the mono-ozonides VIII and IX the activated complexes  may
be presumed to resonate principally among the structures X, XI, and
XII and among XIII, XIV and XV, respectively.  In each case, the

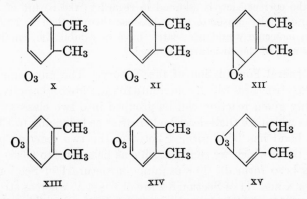

first two structures are those of the reactants, and the third structure
is that of the product.  On account of the similarity of the structures
involved, it seems apparent that there can be no very great difference in
the stabilities of the two activated complexes, whether the stabilities are
measured in terms of $\Delta E^{\ddagger}$ or of $\Delta F^{\ddagger}$.  It follows then from equation 4

that the two mono-ozonides, VIII and IX, should be formed at not very different rates, and that the final reaction product should contain the two triozonides, VI and VII, in not very different amounts. We have, accordingly, come to a conclusion that is qualitatively correct, even though we could not have predicted the exact ratio in which the two triozonides are formed.

The reactions of 2,7-dihydroxynaphthalene cannot be discussed here but will be taken up later in some detail. It will be shown in Section 8·11 that the activated complex for reaction at the 1 (or 8) position should be much more stable than that for reaction at the 3 (or 6) position, even though structures IV and V, as well as III, contribute to the state of the unreacting molecule. The consideration of the nature of the activated complex, therefore, leads to qualitatively correct conclusions here, just as in the ozonization of *o*-xylene.

Apparently as a corollary of the common misconception that a resonating molecule passes successively through all the contributing structures, it seems often to be assumed that such a molecule can enter into reaction with a second reagent only if it happens to be momentarily in a suitable structure at the time of collision. This view is absolutely erroneous, however, since, as was pointed out in Chapter 1 and especially in Section 1·5, a resonating molecule does not actually undergo the assumed transitions among the structures. Indeed, if the present picture were correct, then the failure of 2,7-dihydroxynaphthalene to couple at the 3 or 6 position would be completely inconsistent with the data cited in previous chapters, which showed that the resonance must include the structures IV and V as well as III. On the other hand, if the correct view is adopted in regard to the nature of resonance, the above difficulty ceases to exist, because there is then no reason why a resonating molecule would necessarily have to exhibit the reactions of all, or even of any, of the structures involved.

**8·3 General Formulation of the Theory.** The most important of the various structures which contribute to the state of the activated complex in any given reaction can be grouped into two classes. In those structures which we shall describe hereafter as belonging to Class A, no covalent bond has been formed between the two reacting molecules; while, in those which we shall describe as belonging to Class B, such a bond has been formed. For example, structure I of Section 8·1 and structures X and XI of Section 8·2 are of Class A, whereas structures II of Section 8·1 and XII of Section 8·2 are of Class B. The Class A and Class B structures are seen to be closely related to the original reactants and to the final products, respectively.

Neither of these examples of Class B structures is entirely typical, for, in structure II of Section 8·1, the fragment, $Br^-$, has already broken off and, in structure XII of Section 8·2, *two* bonds have been formed between the reagents.  In the most characteristic examples, on the other hand, no such fragments have become detached and only one new bond is present.  (As a matter of fact, if the correct mechanism of the ozonization reaction were known, the Class B structures contributing to its activated complex might actually be of this more usual type.)  Numerous further examples of Class B structures will be given in Sections 8·5–8·12.

The relative stability of a structure of Class A must be determined largely by the distributions of electric charge in the two reagents.   Thus, it is clear that such a structure is most stable when the most negative center of one reagent is close to the most positive center of the other. It follows therefore that, if these Class A structures were the only ones contributing to the activated complex, then any reagent which either is a positive ion or else has its own reactive center at the positive end of a dipole must attack its reaction partner preferentially at the latter's most negative available position;  and, conversely, that any reagent which either is a negative ion or else has its reactive center at the nega- . tive end of a dipole must attack *its* reaction partner at the latter's most positive available position.   (The meaning of the word " available " in this connection is discussed on page 227.)

The relative stability of a structure of Class B, on the other hand, is not primarily dependent upon the net distribution of electric charge in the two reagents, but rather upon certain other factors which we shall need to consider in some detail.   Before we take up this problem, however, we shall first discuss two points which are fundamental to an understanding of the subsequent theoretical development.   In the first place, we must now call attention, more strongly than we have done hitherto, to the fact that our interest is centered upon the stabilities of the activated complexes *after* they have been formed, and hence upon the stabilities of the contributing structures *after* all the various atoms have assumed the positions which they actually occupy in the respective complexes.   Nevertheless, it proves to be convenient to discuss these stabilities in relation to the changes which must have occurred in the individual reagent molecules *before* the structures in question could be set up.   This manner of speaking must not be taken as implying that we are concerned with the processes by which the activated complexes are formed (although, as a matter of fact, an independent and roughly equivalent treatment of reaction rates can be obtained on such a basis).[10] Instead, whenever we refer, for example, to the polarization of one of

[10] For a discussion of the so-called collision theory of reaction rates, see L. P. Hammett, reference 3, pp. 112 ff.; S. Glasstone, K. J. Laidler, and H. Eyring, *The Theory of Rate Processes*, McGraw-Hill Book Company, New York, 1941, pp. 5 ff.

the reagent molecules by the other in the course of the reaction, we shall do so only for the sake of the light which can be shed thereby upon the stabilities of the Class B structures and of the complex itself.

The second point to be considered here is of a rather different nature from the first, but it is equally essential to an understanding of the theory. According to the definition given above, any structure of Class B contains a new covalent bond, which is of course formed by the sharing of two electrons. Of these two electrons, both may have come originally from one reagent and none from the other, or else one may have come from each reagent. There are, therefore, three distinct types of reagent to be considered: the so-called *electrophilic*, *radical*, and *nucleophilic* reagents, which are defined as contributing 0, 1, and 2 electrons, respectively, to the bond in question. Clearly, every bimolecular reaction must be either between one electrophilic and one nucleophilic reagent, or else between two radical reagents. The problem of determining the type to which any given reagent belongs is a matter for experimental investigation along lines that will be discussed in greater detail in later sections in connection with specific reactions. For the present, it will be sufficient to call attention here to the fact that a given reagent may be of different types in different reactions. We shall find, for example, in Section 8·11 that pyridine is electrophilic when it is aminated with sodamide, radical when it enters into the Gomberg reaction, and nucleophilic when it is nitrated.

Electrophilic and nucleophilic reagents have often been defined as attacking preferentially the most negative and most positive centers, respectively. This definition is based implicitly upon the exclusive consideration of the Class A structures. It is usually equivalent to that adopted here, however, as will be shown later in this section.

The terms *kationoid* (or *cationoid*) and *anionoid* are used by some authors in place of electrophilic and nucleophilic, respectively.[11] It should be noted also that an electrophilic (or kationoid) reagent is an " acid," whereas a nucleophilic (or anionoid) reagent is a " base " in the generalized sense of Lewis.[12]

We are now in position to return to the original problem of establishing criteria for the relative stabilities of the structures of Class B. From what has already been said, it would appear that the relative stabilities of the various structures of this type which can be derived from any

[11] See, for example, the papers of R. Robinson, to which reference was made in footnote 6 of Chapter 1.

[12] G. N. Lewis, *Valence and the Structure of Atoms and Molecules*, Chemical Catalog Company, New York, 1923, pp. 141 f.; *J. Franklin Inst.*, **226**, 293 (1938). See also the discussion in fine print at the end of Section 7·2.

one given reagent should be determined largely by the relative ease with which the necessary 0, 1, or 2 electrons (as the case may be) can be brought by polarization to the various possible points of attack in that reagent. The assumption is thus made implicitly that the behavior of the reagent in question is determined primarily by whether it is electrophilic, radical, or nucleophilic, and only incidentally by the exact identity of its reaction partner. In this way, the treatment can be simplified to a great extent.

Let us examine this criterion for the relative stabilities of the Class B structures more closely. We can think of such a structure as having been established in two steps, which may have been either simultaneous or successive. (The question as to whether the steps are simultaneous or successive is of no significance here, as a matter of fact, because, as was pointed out above, we are not primarily interested in the process by which the structure is produced, but only in its stability after it has been established.) In the first of these steps, the two reagent molecules are polarized by each other in such a way that the electronic configurations necessary for the formation of the new bond are produced. This implies that an incomplete valence shell (usually an open sextet of electrons or else the completely empty valence shell of the hydrogen ion), which is capable of accommodating an unshared pair of electrons, is produced at the reactive center of an electrophilic reagent; that a single, unpaired electron is produced at the reactive center of a radical reagent; and that an unshared pair of electrons is produced at the reactive center of a nucleophilic reagent. In the second step, the bond is actually formed by the sharing of the two electrons produced in the first step. To the extent, then, that all other factors can be ignored, a structure of Class B must be most stable when the new covalent bond which it contains joins the two reagents at the points at which the necessary electron configurations can be provided most easily. Therefore, if these Class B structures were the only ones contributing to the activated complex, the most reactive center of any electrophilic, radical, or nucleophilic reagent would be at that one of its available positions at which an incomplete valence shell of the specified type, a single unpaired electron, or an unshared pair of electrons, respectively, could be created most easily.

The significance of the word " available " in the present connection can be made clear by an example. We shall find in Section 8·11 that, in the nitration of chlorobenzene, the organic molecule acts as a nucleophilic reagent. However, in spite of the fact that its chlorine atom already possesses three unshared pairs of electrons even in the Kekulé structures, the reaction takes place upon a carbon atom of the ring. This apparent discrepancy is due to the fact that any reaction taking place upon the chlorine atom would have to be of an entirely different type from, and hence would not be directly comparable with, the one which actually occurs. The situation can be expressed by the statement that, as an experimental fact, the chlorine atom is not an *available position* for the particular reaction under discussion. The foregoing remarks would not need to be altered in any essential way if attention were centered upon the structures of Class A, and therefore upon the fact that the chlorine atom marks the point with the greatest net negative charge.

In the above discussion, we have derived qualitative rules for the prediction of relative reactivity from two extreme points of view; if the Class A structures alone are considered, the distribution of electric charge is the determining factor; if, on the other hand, the Class B structures alone are considered, the ease of the appropriate electronic displacements is the determining factor. Actually, of course, the truth lies indefinitely somewhere between the extremes, and it is not legitimate for us to restrict our attention to either limiting type of structure alone. Fortunately, however, it appears that this difficulty is not serious in any of the examples in which we shall be interested. The reason for this fact can be seen in the following way. A position, at which an unshared pair of electrons can be easily provided, is ordinarily also a position with a net negative charge, and so it is a center of nucleophilic activity from either point of view; conversely, a position, at which the required kind of incomplete valence shell can be easily provided, is ordinarily also a position with a net positive charge, and so it is a center of electrophilic activity from either point of view. Consequently, if each of the reagents in a given reaction has a charge distribution such that its available positions are appreciably positive or negative, considerations of the Class A and of the Class B structures usually lead to the same qualitative conclusions regarding reactivity. On the other hand, in many reactions, the available positions of one or both of the reagents may have no appreciable charges. This situation is encountered fairly generally in reactions between radical reagents and occasionally also in those between electrophilic and nucleophilic reagents. Under such circumstances, the Class A structures permit no definite conclusions at all to be drawn regarding reactivity. However, since the relative ease of producing the required polarizations may still vary widely, the Class B structures can differ considerably in energy, and so be the decisive factor. Consequently, in these latter types of reaction as well, there is no conflict between the two points of view.

From the above discussion, it follows that we can safely ignore the structures of Class A, since these provide no additional information regarding the reactions either between electrophilic and nucleophilic reagents or between radical reagents.   We shall, accordingly, center our attention in the following sections more upon the structures of Class B, although we shall nevertheless have occasion from time to time to treat certain problems from both points of view.   This procedure, which is adopted here for the sake of convenience, is not to be taken as implying that the relatively neglected structures of Class A are necessarily of secondary importance.   For all we know at present, these may indeed make the major contributions to the states of the activated complex in many, if not in all, reactions.   The point is merely that they have no effect, which we need to consider explicitly, upon the conclusions reached.

**8·4   Symbols for Describing Resonance.**   Up to the present time, in discussing any given molecule, we have indicated the various structures among which resonance is presumed to occur by explicitly writing either all of them or else a few representative examples.   Especially in the discussion of the reactions of electrophilic and nucleophilic reagents, we shall now find it convenient to make use of a more compact, but less generally applicable, system of representation, which has been devised and used largely by the English organic chemists.[13]   The fundamental principle of this system is that one first writes down the most stable structure in the customary manner, and then introduces certain conventional symbols to show the direction in which that structure needs to be modified.   These symbols are of two different types, which will be discussed separately.

A bond between two atoms of different kinds is usually associated with a dipole moment, so that one of the atoms is relatively positive and the other is relatively negative.   (See Chapter 5.)   The situation can be represented graphically if the bond is written not simply as a straight line but as an arrow with its head and tail at the more negative and more positive atoms, respectively.   The direction of the arrow is accordingly in agreement with the usual convention for dipole moments; it is also the same as that in which the electrons have, on the average, been displaced.   The symbol I, for example, implies that the most important structure of the molecule is II, with a pure covalent bond, but that the structure III also makes some contribution.   The further

$$H \rightarrow Cl \qquad H—Cl \qquad H^+ \quad Cl^- \qquad H^- \quad Cl^+$$
$$\text{I} \qquad\qquad \text{II} \qquad\qquad \text{III} \qquad\qquad \text{IV}$$

structure IV makes a still smaller contribution, and is ignored.   The head of an arrow therefore marks a negative center, at which an unshared pair of electrons could be provided with relative ease;   accord-

[13] See, for example, J. Allan, A. E. Oxford, R. Robinson, and J. C. Smith, *J. Chem. Soc.*, 401 (1926).   Cf. also the further references given in footnote 6 of Chapter 1.

ingly, it is a center of nucleophilic activity and a point at which an electrophilic reagent might attack. In a similar way, the tail of an arrow marks a center of electrophilic activity and a point at which a nucleophilic reagent might attack. It is to be noted that these conclusions follow unambiguously, whether the problem is viewed from the point of view of the structures of Class A or of Class B.

The present type of displacement of electric charge is known as the inductive effect, or the $I$-effect. Although, as was shown above, it can be described as due to resonance, it can instead be discussed in purely classical terms; the idea of resonance is not essential to its understanding, since the more electronegative atom can be thought of as merely pulling the electrons toward itself as a result of its greater intrinsic attraction for them. The $I$-effect can be relayed down a saturated chain (with, of course, rapid damping) as is indicated in the structure $H_3C \rightarrow CH_2 \rightarrow CH_2 \rightarrow Cl$ for $n$-propyl chloride.

A second way in which the distribution of electric charge in a molecule can be altered is illustrated by vinyl chloride. If, for simplicity, we ignore the $I$-effect, we can write for this substance the two structures V and VI, of which the former is much the more important. Resonance between these two can be represented by the single symbol VII. Each

$$H_2C\!\!=\!\!CH \qquad\qquad\qquad \overset{-}{H_2C}\!\!-\!\!CH$$
$$\underset{\textstyle V}{\overset{\textstyle |}{Cl}} \qquad\qquad\qquad\qquad \underset{\textstyle VI}{\overset{\textstyle \|}{Cl^+}}$$

curved arrow corresponds here to a transference of a pair of electrons from a position at its tail to a position at its head. If this transference went to completion, the original structure V would have been changed into VI; the symbolism implies, however, that any such transference

VII

is only a minor correction or, in other words, that the structure VI makes only a small contribution. In a similar way, the symbol VIII for chlorobenzene signifies that the structure IX is most important, but that the *ortho* and *para* quinoid structures X and XI make small contributions. The additional Kekulé structure XII and the additional *ortho* quinoid structure XIII are also implied, since the general principles of resonance require that these structures make the same contributions as do IX and X, respectively, to which they are equivalent. And finally, the symbol XIV for nitrobenzene signifies large contributions

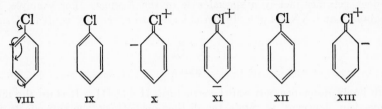

from XV, XVI, XVII, and XVIII and much smaller ones from XIX, XX, and XXI.

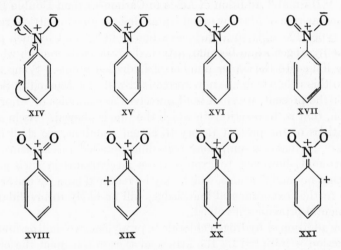

The present type of displacement of electrons was named the tautomeric effect, or *T*-effect, before the essential distinction between resonance and tautomerism was recognized; we shall refer to it hereafter as the resonance effect, or *R*-effect. As with the *I*-effect, the heads and tails of the arrows mark the centers of nucleophilic and electrophilic activity, respectively. This conclusion again follows unambiguously from either of the two extreme points of view regarding the nature of the activated complex. Frequently, the head or the tail of a curved arrow is placed not at a definite atom but on the bond between two atoms. Under such circumstances, the electrophilic or nucleophilic activity is possessed by only such atoms as show a net loss or gain of electrons, respectively. For example, in the structure VII for vinyl chloride, nucleophilic activity is possessed only by the carbon atom to which the chlorine atom is not attached, because it alone shows a net gain of electrons.

As was pointed out in Sections 5·2 and 5·3, the existence of dipole moments and of polarization can be considered to be results of resonance, so that the $I$-effect becomes merely a special case of the $R$-effect. For example, the symbols I and XXII for hydrogen chloride are essentially equivalent since

$$\text{H} \overset{\frown}{-} \text{Cl}$$

XXII

both imply resonance between the structures II and III. It is usually more convenient, however, to retain the distinction between the two effects and between their respective methods of representation.

### 8·5  " Normal " Addition of Acids to Carbon-Carbon Double Bonds.

The familiar rule of Markownikoff states that an unsymmetrical reagent of the type HX adds to a carbon-carbon double bond in such a way that the hydrogen atom becomes attached to the carbon atom which is already linked to the larger number of hydrogen atoms.  Some exceptions to this rule which are now recognized will be discussed in Section 8·6; for the present, we shall limit ourselves to examples of " normal " addition, that is, to reactions in which the rule is obeyed.  As in all the applications of the present theory to actual reactions, we shall find it necessary to make assumptions regarding detailed mechanisms.  We shall attempt, however, to express these mechanisms in such general terms that no modifications, which may be required later by the acquisition of further experimental knowledge, will be likely to invalidate the fundamental principles involved.

In the addition of hydrogen chloride to propylene, we shall assume that the reaction is initiated by the attack of the proton upon the organic molecule.  This assumption is supported by the fact that acids in general are capable of entering into such reactions, but that, except for the hydrogen halides, substances capable of providing halide ions do not ordinarily give rise to corresponding reactions.[14]  The proton, therefore, is probably involved in an essential step of the reaction.  It is, of course, not entirely free but must be combined in some way.  In an ionizing solvent, it is solvated; in a non-polar solvent, such as benzene, or in the absence of a solvent, it is presumably still combined with chlorine in an un-ionized molecule of hydrogen chloride; and in the presence of a catalyst, such as ferric chloride, it may be present in some sort of complex.  In any event, however, the hydrogen is assumed to be transferred to the propylene as a proton, and not as either a hydrogen atom with one electron or as a negative hydride ion with two electrons.

[14] For some possible exceptions to this statement, see K. Nozaki and R. Ogg, Jr., *J. Am. Chem. Soc.*, **63**, 2583 (1941); **64**, 697, 704, 709 (1942).

The initial product is then an organic positive ion, which immediately, or perhaps simultaneously, picks up a chloride ion from the solution to form the final product. This chloride ion may not be, and in fact probably is not, the same one that was combined originally with the proton. (If the reaction is carried out in an ionizing solvent, this last statement is obvious; if in a non-ionizing solvent, it seems reasonable on geometrical grounds.)

Regardless of the exact state of combination of the proton, and regardless of the source of the chloride ion, the essential features of the actual reaction will be reproduced well enough for our purposes if we treat the proton as completely free. Moreover, we can ignore the chloride ion, since it is apparently not involved in an essential way in the primary reaction that determines the mode of addition. With these simplifications, then, we are in position to consider the structures which make the largest contributions to the transition state.

The role of the chloride ion in the reaction may not be quite so simply that of an innocent bystander as is stated above, because the presence of such a negative ion in the fairly immediate neighborhood of the propylene molecule may be required for the easy formation of the organic positive ion. If so, the rate of reaction could then actually be dependent upon the concentration of chloride, as well as of hydrogen, ion. It is doubtful, however, if such refinements in the treatment would necessarily alter the present admittedly oversimplified discussion in any significant regard.

It will be necessary for us to consider separately the two different activated complexes that are involved in the formation of *i*-propyl chloride in agreement with Markownikoff's rule, and of *n*-propyl chloride in violation of that rule. In the former, resonance should occur principally among the structures I, II, and III, of which I is of Class A and II and III are of Class B. In the latter, resonance should occur

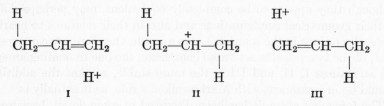

principally between the structures IV and V, which are of Classes A and B, respectively. No structure without formal bonds is possible here analogous to III. Of these various structures, I and IV must be of nearly the same stability. We do not actually know which is the more stable of the two, because we do not know whether the central carbon atom of propylene is positive or negative with respect to the one at the right of the structures as drawn. However, the inequality in charge is doubtless quite small, since the dipole moment of the substance

is only a few tenths of a Debye unit, and consequently the difference in the energies of the structures is doubtless also quite small. Similarly, the structures II and V must be of nearly the same stability, although again we do not know which is the more stable of the two. Inasmuch as both contain the same number of the same kinds of bond, any difference in stability between them must be due largely to a difference in charge distribution. If we assume the central carbon atom to be the more positive, then structure II must be less stable than V, because then the formal charge in the former structure accentuates, whereas that in the latter counterbalances, the inequality in charge distribution. On the other hand, if we assume the central carbon atom to be the more negative, the opposite conclusion regarding relative stabilities follows. In either event, the effect of the Class B structures II and V is in the opposite direction from that of the Class A structures I and IV. Since both of these effects are apparently small and, moreover, tend to cancel each other, as we have just seen, it appears probable that the course of the reaction will be determined by the additional Class B structure, III. This conclusion seems especially reasonable because the structures I and III are nearly, if not completely, equivalent, so that the resonance between them should be especially effective. (Structures I and III, although they appear to be completely equivalent, may perhaps differ in their geometrical configurations and also in their relations to nearby molecules or ions in the solution.) As a result, therefore, we can expect that, of the two possible activated complexes, the one resonating among the structures I, II, and III is the more stable, so that the addition should be in agreement with Markownikoff's rule, as it actually is.

The foregoing example has been discussed in some detail, because it was desired that the essential features of the rather complex problem should be made as clear as possible. The treatment could have been carried through with considerably less labor, however, with the aid of the general considerations of the two preceding sections. The necessary argument proceeds along the following lines. The proton is clearly an electrophilic reagent, since it has no electrons to contribute to the new covalent bond. The propylene must, therefore, be nucleophilic, and its role in the reaction must be to provide an unshared pair of electrons at the point of attack. Consequently, the reaction is initiated at that position of the propylene molecule at which such an unshared pair can be produced most easily. Since the dipole moment of propylene is small, the *I*-effect also is small and can be neglected, but the *R*-effect remains to be considered. For the understanding of the present reaction, the idea of hyperconjugation (Section 3·7) proves to be important. (That hyperconjugation was important also in the preceding treatment follows from the fact that structure III was found to play a decisive role. In this structure, one of the hydrogen atoms of the original propylene molecule is no longer joined to the carbon atom by a valence bond, and that is the essential feature of hyperconjugation.) Accordingly, the structure of propylene can be written in either one of the two approximately equivalent ways, VI and VII. Whichever of these modes of representation is adopted, the center of nucleophilic activity, marked by

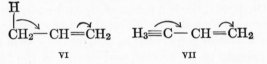

VI                  VII

the head of the curved arrow, is at the terminal carbon atom, so that the reaction is initiated there. The conclusion reached is accordingly the same as that obtained by the preceding, more elaborate method.

The reader may perhaps have wondered why the curved arrows in structures VI and VII are drawn in the particular direction in which they are drawn, and not in the opposite direction as in VIII and IX. Actually, for the unreacting molecule, there would be little reason to prefer one set of

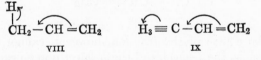

VIII                 IX

structures over the other, unless further information were available regarding the direction and origin of the dipole moment of the substance. We might be inclined, a priori, to regard the hydrogen atoms as less electronegative than the carbon atoms, so that the displacement indicated in the structure VI, or VII, may seem more reasonable than that in structure VIII, or IX. An effect of this nature, however, appears to be quite small and actually is neglected in the treatment, as can be seen from a comparison with the original discussion given above. The essential point at issue is that the propylene is a nucleophilic reagent in the present reaction and, in order to react, must provide an unshared pair of electrons at the point of attack. Such an unshared pair is actually provided at the terminal carbon atom in structure VI, or VII, but not at either of the ethylenic carbon atoms in structure VIII, or IX. In other words, when we are discussing a reaction, we are not so much interested in the structure of the unreacting molecule as in the way the molecule can be polarized during the reaction to provide the necessary electron configuration. The reason then why we write the structure as VI, or VII, and not as VIII, or IX, is that the former, but not the latter, describes the type of polarization that must actually occur in the reaction.

The foregoing simplified argument has been based implicitly on the assumption that the Class B structures of the activated complex are of predominant importance in determining the course of the reaction. A similar argument leading to the same conclusion, however, could be based equally well on the opposite assumption that the Class A structures are predominant; to do this, one would merely have to consider that the primary purpose of the polarization under discussion is to bring negative charge, rather than an unshared pair of electrons, to the point of attack. Obviously, the two points of view are equivalent.

Let us now consider a slightly different sort of example, the addition of hydrogen chloride to vinyl chloride, and, for the sake of brevity, let us confine our remarks to the second, and shorter, of the two treatments illustrated above with reference to propylene. The reader should now be able without difficulty to fill in the missing details of the more complete discussion. In vinyl chloride, the *I*-effect cannot be neglected, as in propylene, because the dipole moment of the molecule is large. Consequently, we must write the structure of the molecule as X. There is no ambiguity here about the directions of the arrows, either straight or curved, because the indicated displacements can occur in only the ways

$$\overset{\frown}{Cl} \longleftarrow CH \Longleftarrow \overset{\frown}{CH_2}$$

X

specified. The course of the reaction, however, cannot be definitely predicted, because the *I*-effect and the *R*-effect oppose each other, and we cannot be sure, without recourse to experiment, which one will predominate. Thus, the *I*-effect (the straight arrows) makes the carbon atom carrying the chlorine the more nucleophilic center, whereas the *R*-effect (the curved arrows) gives nucleophilic activity only to the terminal carbon atom. In such cases, it appears to be a good empirical rule that the *R*-effect wins out. Consequently, the reaction is initiated at the methylenic carbon atom, and the addition is in accordance with Markownikoff's rule. It is to be noted, however, that the *I*-effect does nevertheless exert a noticeable influence, in that it makes this reaction proceed at a slower rate than the corresponding one with unsubstituted ethylene.[15] The situation may be described thus: the $I$-effect decreases the nucleophilic activity of both carbon atoms, whereas the $R$-effect increases that of the terminal carbon atom only; this increase is great enough to make the terminal atom the more reactive of the two, but it is not great enough to bring the reactivity back to the level obtaining in ethylene itself.

The discussion so far has been limited to the addition of hydrogen chloride to two rather simple ethylene derivatives. The present treatment, however, is not restricted to these few reactions but can be extended to a large number of others. It should be evident, for example, that other acids, such as hydrogen bromide, hydrogen iodide, sulfuric acid, and so on, ought also to react in completely analogous manners to form analogous products. This expectation is indeed borne out by the facts, since all these named substances add to propylene and (in so far as the reactions have been studied) to vinyl chloride just as hydrogen chloride does, that is, in agreement with Markownikoff's rule. Moreover, the treatment can be extended in an obvious manner to include other unsymmetrical olefines, so that it is quite general. (For discussions of "abnormal" addition and of the reactions of conjugated systems, however, see Sections 8·6 and 8·9, respectively.)

The hydration of an olefine also can be discussed along the present lines. For example, if propylene is treated with fairly concentrated sulfuric acid, the ion resonating among the structures I, II, and III is presumably formed as above. This ion has several possibilities for subsequent reaction. It could acquire a bisulfate ion from the solution to give $i$-propyl sulfuric acid, XI, or, on the other hand, it could take up a molecule of water to give the oxonium ion XII. Since XII could

$$CH_3—CH—CH_3 \qquad CH_3—CH—CH_3 \qquad CH_3—CH—CH_3$$
$$| \qquad\qquad\qquad | \qquad\qquad\qquad |$$
$$OSO_3H \qquad\qquad +OH_2 \qquad\qquad OH$$
$$\textbf{XI} \qquad\qquad\qquad \textbf{XII} \qquad\qquad\qquad \textbf{XIII}$$

doubtless lose a proton very readily, the product that would be isolated from the reaction mixture would be $i$-propyl alcohol, XIII. The net result of this second possible course of the reaction is therefore addition of water to the olefine in agreement with Markownikoff's rule. It is to be noted that an intermediate formation, and subsequent hydrolysis, of the ester XI does not need to be postulated.

[15] M. S. Kharasch and C. W. Hannum, *J. Am. Chem. Soc.*, **56**, 712 (1934).

**8·6 " Abnormal " Addition of Acids to Carbon-Carbon Double Bonds.**[16] When hydrogen bromide adds to propylene, the reaction can follow either one of two quite different courses, depending upon the experimental conditions. If oxygen and peroxides are rigorously excluded from the reaction mixture, or if an " antioxidant " like diphenylamine or thiocresol is added, only $i$-propyl bromide (the normal product) is obtained; but, if oxygen is present, $n$-propyl bromide (the abnormal product) may also be formed in varying amounts. In fact, if peroxides are added, $n$-propyl bromide may become the only product that can be isolated. Clearly, therefore, there must be two entirely different mechanisms for the addition. Of these, the one leading to normal addition has already been discussed in the preceding section, but the one leading to abnormal addition remains to be considered.

It appears at the present time that the addition of hydrogen bromide to propylene in the presence of oxygen or peroxides is probably a chain reaction proceeding through the steps:

$$HBr + O_2 \longrightarrow (H \cdot O_2) + Br$$

$$HBr + peroxide \longrightarrow (H \cdot peroxide) + Br \qquad (1)$$

$$Br + CH_3CH{=}CH_2 \longrightarrow CH_3\overset{\centerdot}{C}H{-}CH_2Br \qquad (2)$$

$$CH_3\overset{\centerdot}{C}H{-}CH_2Br + HBr \longrightarrow CH_3CH_2CH_2Br + Br \qquad (3)$$

The purpose of the oxygen or peroxide is thus to start the chain by producing a bromine atom in reaction 1. This atom is used up in reaction 2, but a new one is produced in reaction 3 to take its place and to carry on the chain. The sequence of reactions can therefore continue indefinitely, or until the chain is broken by some such reaction as

$$H + Br \longrightarrow HBr \qquad (4)$$

or the like.

We need now to consider why in step 2 the bromine atom, which is clearly a radical reagent, attacks the terminal unsaturated atom of the propylene in preference to the central one. The activated complex for the actual (abnormal) reaction can resonate among the structures I, II, and III, whereas that for the alternative (normal) reaction could resonate only between the structures IV and V. It is difficult to see how the distribution of charge in the propylene molecule could have

---

[16] For a comprehensive survey of the abnormal additions and other related reactions, see F. R. Mayo and C. Walling, *Chem. Rev.*, **27**, 351 (1940). In this paper are given also references to all the experimental work mentioned in this section.

any significant effect upon the relative stabilities of the Class A structures I and IV, or of the Class B structures II and V, because the bromine atom is electrically neutral. It is to be expected, therefore, that the

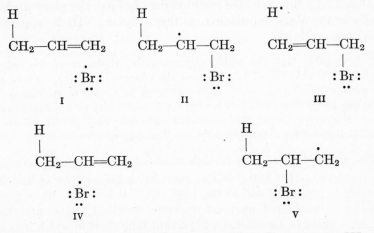

possibility of resonance with the further Class B structure, III, will make the activated complex for abnormal addition the more stable of the two, so that the product should be predominantly *n*-propyl bromide, as it actually is.

The addition of hydrogen bromide to vinyl chloride in the presence of peroxides also occurs abnormally and gives 1-chloro-2-bromoethane as the major product. In this reaction, the activated complex for abnormal addition resonates principally among the structures VI, VII, and VIII, whereas that for normal addition could resonate only between IX and X. The structure VIII cannot be expected to stabilize

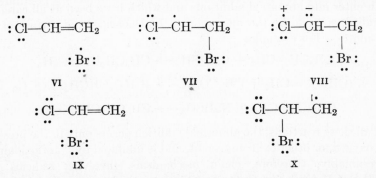

the former activated complex a great deal, for, although it has the same number of bonds as the remaining structures, its charge distribution is unfavorable. (The effect of resonance between VII and VIII is to produce a three-electron bond between the carbon and chlorine atoms, in addition to the two-electron one. Since these atoms are not equivalent, the three-electron bond can therefore be expected to be weak. See Section 2·5.) However, the addition does in fact take place predominantly in the abnormal manner, so that structure VIII is apparently decisive nevertheless.

It is possible that the highly electronegative character of the chlorine atom in vinyl chloride might also favor the abnormal addition. To be sure, our present qualitative point of view gives us no reason to anticipate such an effect, but a more quantitative approach might lead to a definite prediction. See, for example, the somewhat analogous case of the orientation in chlorobenzene for substitution by a radical reagent (Section 8·11).

The above-described mechanism of abnormal addition is, of course, not restricted to the two reactions considered, the addition of hydrogen bromide to propylene and to vinyl chloride. It is instead quite general and can be considered operative whenever a radical reagent attacks an olefine. There is, however, an important limitation to which it is subject: hydrogen bromide is the only one of all the common acids that can be made to enter into an abnormal addition. The reason for this is probably that, with the remaining acids, one or more of the reactions corresponding to the steps 1, 2, and 3 in the above scheme for hydrogen bromide cannot occur. For example, hydrogen chloride and sulfuric acid appear to be too stable to react in the necessary manners with either a peroxide (in step 1) or an organic radical (in step 3); and an iodine atom, although it can be produced from hydrogen iodide (in step 1) is probably not sufficiently reactive to attack a molecule of the olefine (in step 2). The only acids, aside from hydrogen bromide, which can enter into abnormal additions and which have been at all carefully studied, seem to be the mercaptans, the thioacids, and certain of the bisulfites. For example:

$$CH_3CH{=}CH_2 + C_6H_5SH \longrightarrow CH_3CH_2CH_2SC_6H_5$$

$$(CH_3)_2C{=}CH_2 + CH_3COSH \longrightarrow (CH_3)_2CHCH_2SCOCH_3$$

$$CH_3CH{=}CH_2 + NaHSO_3 \longrightarrow CH_3CH_2CH_2SO_3Na$$

In all these reactions, the abnormal addition occurs only in the presence of oxygen, or other oxidizing agent, and is inhibited by "antioxidants." Presumably, therefore, chain mechanisms, involving radicals like $C_6H_5S$, $CH_3COS$, and $HSO_3$ or $SO_3^-$, respectively, are again involved.

Mercaptans add *normally* also, in the presence of certain catalysts, including fairly strong sulfuric acid, elementary sulfur, strong bases, and so

on.  The nature of these reactions is not clearly understood at present.
Bisulfites, on the other hand, appear to add only in the abnormal manner,
and only under oxidizing conditions.

## 8·7  Addition of Halogens to Carbon-Carbon Double Bonds.  Related Reactions.

When bromine adds to even an unsymmetrical olefine
like propylene, only a single product is possible regardless of the mechanism.   We shall find it interesting, however, to consider the nature of
the activated complex, because, in doing so, we can obtain an under-
standing of several related phenomena.   Just as the initial step in the
normal addition of an acid to an olefine is considered to be a reaction
with a positive hydrogen ion, so also the initial step in the addition of
bromine is considered to be a reaction with a positive bromine ion.[17]
This ion, like the hydrogen ion in the addition of an acid, HX, need not
be, and in fact probably is not, completely free; it may be combined
with a negative bromide ion in a polarized bromine molecule, $Br^+Br^-$,
or it may be combined in some way with a catalyst molecule.   In any
event, however, we can carry through the following discussion as if the
ion in question were actually free, because its exact state of combination is not essential to the argument.

The treatment of the addition of bromine to propylene is completely
analogous to that of the addition of hydrogen chloride to propylene,
since in both reactions the inorganic reagent is clearly electrophilic.
The only essential change, in fact, is the replacement of the positive
hydrogen ion, $H^+$, by the positive bromine ion, $Br^+$.   The effect of the
electrostatic interactions in the Class A structures is then qualitatively
the same as before; and, since the bromine ion, just like the hydrogen
ion, is able to accommodate a pair of electrons provided by the unsaturated hydrocarbon, the relation between the Class B structures is also
unaltered.   It follows, therefore, that the attack must be initiated at
the end of the molecule, as before, so that the initial product has the
structure I and not II.   The completion of the reaction is then effected
immediately, or simultaneously with the first step, by the capture of a

negative ion from the solution.   If the reaction is carried out in, say
carbon tetrachloride as solvent, this negative ion can be only a bromide

[17] An excellent survey of this problem is given by L. P. Hammett, pp. 147 ff. of
reference 3.

ion, Br⁻, so that the final product is necessarily propylene bromide, III. On the other hand, if the reaction is carried out in water, hydroxide ions also are available, so that propylene bromohydrin, IV, is a further possible product.     Under such circumstances, the net effect of the reaction is the addition of the unsymmetrical hypobromous acid, HOBr.     Although

$$CH_3—CH—CH_2 \qquad CH_3—CH—CH_2 \qquad CH_3—CH—CH_2$$
$$\quad | \quad\quad | \qquad\qquad\quad | \quad\quad | \qquad\qquad\quad | \quad\quad |$$
$$\quad Br \quad\quad Br \qquad\qquad HO \quad\quad Br \qquad\qquad Br \quad\quad OH$$

$$\qquad III \qquad\qquad\qquad\qquad IV \qquad\qquad\qquad\qquad\qquad V$$

the two products, IV and V, are conceivable in this reaction, only the former is actually produced, as we have just seen.

The above treatment may have been too drastically oversimplified, because it is able only with some difficulty to account for the stereochemical features of certain completely analogous reactions.     For example, *cis* and *trans* stilbene, $C_6H_5CH{=}CHC_6H_5$, give rise on bromination to diastereomeric dibromides, $C_6H_5CHBr—CHBrC_6H_5$ (presumably by trans addition in both reactions).     This fact would be hard to explain if the reactions proceeded through intermediate positive ions of the type $C_6H_5\overset{+}{CH}—CHBrC_6H_5$, because rotation about the central carbon-carbon bonds should occur freely in such ions, and the stereochemical configurations should be lost.     Tarbell and Bartlett[18] have suggested that the concluding phase of the reaction (the capture of a bromide ion from solution) occurs so rapidly that the rotation does not have time to occur.     Roberts and Kimball,[19] on the other hand, have made an alternative proposal that the intermediate positive ion contains a three-membered ring, as in VI.     The rigidity of the structure would then

$$C_6H_5CH{—\!\!—}CHC_6H_5$$
$$\diagdown \overset{+}{Br} \diagup$$

$$VI$$

make possible the maintenance of the configuration.     Moreover, the attack by the bromide ion in the concluding step would presumably be accompanied by a Walden inversion, so that the addition of the bromine should be trans, as it probably is.     The possibility of a mechanism of this type receives further strong support from an extensive series of investigations of related reactions.[20]     The work of Nozaki and Ogg[14] also suggests a more complex

[18] D. S. Tarbell and P. D. Bartlett, *J. Am. Chem. Soc.*, **59**, 407 (1937).

[19] I. Roberts and G. E. Kimball, *J. Am. Chem. Soc.*, **59**, 947 (1937).

[20] S. Winstein and H. J. Lucas, *J. Am. Chem. Soc.*, **60**, 836 (1938); **61**, 1576 (1939). H. J. Lucas and C. W. Gould, Jr., *ibid.*, **63**, 2541 (1941).     S. Winstein and R. E. Buckles, *ibid.*, **64**, 2780, 2787 (1942).     S. Winstein, *ibid.*, **64**, 2791, 2792 (1942). S. Winstein, H. V. Hess, and R. E. Buckles, *ibid.*, **64**, 2796 (1942).     S. Winstein and R. B. Henderson, *ibid.*, **65**, 2196 (1943).

mechanism in which, at any rate under some circumstances, the negative bromide ion plays a more essential role than is assumed here. Regardless of the exact nature of the intermediate, however, we shall continue to treat the problem from the above simpler point of view. It is doubtful if we shall thereby be led into any errors that are important for our present purposes.

Several further reactions analogous to the formation of the halo-hydrins have been reported. For example, the addition of bromine to stilbene in methyl alcoholic solution leads to the methoxybromide, VII;[21] and the addition of bromine to ethylene in the presence of a large concentration of chloride ion or of nitrate ion leads to the bromochloride, VIII, or to the bromonitrate, IX, respectively.[22] None of these reactions involves the problem of orientation, because the olefine in each is

$$C_6H_5—CH—CH—C_6H_5 \qquad H_2C—CH_2 \qquad H_2C—CH_2$$
$$\quad\;\; | \quad\;\; | \qquad\qquad\quad | \quad | \qquad\qquad\quad | \quad |$$
$$\quad\;\; Br \quad OCH_3 \qquad\qquad Br \;\; Cl \qquad\qquad Br \;\; ONO_2$$

|      VII      |      VIII      |      IX      |
| --- | --- | --- |

symmetrical. We could predict, however, that under comparable conditions propylene should give the substances X, XI, and XII, respectively. These reactions seem never to have been reported.

$$CH_3—CH—CH_2 \qquad CH_3—CH—CH_2 \qquad CH_3—CH——CH_2$$
$$\quad | \quad\;\; | \qquad\qquad\qquad | \quad\;\; | \qquad\qquad\quad | \qquad\qquad |$$
$$CH_3—O \;\; Br \qquad\qquad Cl \;\; Br \qquad\qquad ONO_2 \;\; Br$$

|      X      |      XI      |      XII      |
| --- | --- | --- |

## 8·8 Addition to Carbon-Oxygen Double Bonds.[23]

Whereas the reagents which can add to carbon–carbon double bonds have been found to be either electrophilic or radical, those which can add to carbon–oxygen double bonds are on the whole nucleophilic. In an aldehyde or ketone, for example, the distribution of electric charge is that represented by either of the equivalent structures, I and II. The

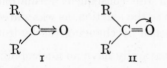

carbon atom, therefore, is a center of electrophilic activity and a point of attack by a nucleophilic reagent.

[21] P. D. Bartlett and D. S. Tarbell, *J. Am. Chem. Soc.*, **58**, 466 (1936).
[22] A. W. Francis, *J. Am. Chem. Soc.*, **47**, 2340 (1925).
[23] For an excellent and detailed discussion of these reactions, see L. P. Hammett, Chapter XI of reference 3.

A characteristic example of a nucleophilic reagent is given by the cyanide ion, CN⁻, which not only has an unshared pair of electrons upon the carbon atom, but also is negatively charged. The initial product in the reaction with, say acetaldehyde is presumably the ion III, which then acquires a proton from the solution and becomes the cyanhydrin, IV.

The formation of an oxime presents a rather complex problem. The nucleophilic reagent in this reaction is hydroxylamine, $H_2NOH$, which has an unshared pair of electrons upon the nitrogen atom. Since the reaction is acid-catalyzed, the electrophilic reagent is presumably not the free carbonyl compound, $RR'CO$, but is instead the more actively electrophilic ion, $[RR'COH]^+$. The initial product is therefore V. The reaction can now be completed in either one of two ways. With chloral ($R = CCl_3$, $R' = H$) a proton is lost to the solution to give the product VI, and with a few other negatively substituted carbonyl compounds the reactions are similar. With acetaldehyde ($R = CH_3$, $R' = H$), however, and in general with most remaining aldehydes and

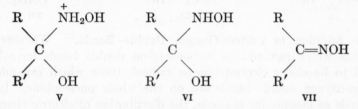

ketones, the concluding step consists in the loss of both a proton and a water molecule, with the consequent formation of the oxime, VII. Although acids catalyze the reaction, as was stated above, they can also act in the opposite sense by changing the hydroxylamine into the ion $H_3\overset{+}{N}OH$, which can naturally have no nucleophilic activity at all, since it has no unshared pair of electrons. (Similarly, the fact that the cyanhydrin reaction, discussed above, does not occur in too acid solution is to be related to the transformation of the nucleophilic cyanide ion into the non-nucleophilic hydrogen cyanide molecule.) Consequently, the reaction of oxime formation has an optimum $pH$, at which its rate reaches a maximum value. In strongly basic solution, the rate again rises, doubtless as a result of the transformation of the hydroxylamine into the ion $H_2NO^-$, which is strongly enough nucleophilic to react rapidly with the carbonyl compound $RR'CO$ itself. This complex problem has been discussed elsewhere[23] in considerable detail, and nothing further will be said about it here.

**8·9  Addition to Conjugated Systems.**  The addition of bromine to butadiene doubtless proceeds by a mechanism similar to that outlined in Section 8·7 for the addition to propylene. That is to say, the active reagent is probably a positive bromine ion (or its equivalent) which is, of course, electrophilic. The attack therefore occurs at that point of the butadiene molecule at which an unshared pair of electrons can be provided most easily. The structures I and II indicate the ways in

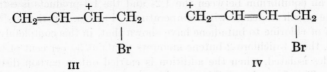

which an unshared pair can be brought to one of the terminal, or to one of the central carbon atoms, respectively, as the molecule is polarized in the reaction. Clearly, the former process is the easier of the two, because it permits the electrons in question to be brought from either or both of two atoms instead of from only one. Consequently, the reaction must commence at the terminal atom, so that the initial product is a resonance hybrid of III and IV.

$$CH_2=CH-\overset{+}{C}H-CH_2 \qquad \overset{+}{C}H_2-CH=CH-CH_2$$
$$\quad\qquad\qquad\qquad | \qquad\qquad\qquad\qquad\qquad\qquad |$$
$$\qquad\qquad\qquad Br \qquad\qquad\qquad\qquad\qquad\qquad Br$$
$$\qquad\qquad\textbf{III} \qquad\qquad\qquad\qquad\qquad\qquad\textbf{IV}$$

This same conclusion could have been obtained from a completely equivalent, but more laborious treatment along the lines followed in Section 8·5. Thus, the activated complex for reaction at one of the terminal carbon atoms can resonate among the structures V, VI, and VII, whereas that for reaction at one of the central atoms can resonate only between VIII and IX. The former therefore is the more stable and is the one actually formed. (The

$$CH_2=CH-CH=CH_2 \qquad CH_2=CH-\overset{+}{C}H-CH_2 \qquad \overset{+}{C}H_2-CH=CH-CH_2$$
$$\qquad\qquad\qquad\qquad\qquad\qquad\qquad\qquad | \qquad\qquad\qquad\qquad\qquad |$$
$$\qquad Br^+ \qquad\qquad\qquad\qquad Br \qquad\qquad\qquad\qquad\qquad Br$$
$$\qquad\textbf{V} \qquad\qquad\qquad\qquad\textbf{VI} \qquad\qquad\qquad\qquad\textbf{VII}$$

$$CH_2=CH-CH=CH_2 \qquad\qquad CH_2=CH-CH-\overset{+}{C}H_2$$
$$\qquad\qquad\qquad\qquad\qquad\qquad\qquad\qquad\qquad\qquad |$$
$$\qquad\quad Br^+ \qquad\qquad\qquad\qquad\qquad\qquad\qquad Br$$
$$\qquad\qquad\textbf{VIII} \qquad\qquad\qquad\qquad\qquad\qquad\textbf{IX}$$

foregoing discussion has ignored all structures with formal bonds. Such structures are less stable than the ones considered and make negligible contributions for our present purposes.)

The reaction can now be completed by the coming up of a negative bromide ion, to produce either the product X (related to the structure III of the intermediate) or else the product XI (related to the structure IV of the intermediate). In the former case, the net result of the reaction is 1,2-addition to one of the double bonds, whereas in the latter case, it is 1,4-addition to the conjugated system. We are unable to predict which of the two possible products will predominate, but our

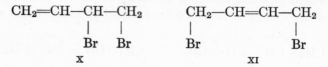

$$
\begin{array}{cc}
\underset{\substack{| \quad | \\ \text{Br} \quad \text{Br}}}{CH_2{=}CH{-}CH{-}CH_2} & \underset{\substack{| \qquad\qquad | \\ \text{Br} \qquad\qquad \text{Br}}}{CH_2{-}CH{=}CH{-}CH_2} \\
\text{x} & \text{xi}
\end{array}
$$

discussion has been of value nevertheless in that it has provided a simple and logical explanation of the *possibility* of 1,4-addition.

The proportion of 1,4-dibromo-2-butene, XI, has been reported[24] to vary from 38.4 per cent of the total dibromides isolated, when the addition is carried out in hexane as solvent, to 70.0 per cent, when it is carried out in acetic acid. Although the first of these reactions was performed at $-15°$ and the second at $4°$, the above figures are subject to some small uncertainty, because an equilibrium between the 1,2- and the 1,4-products is established at a rate which increases with temperature. Further experiments[25] on the addition of chlorine to butadiene have shown that, in this completely similar reaction, the 1,4-dichloro-2-butene amounts to about 30 per cent of the total dichlorides isolated, when the addition is carried out in carbon disulfide as solvent. This figure is possibly somewhat more reliable than the corresponding ones for the addition of bromine, because the equilibrium between the two dichlorides is not at all mobile at the temperature of the experiments.

In the addition of other electrophilic reagents to other conjugated systems, completely similar situations are encountered. For example, the structures XII and XIII for styrene show the types of polarization

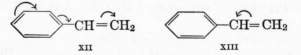

$$
\begin{array}{cc}
{-}CH{=}CH_2 & {-}CH{=}CH_2 \\
\text{xii} & \text{xiii}
\end{array}
$$

that are possible when the attack is at the terminal atom or at the atom adjacent to the benzene ring, respectively. It is evident from these

[24] E. H. Farmer, C. D. Lawrence, and J. F. Thorpe, *J. Chem. Soc.*, 729 (1928).
[25] I. E. Muskat and H. E. Northrup, *J. Am. Chem. Soc.*, **52**, 4043 (1930).

structures that the attack must again be initiated at the end of the conjugated system.   The addition of hydrogen chloride must therefore be
in accordance with Markownikoff's rule, as is observed.

When hydrogen chloride adds to an $\alpha,\beta$-unsaturated acid, such as
acrylic acid, the reaction doubtless begins as usual with the addition of a
proton at the end of the conjugated system.   In this reaction, two possibilities exist, as is shown in the structures XIV and XV for the original

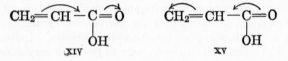

acrylic acid.   Since oxygen is a more electronegative element than
carbon, the first of these modes of polarization must presumably be the
more easily effected, and consequently the initial product should be the
one represented by the three resonating structures XVI, XVII, and
XVIII.   (Here, and below, the resonance within the carboxyl group

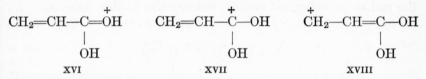

itself may be ignored as not affecting the final conclusions reached.)
When this ion acquires a chloride ion, to complete the reaction, the
resulting neutral molecule might be either XIX, by 1,2-addition, or XX,
by 1,4-addition.   The former structure, however, is of a type known to
be unstable.   If such a molecule were formed, it would presumably
break up again immediately to regenerate the hydrogen chloride and
acrylic acid; we therefore need consider it no further.   A molecule with

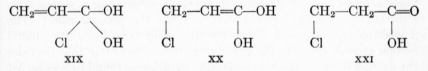

the second structure, XX, would also be unstable, but, if it were formed,
it could rearrange irreversibly to the stable keto form, XXI, and would
not be restricted to merely decomposing into the original reactants.
This is apparently what happens, since the product actually obtained
is indeed the $\beta$-chloropropionic acid, XXI.   It is to be noted that the
addition has occurred in violation of Markownikoff's rule, but that
the mechanism is probably entirely different from that involved in the
peroxide-induced addition of hydrogen bromide to an olefine.   With the

remaining $\alpha,\beta$-unsaturated acids, and with the $\alpha,\beta$-unsaturated alde-hydes and ketones, the reaction would be expected to follow the same course as with acrylic acid; in all these reactions the chlorine atom (or, in general, the halogen atom) actually ends up in the $\beta$ position, regard-less of Markownikoff's rule, in agreement with expectation.

The above discussion of acrylic acid may seem inconsistent with the con-clusion reached in Section 3·2 that the carbonyl part of a carboxyl group cannot be effectively conjugated with an ethylenic double bond. This con-clusion was derived, however, only for normal, unreacting molecules, and may not be valid when applied to activated complexes. Indeed, the struc-tures XVI, XVII, and XVIII, above, seem to be of not very different energy, so that resonance among them might be expected to produce an appreciable stabilization. In any event, there can be little doubt that an oxonium cation, to which XVI, XVII, and XVIII can contribute, is actually formed to some extent in strongly acid solution. (See Section 7·3.)

Nucleophilic reagents also have a tendency to attack preferentially the end of a conjugated system, unless other factors intervene. An $\alpha,\beta$-unsaturated carbonyl compound is seen from the structure XXII to

$$R-CH=CH-C=\overset{\cdot\cdot}{O}$$
$$|$$
$$R$$

XXII

have centers of electrophilic activity at the carbonyl carbon atom and at the $\beta$ position. (A phenyl group is sometimes included in the con-jugated system, as with benzalacetophenone and cinnamic aldehyde, discussed below. Addition to such compounds would hardly be ex-pected to be initiated in the ring, however, since then the large stabiliza-tion resulting from resonance between the Kekulé structures would necessarily be lost. Consequently, reactions proceeding in such a way, although occasionally encountered, are not the general rule.) The $\beta$ position is at the end of the conjugated system, but the carbonyl carbon atom is closer to the electronegative oxygen atom that provides the driving force for the electronic shift (which was found in Section 5·4 to be appreciable even in the unreacting, unpolarized molecule). Ap-parently the two factors are fairly evenly balanced. Benzalacetophe-none, XXIII, for example, can react with a nucleophilic reagent either at the carbonyl carbon atom or at the $\beta$ position, depending upon the

$$C_6H_5-CH=CH-C=O \qquad\qquad C_6H_5-CH=CH-CH=O$$
$$|$$
$$C_6H_5$$

XXIII XXIV

reagent and upon the conditions. With hydroxylamine, it forms an oxime in the usual manner in acid solution, but it behaves in a much more complex manner in basic solution and reacts at least partially at the $\beta$ position.[26] Moreover, cinnamic aldehyde, XXIV, reacts by 1,2-addition with sodium malonic ester to form the compound XXV, whereas benzalacetophenone reacts by 1,4-addition with the same reagent to give XXVI. The actual nucleophilic reagent in these last

$$C_6H_5—CH{=}CH—CH{=}C(CO_2C_2H_5)_2$$
XXV

$$C_6H_5—CH—CH_2—CO—C_6H_5$$
$$|$$
$$CH(CO_2C_2H_5)_2$$
XXVI

two reactions is doubtless the negative ion $[HC(CO_2C_2H_5)_2]^-$. Just as in the addition of bromine to butadiene, the present theory does not make possible a prediction of the actual mode of addition, but it does account for the possibility of 1,4- as well as 1,2-addition.

The addition of Grignard reagents to $\alpha,\beta$-unsaturated carbonyl compounds seems to be analogous to the addition of sodium malonic ester, since a negative organic ion, or its equivalent, may be assumed to be involved. Such an obviously nucleophilic reagent would be expected to attack either the carbon atom of the carbonyl group or the one in the $\beta$ position, so that either 1,2- or 1,4-addition could result, as before. This conclusion appears to be in agreement with experiment.[27] However, a detailed discussion of the complex problem would seem especially dangerous at the present time, in view of the surprisingly great, and not yet completely understood, effect which traces of metal salts have recently been found to exert upon the courses of such reactions.[28]

When a radical reagent reacts with a conjugated system, it also should attack the terminal position. That this statement is correct can be seen from a consideration of the peroxide-induced addition of hydrogen bromide to styrene. If the addition occurs in accordance with Markownikoff's rule, the activated complex can resonate among several structures, of which XXVII and XXVIII are typical examples. On the other hand, if addition occurs contrary to Markownikoff's rule, the

[26] K. v. Auwers and H. Müller, *J. prakt. Chem.*, **137**, 57 (1933).

[27] For example, see E. P. Kohler, *Am. Chem. J.*, **38**, 511 (1907); C. F. H. Allen and A. H. Blatt in H. Gilman, *Organic Chemistry*, John Wiley & Sons, New York, 1st ed., 1938, vol. I, pp. 581 ff.; 2nd ed., 1943, vol. I, pp. 672 ff.

[28] M. S. Kharasch and P. O. Tawney, *J. Am. Chem. Soc.*, **63**, 2308 (1941). M. S. Kharasch and D. C. Sayles, *ibid.*, **64**, 2972 (1942).

activated complex can resonate not only with structures like XXIX and XXX (analogous to XXVII and XXVIII respectively) but also

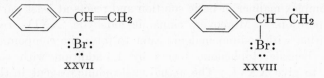

with *ortho* and *para* quinoid structures like XXXI, which have no analogs in the preceding example. Evidently, therefore, the latter complex

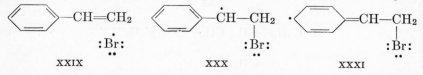

must be the more stable of the two, so that the presence of the peroxide should reverse the direction of addition here just as with propylene (Section 8·6).

The addition of hydrogen bromide to acrylic acid (as to any other $\alpha,\beta$-unsaturated acid, aldehyde, or ketone) is unaffected by the presence of peroxides. This fact is easily accounted for by the present theory. Under peroxide-free conditions, the hydrogen bromide presumably acts as an electrophilic reagent and so behaves in exactly the same manner as hydrogen chloride, which has been considered previously. The product of the addition is therefore $\beta$-bromopropionic acid. In the presence of peroxides, the hydrogen bromide may act as a radical reagent, and, if so, the reaction should be initiated by the attack of a bromine atom at the end of the conjugated system to give either XXXII or XXXIII. There can be little question that the first of these must be the one actually

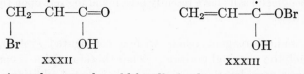

formed, since the second could hardly lead to any stable final product. The result of the addition must therefore be again $\beta$-bromopropionic acid, just as in the absence of peroxides. It is interesting that in this reaction a change in mechanism cannot reverse the direction of addition, as it does with propylene or even with such conjugated systems as styrene.[28a] (In regard to the question of conjugation in acrylic acid, see the section in fine print on page 248.)

---

[28a] For a discussion of some further reactions in which radical reagents attack $\alpha,\beta$-unsaturated carbonyl compounds, and which can be interpreted in a similar manner, see C. F. Koelsch and V. Boekelheide, *J. Am. Chem. Soc.*, **66**, 412 (1944).

A rather different kind of reaction between a radical reagent and a conjugated olefine is presented by the addition of hexaphenylethane to butadiene.[29] The first step is undoubtedly the addition of a triphenylmethyl radical to one end of the butadiene molecule to form an initial product resonating between XXXIV and XXXV. The reaction is then completed by a second triphenylmethyl radical. As might have been anticipated on steric grounds, the addition is 1,4 instead of 1,2 so that the final product is XXXVI.

$$(C_6H_5)_3C—CH_2—\overset{\centerdot}{C}H—CH=CH_2 \qquad (C_6H_5)_3C—CH_2—CH=CH—\overset{\centerdot}{C}H_2$$

XXXIV                                    XXXV

$$(C_6H_5)_3C—CH_2—CH=CH—CH_2—C(C_6H_5)_3$$

XXXVI

**8·10  Polymerization of Olefines.**[30]  When *i*-butene is treated with sulfuric acid, it is changed into a complex mixture of polymers, containing the two isomeric diisobutenes, I and II, a number of isomeric triisobutenes, and also some higher polymers.  Since the original *i*-butene

$$CH_2=C—CH_2—C(CH_3)_3 \qquad\qquad CH_3—C=CH—C(CH_3)_3$$
$$\quad\ |\qquad\qquad\qquad\qquad\qquad\qquad\quad\ |$$
$$\quad\ CH_3 \qquad\qquad\qquad\qquad\qquad\qquad CH_3$$

I                                           II

is an unsymmetrical olefine, there exist several conceivable ways in which the molecules could be linked to each other in the polymerization.  For example, the carbon skeleton of a diisobutene might be that represented by III, IV, or V.  The fact that only the first of these seems actually to occur means, of course, that the reaction leading to this particular

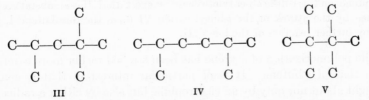

III                       IV                           V

skeleton proceeds much faster than either of those leading to the other two.  We shall find it interesting to consider the reason for this difference in rates.

The first step in the polymerization of *i*-butene by sulfuric acid pre-

[29] J. B. Conant and B. F. Chow, *J. Am. Chem. Soc.*, **55**, 3475 (1933).

[30] See C. S. Marvel and E. C. Horning, in H. Gilman, *Organic Chemistry*, John Wiley & Sons, New York, 2nd ed., 1943, vol. I, pp. 739 ff.; G. Egloff, *ibid.*, pp. 10 ff.  See also *The Chemistry of Large Molecules* (R. E. Burk and O. Grummitt, editors), Interscience Publishers, New York, 1943; the chapters by H. Mark (pp. 1 ff.) and by C. S. Marvel (pp. 219 ff.) are of particular interest in the present connection.

sumably consists in the acquisition of a proton, which is of course an electrophilic reagent, by the organic molecule. The resulting positive ion could be either VI or VII, but, as should be apparent from the discussion in Section 8·5, the first of these must be formed in preference to

$$(CH_3)_2\overset{+}{C}{-}CH_3 \qquad\qquad (CH_3)_2C{-}\overset{+}{C}H_2$$
$$\underset{\text{VI}}{} \qquad\qquad\qquad \overset{|}{\underset{\text{VII}}{H}}$$

the second. On being changed into the ion, VI, the molecule of *i*-butene, which was originally a nucleophilic reagent, obviously becomes a powerful electrophilic one. Its center of electrophilic activity is, of course, situated at the central carbon atom, since this has an open sextet of electrous. Consequently, in the subsequent reaction between the ion and a second molecule of *i*-butene, the more complex ion VIII, must be formed by union of the two reagents at their most electrophilic and nucleophilic positions, respectively. Several possibilities now arise. On the one hand, the ion, VIII, may lose a proton to give one or the

$$(CH_3)_2\overset{+}{C}{-}CH_2{-}C(CH_3)_3$$
$$\underset{\text{VIII}}{}$$

other of the two neutral diisobutenes, I and II; or, on the other hand, this ion may react further with unchanged *i*-butene to yield ultimately either a triisobutene or else a still more highly polymerized product.

Actually, the known structures of the triisobutenes, 2,2,4,6,6-pentamethyl-3-heptene and 1,1-di-*neo*-pentylethylene, suggest that these substances are formed by the attack of the *t*-butyl cation VI upon the diisobutene I, and not by further reaction of the ion VIII.

The polymerization of styrene has been studied rather more carefully than that of *i*-butene. It is of particular interest in that it can be brought about not only by an electrophilic but also by either a radical or a nucleophilic reagent as well. For example, stannic chloride, the phenyl radical, and triphenylmethyl sodium are effective (together with numerous further reagents of all three types). The first of these is electrophilic, because the octet of electrons about the tin atom can be expanded to include as many as twelve electrons; the second, which can be generated in the reaction mixture by the thermal decomposition of benzoyl peroxide, is obviously a radical reagent; and the last is a powerfully nucleophilic reagent because it contains the triphenylmethyl anion. The mechanism of the polymerization and the essential part of the structure of the polymer are probably very similar for the three different types of reaction and can be discussed together.   We shall let the symbol R represent the stannic chloride molecule, the phenyl radical, or the triphenylmethyl anion, as the case may be; and we shall let the letter $z$ represent a vacancy (capable of accommodating a pair of electrons), a single unpaired electron, or an unshared pair of electrons, respectively. (When R is electrophilic or nucleophilic, the letter $z$ may imply in addition a positive or negative charge, respectively.)   In each of the reactions, the first step is presumably an attack by the reagent R upon the terminal carbon atom of a styrene molecule, to give the product IX. The electrophilic, radical, or nucleophilic activity, which is indicated by the letter $z$, is thereby transferred to the carbon atom attached

$$\overset{z}{C_6H_5—CH—CH_2—R}$$

IX

directly to the benzene ring in this initial product, so that the second and subsequent steps should lead successively to the products X, XI, XII, and so on.   The polymerization is therefore presumably of the

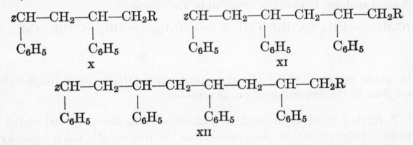

X                                          XI

XII

" head-to-tail " type, regardless of the nature of the reagent which induces it.   On the whole, this conclusion seems to be in satisfactory agreement with the facts.   The dimer that is formed when the polymerization is brought about by an electrophilic reagent like sulfuric acid has been identified[31] as the " head-to-tail " product XIII; and the

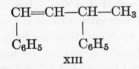

XIII

polymers of high molecular weight that are formed with various different reagents seem also to be predominantly " head-to-tail," although, in these, some randomness of orientation may possibly exist.[30]   (See the discussion of the polymerization by sodium at the end of this section.)

[31] See R. Stoermer and H. Kootz, *Ber.*, **61**, 2330 (1928).   J. Risi and D. Gauvin, *Can. J. Research*, **14**, 255 (1936).

Several features of the above mechanism merit further discussion. In the first place, each styrene molecule is considered to react initially at its terminal carbon atom or, in other words, at the end of its conjugated system, whether the polymerization is induced by an electrophilic, radical, or nucleophilic reagent. The reason for this identical behavior has already been given in Section 8·9 and need not be repeated here. It is of especial interest, however, that electrophilic and nucleophilic reagents attack styrene at the same position; this fact could hardly have been explained on the basis of the Class A structures of the activated complex, because the two types of reagent would be expected to be affected differently by the distribution of charge (whatever it may be) in the styrene molecule.

Although independent experimental evidence was advanced in Section 8·9 to show that electrophilic and radical reagents actually do attack styrene in the manner indicated above, similar evidence showing the behavior of nucleophilic reagents is more difficult to obtain, because a reagent of this type, if it is active enough to react at all, ordinarily polymerizes the styrene. A close analogy, however, is provided by the reaction[32]

$$(C_6H_5)_2C{=}CH_2 + C_6H_5C(CH_3)_2K \longrightarrow (C_6H_5)_2C{-}CH_2{-}C(CH_3)_2C_6H_5$$
$$\underset{K}{|}$$

in which the nucleophilic phenyl-$i$-propyl anion attacks the 1,1-diphenylethylene at the terminal position, as expected.

A further point of interest in connection with the proposed mechanism of polymerization of styrene is that the reagent $R$ is not necessarily regenerated but instead may be contained in the final polymer. In the latter event, it is therefore not strictly a catalyst, even though only a trace of it may be required to polymerize a large quantity of styrene. This, of course, is because a molecule of the polymer may contain an enormous number of styrene residues but only a single R. And finally, it should be noted that the polymerization must terminate in some manner, since it cannot continue forever. Clearly, therefore, there must be a further reaction, that we have not considered, which destroys the active electrophilic, radical, or nucleophilic center. The nature of this reaction, and hence of the "end group," is not completely established; it doubtless varies with the substance being polymerized and with the experimental conditions. This fact has no direct bearing, however, upon the problems in which we are primarily interested

[32] K. Ziegler and K. Bähr, *Ber.*, **61**, 253 (1928). For additional related reactions, see W. D. McPhee and E. G. Lindstrom, *J. Am. Chem. Soc.*, **65**, 2177 (1943), and further references given there.

at present, namely, the mechanism of the polymerization itself and the structure of the polymer, exclusive of the end groups.

The polymerization of styrene by metallic sodium may be of the radical type inasmuch as a sodium atom has a single unpaired electron. An alternative mechanism is possible, however. The first step in the polymerization may consist in the addition of two atoms of sodium to a molecule of styrene to give the substance XIV. This can now induce polymerization in the same way as the nucleophilic triphenylmethyl

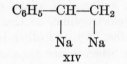

$$C_6H_5—CH—CH_2$$
$$|\qquad\quad|$$
$$Na\qquad Na$$

XIV

sodium, which it resembles closely. If this interpretation is correct, the next step in the polymerization should be the reaction of the disodium compound XIV with a second molecule of styrene to give the product XV. The reason for this " head-to-head," instead of the

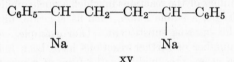

$$C_6H_5—CH—CH_2—CH_2—CH—C_6H_5$$
$$|\qquad\qquad\qquad\qquad\quad|$$
$$Na\qquad\qquad\qquad\qquad Na$$

XV

usual " head-to-tail," polymerization is that the terminal carbon atom of the disodium compound XIV must be the seat of its greatest nucleophilic activity, inasmuch as sodium methyl is more strongly nucleophilic than sodium benzyl. This second phase of the reaction is therefore analogous to the well-known " dimerizing addition " of sodium to 1,1-diphenylethylene, to yield the product XVI.[33] When once the substance XV has been formed, the subsequent reactions, which can

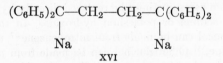

$$(C_6H_5)_2C—CH_2—CH_2—C(C_6H_5)_2$$
$$|\qquad\qquad\qquad\qquad|$$
$$Na\qquad\qquad\qquad Na$$

XVI

proceed in both directions simultaneously, should be " head-to-tail " as in the polymerization by triphenylmethyl sodium, so that the structure of the final polymer can be expressed as XVII. This interpretation provides a possible way of reconciling the chemical evidence sup-

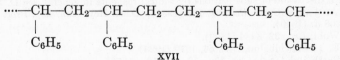

$$\cdots\!\cdots\!—CH—CH_2—CH—CH_2—CH_2—CH—CH_2—CH—\cdots\!\cdots$$
$$|\qquad\qquad|\qquad\qquad\qquad\quad|\qquad\qquad|$$
$$C_6H_5\qquad C_6H_5\qquad\qquad C_6H_5\qquad C_6H_5$$

XVII

[33] W. Schlenk, J. Appenrodt, A. Michael, and A. Thal, *Ber.,* **47,** 473 (1914).

porting a predominantly " head-to-tail " arrangement in polystyrene[30] with the fact that, when the polymerization by sodium is stopped at the dimeric stage by being conducted in alcoholic solution, the substance actually isolated is the " head-to-head " product, 1,4-diphenylbutane.[34]

**8·11   Orientation of Substituents in Aromatic Systems.**   It has been found that substitution in benzene and in other aromatic ring systems can be effected by reagents of all three possible types, electrophilic, radical, and nucleophilic.   In most of the common reactions, such as halogenation, nitration, sulfonation, diazo coupling, and so on, the substituting reagent is electrophilic, so that the aromatic compound itself must be nucleophilic.   On the other hand, in the Gomberg reaction,[35,36] both of the reagents are apparently radical; and in the hydrolysis, alcoholysis, and aminolysis of aryl halides, amines, ethers, and the like, the substituting reagent is nucleophilic.   (This list of reactions is intended to be illustrative rather than exhaustive; several further reactions belonging to these three types will be mentioned later.)

In the most familiar of the reactions in which a nucleophilic reagent attacks an aromatic molecule, a stable anion, such as chloride, nitrite, or the like, is displaced by the entering substituent.   (For examples, see the preceding paragraph.)   A number of further reactions have been found, however, in which a hydrogen atom, presumably in the form of a negative hydride ion, is displaced instead.   (This hydride ion, of course, is immediately, or perhaps simultaneously, transformed into either molecular hydrogen, $H_2$, by interaction with one of the reagents, or into water in the presence of the air or other oxidizing agent.)   Since the reactions of this latter type are relatively little known, and since, moreover, no comprehensive survey of them has appeared recently (such as has appeared for the corresponding reactions of the radical reagents),[36] a brief digression for the purpose of summarizing the pertinent facts would seem desirable here.

A hydrogen atom can sometimes be replaced directly by a hydroxyl group by the action of sodium or potassium hydroxide.   In this way, o- and a trace of p-nitrophenol can be made from nitrobenzene;[37] α-pyridone can be made from pyridine;[38] phloroglucinol can be made from phenol or from resorcinol;[39] and alizarin (1,2-dihydroxyanthraquinone) can be made from 1- or 2-hydroxyanthraquinone.[40]   In a similar way, by the action of so-

---

[34] T. Midgley, Jr., A. L. Henne, and H. M. Leicester, *J. Am. Chem. Soc.*, **58**, 1961 (1936).

[35] M. Gomberg and W. E. Bachmann, *J. Am. Chem. Soc.*, **46**, 2339 (1924).

[36] For a discussion of substitutions by radical reagents in general, see D. H. Hey and W. A. Waters, *Chem. Rev.*, **21**, 169 (1937); D. H. Hey, *Ann. Rep. Prog. Chem.*, **37**, pp. 268 ff. (1940).

[37] A. Wohl, *Ber.*, **32**, 3486 (1899).

[38] A. E. Tschitschibabin, *Ber.*, **56**, 1879 (1923).

[39] L. Barth and J. Schreder, *Ber.*, **12**, 417, 503 (1879).

[40] A. Baeyer and H. Caro, *Ber.*, **7**, 968 (1874).

dium or potassium amide, $\alpha$-aminopyridine can be made from pyridine;[41] 2- and 4-aminoquinoline can be made from quinoline;[41] 4-amino-2,6-dimethylpyridine can be made from 2,6-dimethylpyridine;[41] and $\alpha$-naphthylamine and 1,5-diaminonaphthalene can be made from naphthalene.[42] (Strangely enough, however, neither *o*- nor *p*-nitroaniline can be made from nitrobenzene in this way, because the reaction leads only to sodium benzene diazotate in rather small yield.)[43] Moreover, by the action of hydroxylamine, $\alpha$- and $\beta$-naphthylamine can be made in small yield from naphthalene;[44] 1-amino-2-nitronaphthalene can be made from 2-nitronaphthalene;[45] and 2,4-dinitroaniline and 2,4-dinitro-*m*-phenylenediamine can be made from *m*-dinitrobenzene.[45] And finally, by the action of potassium cyanide, 2-nitro-6-ethoxybenzonitrile can be made from *m*-dinitrobenzene (in alcoholic solution);[46] and isopurpuric acid (2-hydroxylamino-3,5-dicyano-4,6-dinitrophenol) can be made from picric acid.[47] The actual nucleophilic reagents in these different groups of reactions are doubtless the hydroxide ion, the amide ion, the hydroxylamine molecule, and the cyanide ion, respectively.

The above discussion is, of course, far from complete, but it should be sufficient to illustrate the nature and scope of the reactions in question. As the reader has possibly already observed, the aromatic substances which undergo the substitutions by these nucleophilic reagents are usually of rather special types and, more frequently than not, are relatively inert toward the usual electrophilic reagents (at any rate, at the points at which the substitutions actually occur). The reasons for these facts, and also for the observed orientations, should become apparent from the following discussion in this section.

It appears that the difficulty referred to in Section 8·1 in connection with the entropy of activation is relatively unimportant in the substitution reactions of aromatic compounds (at any rate, when the second reagent is electrophilic). In other words, if the two reactions being compared with each other are substitutions by the same reagent at two different positions in the same molecule, then $\Delta\Delta S^{\ddagger}$ is found experimentally to be very small.[3,48] Contrary to what might have been expected, this generalization seems to hold even when one of the

[41] For a general discussion of reactions of this type, see M. T. Leffler in *Organic Reactions* (R. Adams, editor-in-chief), John Wiley & Sons, New York, 1942, Chapter 4.

[42] F. Sachs, *Ber.*, **39**, 3006 (1906).

[43] F. W. Bergstrom and J. S. Buehler, *J. Am. Chem. Soc.*, **64**, 19 (1942).

[44] C. Graebe, *Ber.*, **34**, 1778 (1901).

[45] J. Meisenheimer and E. Patzig, *Ber.*, **39**, 2533 (1906).

[46] C. A. Lobry de Bruyn, *Rec. trav. chim.*, **2**, 205 (1883).   C. A. Lobry de Bruyn and J. W. van Geuns, *ibid.*, **23**, 26 (1904).

[47] W. Borsche and E. Böcker, *Ber.*, **37**, 4388 (1904).

[48] F. E. C. Sheffer and W. F. Brandsma, *Rec. trav. chim.*, **45**, 522 (1926).   A. E. Bradfield and B. Jones, *J. Chem. Soc.*, 1006 (1928).

reactions in question occurs in the *ortho* position with respect to a substituent already present.

As in the discussions of the addition reactions of unsaturated substances, we shall find it necessary here also to make rather detailed assumptions regarding the natures of the actual reagents, and regarding the mechanisms of the various reactions. As before, however, the exact forms in which we express these assumptions are of minor importance, provided only that they are not at variance with the fundamental principles upon which the treatment is based. In the bromination of benzene, for example, we shall consider that the reaction is initiated by the attack of a positive bromine ion upon the organic molecule. Actually, of course, just as in the addition of bromine to an olefine, the bromine may instead enter into the activated complex in the form of a polarized molecule, $\overset{+}{Br}\,\overset{-}{Br}$, or, more probably, of a complex with a catalyst molecule, such as $\overset{+}{Br}$—$\overset{-}{Br}$—$FeBr_3$, or the like. The essential point, however, is that the bromine atom is transferred to the product as a positive ion with only six electrons in its valence shell or, in more general terms, that it behaves as an electrophilic reagent. In a similar manner, we shall consider that in chlorination, iodination, nitration, sulfonation, and diazo coupling the actual reagents are, respectively, the ions or molecules Cl, I, $\overset{+}{NO_2^+}$, $\overset{+}{SO_3}$, and $ArN_2^+$. All these are clearly electrophilic since each either is a positive ion or has its reactive center at a relatively positive position, and since moreover each has an open sextet of electrons at its reactive center in at least one of its important resonating structures. Furthermore, we shall also consider that, in the Gomberg reaction, the actual reagent is a free aryl radical, which has an odd electron and is clearly a radical reagent; that in the hydrolysis, alcoholysis, and aminolysis reactions the reagents are, respectively, the clearly nucleophilic hydroxide ion, alkoxide ion, and amine molecule (or amide anion); and similarly for all further reactions that we shall have occasion to consider.

In addition to the foregoing assumptions regarding the actual reagents which attack the aromatic molecules, we shall have to make further assumptions regarding the natures of the activated complexes. A single example will suffice to illustrate the general principles that are common to all the reactions being considered. For the bromination of benzene, it seems probable that the structures which make the largest contributions to the activated complex are I–VII. (For the sake of simplicity, only the hydrogen atom being replaced in the reaction is written explicitly.) Of these, structures I and II are of Class A, whereas the others are of Class B. It is to be noted, however, that III and IV

resemble the Class A structures in that their relative stabilities are
determined largely by charge distributions rather than by the ease

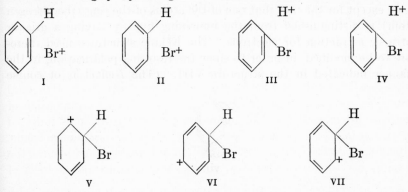

with which a pair of electrons can be brought by polarization to the
point of attack; consequently any further reference to Class B structures is to be considered to apply only to the ones like V, VI, and VII
in which the carbon atom attacked is joined by single bonds to four
different atoms, and in which the benzene ring has an *ortho* or *para*
quinoid structure.

In discussing the relative stabilities of the activated complexes for
various substitution reactions, we have the same two choices as in the
previous discussions of the addition reactions. On the one hand, we
can center our attention upon the Class A structures (including now
those like III and IV) and thereby emphasize the importance of the
electrostatic interactions; or, on the other hand, we can center our
attention upon the Class B structures (exclusive of III and IV) and
thereby emphasize the importance of the ease with which the necessary
polarizations can be produced. As before, these two points of view
seem always to lead to identical conclusions, except for certain reactions like those between radical reagents, for which the former leads
again to no very definite conclusions at all. We shall, accordingly,
lay the greater emphasis upon the second point of view in order to be
able to treat in a unified manner as large a number of reactions as possible. In other words, we shall consider that an aromatic substance
will react the more easily with an electrophilic, radical, or nucleophilic
reagent, the more easily an unshared pair of electrons, a single unpaired
electron, or an open sextet of electrons can be provided at the point of
attack.

The first aromatic compound to which we shall apply the above general considerations will be pyridine. Although not actually a benzene
derivative, this substance, on account of its simplicity, provides a par-

ticularly convenient introduction to the subject.  For our purposes, we may think of a molecule of pyridine as being just like one of benzene, except for the fact that one of the atoms of the ring (the nitrogen atom) is distinguished from the remaining five by having a greater intrinsic attraction for electrons.  The Kekulé structures need therefore to be modified, in order to show the resulting polarization, in the manner indicated in the structure VIII.  (The *I*-effect is of course

VIII

also operative.  It could be represented in the above structure by replacing each valence bond in it with a straight arrow pointing toward the nitrogen atom.  The figure would then, however, be unnecessarily cluttered up.  We shall, therefore, ignore the *I*-effect for the moment, but we shall return to it again shortly.)  The effect of the resonance in pyridine, as is indicated by the curved arrows in structure VIII, is to bring electrons from the $\alpha$ and $\gamma$ positions to the nitrogen atom. As a result, the attack by an electrophilic reagent will be made more difficult at the $\alpha$ and $\gamma$ positions, and that by a nucleophilic reagent will be made more easy.  Since, to the present approximation, the $\beta$ position is not affected, it follows that the orientation is $\beta$ for an electrophilic, and $\alpha$, $\gamma$ for a nucleophilic reagent.  Moreover, since the *I*-effect, which has been neglected heretofore, removes electrons to some extent also from the $\beta$ position, the further conclusion can be drawn that substitution by an electrophilic reagent should be more difficult, even in the favored $\beta$ position, than in benzene.  All these predictions are in agreement with experiment; nitration of pyridine, for example, occurs with great difficulty and leads to the $\beta$-nitro derivative, whereas the reaction with sodamide (in which the actual reagent must be the very strongly nucleophilic ion, $NH_2^-$, or its equivalent) occurs with comparative ease and leads to the $\alpha$-amino derivative.[41]  A further, and it is assumed completely comparable, example of orientation with respect to a nucleophilic reagent is given by the fact that $\alpha$- and $\gamma$-chloropyridine can be hydrolyzed by a base much more readily than either $\beta$-chloropyridine or chlorobenzene.

The nitration of pyridine is, of course, carried out in a strongly acidic medium, so that the entity nitrated must actually be the ion $C_5H_6N^+$.  On account of the positive charge upon the nitrogen atom in this ion, the electrons are drawn to the nitrogen from the rest of the molecule even more strongly than in the electrically neutral pyridine molecule itself. Consequently, the reactivity of all the positions, and expecially of the $\alpha$ and $\gamma$ positions, toward the electrophilic reagent is decreased to an even greater extent. A further point of interest in connection with the substitution reactions of pyridine is that sometimes the rule of orientation appears to change with temperature. For example, bromination leads largely to $\beta$-bromopyridine, as expected, at 300°, but to $\alpha$-bromopyridine at 500°. The explanation may be that, at the higher temperature, the bromine dissociates into bromine atoms, so that the substituting agent becomes radical instead of electrophilic. (See below.)

The purely qualitative arguments employed in the preceding paragraphs for the interpretation of the reactions of electrophilic and nucleophilic reagents with pyridine are no longer able to lead to a definite prediction when applied to the reactions of radical reagents. This is true even when the problem is considered from the viewpoint of the Class B structures. There is, indeed, no immediately obvious reason why a single unpaired electron could be provided more easily at any one position in this molecule than at any other. However, some semi-quantitative calculations have been made[49] which show unambiguously that an unpaired electron (as well as an open sextet) can be provided at the $\alpha$ or $\gamma$ position more easily than at the $\beta$ position. This conclusion also is in agreement with experiment, since, in the Gomberg reaction between sodium benzene diazotate and pyridine,[50] the product isolated in largest amount is $\alpha$-phenylpyridine. As usual, the theory does not permit a prediction to be made of the relative importance of the reactions at the $\alpha$ and $\gamma$ positions, but it does permit a distinction to be drawn between those two positions (considered as a unit) and the $\beta$ position.

Contrary to the statement often made in the older literature, appreciable quantities of the $\beta$ isomer (or of the *meta* isomer in reactions with benzene derivatives) often appear to be formed when substitution is brought about by a radical reagent.[51] We shall follow the customary convention, however, of considering the orientation to be $\alpha$, $\gamma$ (or *ortho, para*) whenever the amount of $\beta$ (or *meta*) isomer isolated is less than 40 per cent of the total. This figure of 40 per cent expresses the fact that only two of the five available positions at which substitution could occur are $\beta$ (or *meta*).

A further simple example is provided by the trimethylanilinium ion, $[C_6H_5N(CH_3)_3]^+$. The effect of the positively charged substit-

[49] G. W. Wheland, *J. Am. Chem. Soc.*, **64**, 900 (1942). In this paper references are given to several earlier calculations of similar type.

[50] J. W. Haworth, I. M. Heilbron, and D. H. Hey, *J. Chem. Soc.*, 349 (1940).

[51] D. H. Hey, *J. Chem. Soc.*, 1966 (1934). See also D. H. Hey, p. 282 of reference 36.

uent here must be to pull electrons away from, and hence to increase the electron affinity of, the carbon atom to which it is attached. The aromatic ring is accordingly qualitatively similar to that of pyridine, and the rules of orientation can be expected to be the same. Thus, substitution by an electrophilic reagent should be difficult and should occur in the *meta* (analogous to the $\beta$) position, and substitution by either a radical or a nucleophilic reagent should occur in the *ortho* and *para* positions (analogous to the $\alpha$ and $\gamma$, respectively). The first of these predictions is verified by the fact that nitration, for example, proceeds slowly and gives the *meta* isomer; the two final predictions, however, appear not to have been tested experimentally.

The structure IX for nitrobenzene shows that, just as with pyridine,

IX

an electrophilic reagent should attack the *meta* position with deactivation, and a nucleophilic reagent should attack the *ortho* and *para* positions with activation. (The terms " deactivation " and " activation " are applied to reactions which proceed less, or more, rapidly, respectively, than the corresponding reactions with benzene itself.) In considering the orientation with respect to a radical reagent, we can note first that the situation is somewhat analogous to that in pyridine, with the nitrogen atom in the ring of the latter substance being replaced here by the carbon atom which carries the nitro group. This is because the nitro group removes electrons from, and so increases the electron affinity of, the carbon atom to which it is attached. Consequently, we may expect a radical reagent to attack the *ortho* and *para* positions. A further factor which also leads to *ortho, para* orientation is that the Class B structures X and XI (where R represents the radical reagent) should be much more stable than the corresponding one, XII, which would be required for *meta* substitution, but which contains a formal bond. As should be apparent, the situation here is closely analogous to that encountered in Section 8·9, where it was found that a radical reagent attacks preferentially the *end* of a conjugated system. Again, all these predictions are in agreement with experiment. Nitration of nitrobenzene, for example, does indeed occur with some difficulty and lead predominantly to the *meta* derivative; the hydrolysis of *o*- or *p*-nitrochlorobenzene occurs much more easily than that of either *m*-nitrochlorobenzene or chlorobenzene; and the decomposition of benzoyl peroxide in nitrobenzene solution gives a mixture of *o*- and

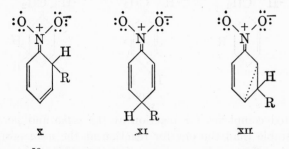

X                    XI                    XII

*p*-nitrobiphenyl.[52]  (In this last reaction, free phenyl radicals are apparently formed in the decomposition of the benzoyl peroxide.)

In toluene, if hyperconjugation of the methyl group with the benzene ring is neglected, the rules of orientation might be expected to be just the opposite of those applying to the trimethylanilinium ion. This is because here the substituent does not remove electrons from, but actually gives them up to, the benzene ring, as is shown by the observed direction of the dipole moment of the molecule.[53]  Thus, electrophilic reagents should attack the *ortho* and *para* positions with activation, whereas radical and nucleophilic reagents should attack the *meta* position with deactivation.  The predictions for the electrophilic and nucleophilic reagents are correct, but that for the radical reagents is incorrect.  For example, nitration of toluene gives largely the *ortho* and *para* isomers, and the reaction takes place more easily than the nitration of benzene;[54] methyl groups make the replacement of a halogen atom by the action of a nucleophilic reagent more difficult, and are especially effective in that regard when *ortho* or *para* to the point of attack;[55] and the decomposition of benzoyl peroxide in the presence of toluene gives mostly *p*-methylbiphenyl.[56]  The explanation of the discrepancy with the radical reagents is presumably to be found in the neglect of hyperconjugation.  In reactions with radical reagents at the *ortho* and *para* positions, the structures XIII and XIV (where R represents a radical reagent) can contribute to the activated complex, whereas, in a reaction at the *meta* position the only analogous struc-

[52] D. H. Hey, *J. Chem. Soc.*, 1966 (1934).

[53] J. W. Williams, *Fortschr. Chem. Physik physik. Chem.*, **20**, 257 (1930), Table 11.

[54] C. K. Ingold, A. Lapworth, E. Rothstein, and D. Ward, *J. Chem. Soc.*, 1959 (1931).

[55] H. Lindemann and A. Pabst, *Ann.*, **462**, 24 (1928).   N. Campbell, W. Anderson, and J. Gilmore, *J. Chem. Soc.*, 446 (1940).

[56] W. Dietrich, *Helv. chim. acta*, **8**, 149 (1925).

tures that are possible are some relatively unstable ones with formal bonds, like XV. Consequently, as a result of the hyperconjugation,

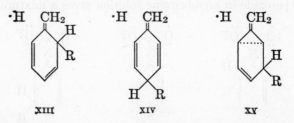

XIII          XIV          XV

the activated complexes for reaction at the *ortho* and *para* positions are more stable than the one for reaction at the *meta* position. The fact that the effect of hyperconjugation is sufficient to outweigh the opposing effect of the transfer of the electrons to the ring is consistent with approximate calculations.[49] It is to be noted that the hyperconjugation does not necessarily alter the conclusions reached for the reactions with electrophilic and nucleophilic reagents, as is evident from a consideration of the structure XVI. In this, the arrows are

XVI

drawn in the direction suggested by the observed direction of the dipole moment of the molecule.

In benzyl chloride, XVII, benzal chloride, XVIII, and benzotrichloride, XIX, the electronegative chlorine atoms oppose the shift of electrons toward the ring. As a result, the proportion of *meta* isomer

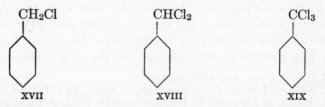

XVII          XVIII          XIX

formed in the reactions with electrophilic reagents increases progressively as the number of chlorine atoms increases, as is shown in Table 8·1. A similar steady transition between the two types of orientation

TABLE 8·1

PER CENTS OF META ISOMER FORMED IN NITRATIONS

| Substance Nitrated | $n = 0$ | $n = 1$ | $n = 2$ | $n = 3$ |
|---|---|---|---|---|
| $C_6H_5—CCl_nH_{3-n}$ [a] | 4.4 | 4.2 | 33.8 | 64.5 |
| | | 11.6 | 32.8–33.3 | 48.3–48.6 |
| $C_6H_5—(CH_2)_n \overset{+}{N}(CH_3)_3$ [b] | 100 | 88 | 19 | 5 |

[a] For this series of substances, the figures in the top row are those of M. A. F. Holleman, *Rec. trav. chim.*, **33**, 1 (1914); the ones in the second row are those of B. Flürscheim and E. L. Holmes, *J. Chem. Soc.*, 1607 (1928).

[b] These figures are taken from the compilation of C. K. Ingold, *Rec. trav. chim.*, **48**, 797 (1929).

is illustrated by the series of ions, XX–XXIII. The trimethylanilinium ion, XX, is attacked in the *meta* position by an electrophilic reagent, as we have already seen, but the ion XXIII is attacked predominantly in the *ortho* and *para* positions, and the intermediate ions, XXI and XXII, exhibit intermediate behaviors. (See Table 8·1.) Ap-

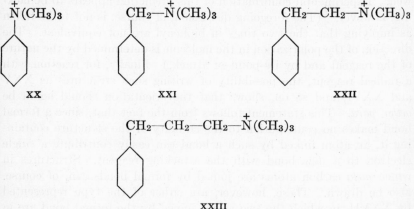

parently here, the inductive effect which results from the attraction of the positively charged nitrogen atom for the electrons is damped fairly rapidly as it is transmitted along the saturated chain. The natural tendency of alkyl groups to produce *ortho, para* orientation with respect to electrophilic reagents, therefore, gradually assumes greater importance as the chain is lengthened, and it finally becomes predominant. No corresponding data, exhibiting the gradual modification of orienting effect, seem to be available for reactions in which the aromatic molecule is attacked by radical or nucleophilic reagents.

Aryl, like alkyl, groups are also *ortho, para* directing toward electrophilic reagents. The structure XXIV for biphenyl, for example, shows that the required unshared pair of electrons can indeed be readily provided at the *ortho* and *para* positions (of the ring at the right of the figure as drawn) in consequence of the polarization during the reaction.

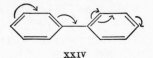

XXIV

The same structure shows also that open sextets of electrons can also be readily provided at the *ortho* and *para* positions (of the ring at the left of the figure in this case).   Consequently, the phenyl group should

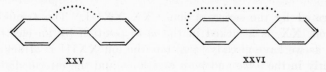

XXV                                    XXVI

be *ortho, para* directing for substitution by a nucleophilic reagent as well.   Experimental confirmation of this prediction appears to be lacking, however.   (The foregoing discussion, of course, is not to be taken as implying that the two rings in biphenyl are not equivalent.   The direction of the polarization in the molecule is determined by the nature of the reagent and by its point of attack.)   Finally, for reaction with a radical reagent, the possibility of writing such structures as XXV and XXVI, and so on, shows that the orientation should again be *ortho, para*.   This statement follows from the fact that, since a formal bond makes no contribution to the stability of the structure containing it, an atom linked by such a bond can easily contribute a single electron to a new bond with the attacking reagent.   Structures in which *meta* carbon atoms are joined by formal bonds can, of course, also be drawn.   These, however, are either of the type represented by XXVII, in which the two atoms joined by the formal bond are in the same ring, or of the type represented by XXVIII, which is rela-

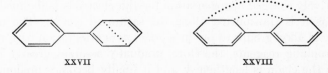

XXVII                                   XXVIII

tively unstable in consequence of the additional formal bond.   In neither event, however, could these further structures be expected to have as great an effect upon the orientation as those like XXV and XXVI.   This prediction is verified by the fact that the decomposition of benzoyl peroxide in biphenyl as solvent leads to *p*-terphenyl.[57]

[57] H. Gelissen and P. H. Hermans, *Ber.*, **58**, 285 (1925).

Naphthalene is a further substance which can be expected to exhibit the same orientation for all three types of reagent. The arguments leading to this conclusion are somewhat more complicated than those outlined above in connection with biphenyl (without, however, being essentially different), and so they will be left for the interested reader to work out for himself. Experimentally, it has been found that nitric acid, diazotized methyl anthranilate[58] (in the Gomberg reaction), and sodamide[42] all attack at the $\alpha$ position. It is of particular interest that the identical orientation for these widely different reagents could hardly have been explained on the basis of any assumed distribution of charge in the unreacting naphthalene molecule. (The sulfonation of naphthalene at the $\beta$ position at high temperatures seems to be a matter of equilibrium rather than of rate, since the $\alpha$-sulfonic acid is apparently formed first, just as at low temperatures, but then " rearranges " by a mechanism involving desulfonation and subsequent resulfonation to the more stable product.)

In chlorobenzene, there are two different effects that need to be considered separately. The first of these results from the fact that the chlorine atom is strongly electronegative, and so pulls electrons away from the carbon atom to which it is attached. If this displacement of charge were the only factor to be considered, the orientation should be just as in pyridine or in the trimethylanilinium ion — *meta* with deactivation for electrophilic reagents, and *ortho*, *para* with activation for radical or nucleophilic reagents. The situation could then be represented by the structure XXIX. The second effect to be considered results from the fact that the chlorine atom has an unshared pair of electrons and so can initiate the $R$-effect symbolized by the structure XXX. If this displacement of charge were the only factor involved, the orientation would be *ortho*, *para* with activation for an electrophilic reagent,

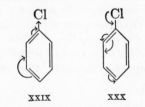

XXIX            XXX

indeterminate for a radical reagent, and *meta* with deactivation for a nucleophilic reagent. (However, resonance with structures like XXXI might favor *ortho*, *para* orientation for a radical reagent. Cf. the somewhat analogous situation in the peroxide-induced addition of hydrogen bromide to vinyl chloride, discussed in Section 8·6.) The two effects,

[58] W. S. M. Grieve and D. H. Hey, *J. Chem. Soc.*, 108 (1938).

due respectively to the electronegativity and to the unshared pair of electrons of the chlorine atom, are largely in conflict with each other.

XXXI

We cannot, therefore, predict with any assurance what the actual orientation will be for any of the different types of reagent.   Experimentally, it is found that the orientation is *ortho, para* with deactivation for an electrophilic reagent and *ortho, para* for a radical reagent.   Little is known about the orientation for a nucleophilic reagent.   It is evident, therefore, that some sort of compromise between the opposed effects is reached, so that each determines some features of the total picture. This result, although it could not have been foreseen in its entirety, is eminently reasonable.[49]

For phenol and aniline, the theoretical treatment is the same as for chlorobenzene.   Here also, there are two opposed effects, and we cannot tell a priori which will predominate.   In these substances, however, the *R*-effect wins out completely, at any rate as far as substitution by an electrophilic reagent is concerned, so that the orientation for such a reagent is *ortho, para*, with very great activation.   This result, although again it could not have been foreseen, is nevertheless entirely reasonable.[49]

In connection with the present difference in behavior between chlorobenzene, on the one hand, and phenol and aniline, on the other, it is of interest to recall a conclusion reached in Section 5·4.   Attention was called there to the fact that the dipole moment of *p*-nitroaniline requires a relatively large contribution from a structure like XXXII, whereas the moment of *p*-nitrochlorobenzene requires only a small contribution from the analogous structure XXXIII.   It appears, therefore, that the unshared pair of elec-

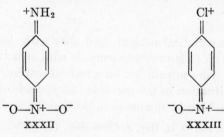

XXXII                               XXXIII

trons on the nitrogen atom of an amino group is better able to initiate an *R*-effect than is any of the three unshared pairs on a chlorine atom. On this basis, the difference in orienting effect under discussion is seen to be, at any rate, in the expected direction.

We are now in position to consider in greater detail the problem that was briefly mentioned in Section 8·2, in connection with the reactions of 2,7-dihydroxynaphthalene. The point of interest is that this substance couples readily with a diazonium compound at the 1 (or 8) position, but cannot be forced to couple at the 3 (or 6) position.[7] In order to understand this striking experimental result, let us consider the natures of the activated complexes that would be involved in the reactions at the 1 and at the 3 position. As usual, we shall center our attention principally upon the Class B structures; and moreover, since the *R*-effect, which is made possible by the hydroxyl group, seems to be an essential feature of the coupling reaction, we shall consider only those structures in which the oxygen atom is joined to the naphthalene nucleus by a double bond. In any event, structures of this type would be expected to be especially stable, and so especially important, since they contain one more bond than any of the others. With these simplifications, then, we can write the structures XXXIV and XXXV for coupling in the 1 position, but only the single structure XXXVI for coupling in the 3 position. It will be remembered that in diazo coupling

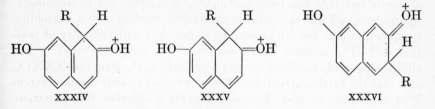

the active reagent, which is presumably the diazonium cation and which is abbreviated as simply "R" in structures XXXIV–XXXVI, is electrophilic and so contributes no electrons to the C–R bond. (The situations for coupling in the 8 and 6 positions are of course equivalent to the two above and need not be discussed further.) It is now apparent that the activated complex for coupling at the 1 position must be much the more stable of the two, since it alone retains the full resonance energy of an intact benzene ring. If, for example, the activation energies for the two reactions differed by just this resonance energy, say 36 kcal per mole, the ratio of the rate constants would be as about $10^{26}$ to 1. This enormous value is, of course, only an upper limit and cannot be taken very seriously. When the fact is taken into account that actually the

ignored Class A structures must be important in the activated complexes
and that, moreover, the numerous further Class B structures with merely
single bonds between the oxygen and carbon atoms are involved, the
ratio must be much smaller.    There can be no reasonable doubt, however, that it still is very large, so that the coupling should occur with
tremendously greater ease at the 1 (or 8) position than at the 2 (or 6)
position, as is observed.    In fact, a value of about 10.4 kcal per mole for
the difference in energy of activation, and hence of about $3 \times 10^7$ for the
ratio of rate constants, has been derived[49] by a semiquantitative method,
in which all the Class B structures (but not the Class A structures) are
taken into account.    This figure cannot be relied upon as even approximately correct numerically, but the fact that it is still very large is
significant.    It is especially to be noted that the conclusion that 2,7-di-
hydroxynaphthalene should couple only in the 1 (or 8) position has been
derived without the necessity of postulating that the unreacting molecule is fixed rigidly in the Erlenmeyer structure XXXVII.

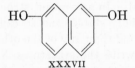

XXXVII

A somewhat similar situation, in which a fixation of bonds in an
aromatic molecule has been postulated, is encountered in 5-hydroxy-
hydrindene, XXXVIII.    In this substance, coupling with a diazonium
compound occurs readily at position 6, but only with difficulty at position 4.[59]    The original interpretation of the experimental data was
that the molecule was held more or less rigidly in the structure XXXIX,
and that the further structure XL was involved to only a minor extent
if at all.    We can now, however, provide a different interpretation,

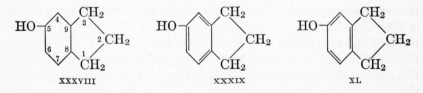

which makes no such drastic assumption regarding the unreacting
molecule.    With the same neglect as before of all Class A structures
and of those Class B structures in which there is only a single bond
between the oxygen and carbon atoms, we can write the structures XLI

[59] W. H. Mills and I. G. Nixon, *J. Chem. Soc.*, 2510 (1930).    See also L. F. Fieser
and W. C. Lothrop, *J. Am. Chem. Soc.*, **58**, 2050 (1936); **59**, 945 (1937).

and XLII for the activated complexes involved in the reactions at positions 6 and 4, respectively.    There is no obvious difference in resonance

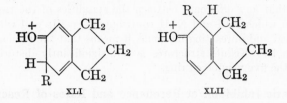

XLI                              XLII

energy possible here to make one activated complex more stable than the other, but a difference in bond energies seems reasonable.    In structures XLI and XLII, the bond between carbon atoms 8 and 9 is represented as single and double, respectively.    Mills and Nixon[59] suggested that the bond angles that are enforced by the fused five-membered ring are such as to make the structure XLI, in which the bond in question is single, more stable than XLII, in which it is double.    The further suggestion, pointing in the same direction, has been made[49] that the $C_8$—$C_9$ bond is stretched by a spring-like action of the five-membered ring, so that its length is nearer to the single-bond value than in, say, phenol.    In either event, the structure XLI is more stable than XLII, and consequently the coupling can be expected to occur more readily in position 6 than in position 4, as is observed.    Again this prediction must be modified by the inclusion of the Class A, and of the remaining Class B, structures in the discussion.    The qualitative aspects remain unaltered, however, and are probably significant.    It is to be noted that, as in the discussion of 2,7-dihydroxynaphthalene, no assumption has been made regarding any extreme fixation of the bonds in the unreacting molecule.

Recent work has suggested that the Mills-Nixon effect is much smaller than was originally thought and may actually be non-existent.    Arnold and Evans,[60] for example, in a study of the acid strengths of related nitroxylenols and nitrohydrindenols, could find no evidence of any fixation of bonds; and Kossiakoff and Springall,[61] in an electron-diffraction investigation of a related dibromoxylene and dibromohydrindene could find no appreciable variation in the carbon-bromine bond distances or in any of the comparable bond angles.    On the other hand, Arnold and Zaugg[62] found small variations in the oxidation-reduction potentials of related quinones, which they interpreted as showing some fixation of bonds in the hydrindene derivative.    The significance of these various methods of attack is not entirely clear (in particular, we have no completely reliable way of predicting what the effect of

[60] R. T. Arnold and R. L. Evans, *J. Am. Chem. Soc.*, **62**, 556 (1940).
[61] A. Kossiakoff and H. D. Springall, *J. Am. Chem. Soc.*, **63**, 2223 (1941).
[62] R. T. Arnold and H. E. Zaugg, *J. Am. Chem. Soc.*, **63**, 1317 (1941).

a fixation of bonds would be upon the bond distances in question or upon the bond angles), but, in any event, it seems certain that no great fixation exists. With reference to the original experiments of Mills and Nixon, this conclusion means that any difference between the stabilities of the two activated complexes to which XLI and XLII contribute is small; and with reference to the isolated and unreacting molecule, it means that the normal resonance between the two Kekulé structures is not significantly disturbed by the presence of the five-membered ring.

**8·12   Steric Inhibition of Resonance and Rates of Reaction.**   The hydrolysis and other similar reactions of an aryl halide, such as chlorobenzene, for example, proceed with greater difficulty than the corresponding reactions of any comparable alkyl halide.   A partial explanation of this relative inertness may be that the unreacting molecule is stabilized by resonance with structures, of which I is a typical example, in which the chlorine atom is joined to the ring by a double bond.   The activated complex, however, has smaller possibilities for resonance,

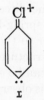

since no Class B structures analogous to I can be written.   Consequently, the activation energy should be somewhat higher and the rate should be somewhat lower, than for the corresponding reaction of an alkyl halide, in which no resonance at all of the present type is involved. (Obviously, this same explanation may be partly responsible also for the inertness of the unsaturated aliphatic halides of the vinyl chloride type.) However, the stabilization of the unreacting molecules by the resonance under consideration can amount at most to only a very few kilocalories per mole, so that this present effect is much too small to be responsible for all of the great difference in reactivity.   A further factor which may be involved in the reactions of the aromatic halides (but which cannot be in those of the vinyl halides) is that the resonance of the benzene ring must be largely destroyed in the Class B structures of the activated complexes; this fact should decrease the stabilities of these complexes. And finally, attention should be called to the possibility that the mechanism of substitution at an unsaturated atom may be sufficiently different from that at a saturated atom to make a direct comparison between the rates of the two types of reaction of questionable significance.   (Cf. Section 8·1.)

Whatever the complete explanation of the relative inertness of the aryl halides may be, however, it is an important empirical fact that a nitro group in a position *ortho* or *para* with respect to the halogen atom enables the reactions under discussion to take place much more easily. In the preceding section we accounted for this activating effect of a nitro group (for substitution by a nucleophilic reagent) on the basis of resonance with quinoid structures like II.   Since such structures are most

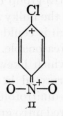

II

stable when the nitro group lies in the plane of the benzene ring, we can anticipate that the activating effect of the nitro group would be decreased if the molecule could be forced out of the planar configuration.   A certain amount of experimental evidence is available in confirmation of this expectation.   The data quoted below are of varying types, but they are all directly comparable since they refer to reactions in which substitution by a nucleophilic reagent is facilitated by an *ortho* or *para* nitro group.

When 2,5-dinitro-*m*-xylene, III, is heated in a sealed tube with aqueous ammonia, the nitro group in position 2 is replaced by an amino group to give the nitroxylidine, IV.[63]   At first sight, this reaction seems

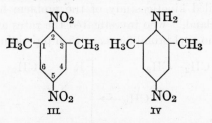

highly anomalous, because one might have predicted that the nitro group in position 5 ought to be the more easily replaced of the two.   In the first place, the 5 nitro group is less surrounded by the methyl radicals and so is more open to attack by the ammonia molecule; and, in the second place, methyl groups are known to be more effective in deactivating an aromatic molecule for substitution by a nucleophilic reagent when they are *ortho* or *para*, than when they are *meta*, to the position at which

[63] K. Ibbotson and J. Kenner, *J. Chem. Soc.*, **123**, 1260 (1923).

the reaction occurs.[55]   The fact that the 2 nitro group is actually the one replaced, in spite of the steric hindrance and in spite of the unfavorable positions of the methyl groups, is readily understandable, however, on the basis of an inhibition of resonance.   Position 2 is, in fact, activated to the full extent for reaction with a nucleophilic reagent, because the nitro group in position 5 is free to assume the necessary coplanar configuration;   position 5, on the other hand, is activated to a much smaller extent, because the nitro group in position 2 is effectively held out of the plane of the ring by the bulky methyl groups.   The observed course of the reaction, although it could hardly have been predicted in advance, is therefore entirely reasonable.

Several further reactions, which likewise appear anomalous at first sight, but which can be interpreted in a similar manner, have been reported.   For example, in 2,3-dinitrotoluene, V, and 2,5-dinitrotoluene, VI, the apparently more hindered nitro group, *ortho* to the methyl group, is replaced the more rapidly by an amino group on treatment with

aqueous ammonia.[64]   In each of these reactions, the group replaced is the one which is *ortho* or *para* to the nitro group that encounters the less hindrance to taking up the coplanar configuration.

A rather detailed kinetic study of the problem has been made by Spitzer and Wheland,[65] who investigated the rates at which a number of nitro and cyano aryl bromides react with piperidine:

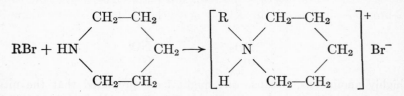

They found, for example, that the rate constant for 2-nitro-5-bromo-*m*-xylene, VII, was only about one thirty-fifth as great as that for *p*-nitro-bromobenzene, VIII.   In order to exclude the possibility that this result might be due merely to the recognized deactivating effect of the methyl

[64] H. Burton and J. Kenner, *J. Chem. Soc.*, **119**, 1047 (1921).   J. Kenner and M. Parkin, *ibid.*, **117**, 852 (1920).
[65] W. C. Spitzer and G. W. Wheland, *J. Am. Chem. Soc.*, **62**, 2995 (1940).

groups, they studied also the corresponding reactions of 2-cyano-5-bromo-*m*-xylene, IX, and *p*-cyanobromobenzene, X.  The rate constant for the first of these two substances was found to be about one-third as

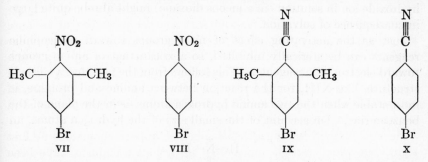

VII          VIII          IX          X

great as that for the second.   Inasmuch as resonance of the type summarized in structure XI cannot be inhibited sterically (on account of the linearity of the cyano group), this figure provides a measure of the direct

XI

deactivating effect of the methyl groups.   Since the deactivation in the nitro compound was considerably greater, it appears that, in this substance, the inhibition of resonance must be important.   The proof is not as complete as might be desired, however, because it was found that 2-bromo-5-nitro-*m*-xylene, XII, reacted  much  more  slowly  than  its

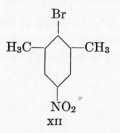

XII

isomer, VII.  For this discrepancy, the explanation was offered that the steric hindrance caused by the methyl groups ought to be very large in view of the size of the piperidine molecule.   In examining this possibility, Spitzer and Wheland showed that, even toward hydroxide ion, the bromonitroxylene XII was less reactive than its isomer VII. The significance of this result is not completely clear, however, since the hydroxide ion in solution (in aqueous dioxane) might also be quite large in consequence of solvation.

Just as the activating effect of nitro groups toward nucleophilic reagents can be sterically inhibited, so also can that of amino groups toward electrophilic reagents. This follows from the fact that a Class B structure, like XIII, for the reaction between aniline and bromine, is most stable when the two amino hydrogen atoms lie in the plane of the benzene ring. On account of the small size of the hydrogen atoms, an

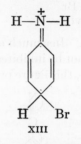

XIII

observable effect of this sort could hardly be expected in substances possessing only the unsubstituted amino group, —NH₂, but it should be demonstrable in analogous substances with, say, a dimethylamino group, —N(CH₃)₂.

It should perhaps be mentioned that the present discussion does not require complete coplanarity of the nitrogen atom and the three atoms joined to it, since an appreciable (even though probably smaller) effect could result from any reasonably close approximation to coplanarity. The essential point at issue is that the hydrogen atoms of the amino group (or the radicals which replace them) should lie on the same side of the benzene ring if the resonance under discussion is to have a great effect upon the rates.

Considerable evidence is to be found in the literature which confirms this expectation. For example, dimethyl-*vic-m*-xylidine, XIV, is reported[66] not to react with nitrous acid, aldehydes, or diazonium com-

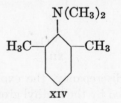

XIV

[66] P. Friedlaender, *Monatsh.*, **19**, 627 (1898).

pounds. Since these three types of reaction are characteristic of very highly activated aromatic substances, a small inhibition of the resonance might be sufficient to produce the observed result.

Brown and his co-workers[67] have made a careful study of hydrogen exchange in aromatic amines. In the reaction

$$(CH_3)_2NC_6H_5 + D^+ \longrightarrow (CH_3)_2NC_6H_4D + H^+$$

the deuteron, $D^+$, must be an electrophilic reagent, since it can attack only at those positions at which an unshared pair of electrons can be provided. This conclusion is confirmed by the fact that exchange reactions of the above type have been found[68] to obey the customary rules of orientation for electrophilic reagents. Consequently, the rate of exchange should decrease if the resonance of the dimethylamino group with the ring is inhibited. For example, the rate could be expected to decrease in the order: *o*-fluorodimethylaniline > *o*-chlorodimethylaniline > *o*-bromodimethylaniline, as the size of the *ortho* substituent increases. This prediction has been confirmed experimentally.[67] More conclusive evidence pointing in the same direction can be derived from the further order of decreasing rate of reaction: N-methylindoline, XV > N-methyltetrahydroquinoline, XVI > N-methyl-homo-tetrahydroquinoline, XVII. In the first of these, the five-membered ring holds the molecule rigidly in the planar configuration; in the second, the puckered six-membered ring prevents planarity from being achieved;

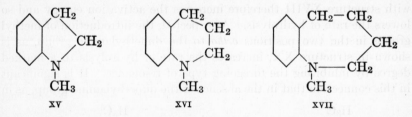

and, in the third, the seven-membered ring makes the departure from planarity still greater. The observed decrease in rate of reaction therefore parallels the decrease in resonance.

In the examples considered so far, the resonance that is inhibited is of such nature that it would otherwise have facilitated reaction. The inhibition therefore has the result of slowing the reaction. The opposite situation, however, is also conceivable, in which the resonance would have made the reaction more difficult. In such an event, an inhibition

[67] W. G. Brown, A. H. Widiger, and N. J. Letang, *J. Am. Chem. Soc.*, **61**, 2597 (1939).

[68] A. P. Best and C. L. Wilson, *J. Chem. Soc.*, 28 (1938).

of resonance must make the reaction faster. It is possible, for example, that the relative ease of dinitrating mesitylene (as compared with benzene) is due not only to the direct activating effect of the methyl groups for the reaction with the electrophilic reagent but also to a decrease in the deactivating effect of the first nitro group after it has been introduced.[69] This is, of course, just the converse of the situation considered above in which the methyl groups decrease the activating effect of a nitro group for substitution by a nucleophilic reagent.

A further example, which has been more carefully examined, has to do with the rates of saponification of the esters of aminobenzoic acids.[70] In the alkaline hydrolysis of an ester, an important structure contributing to the activated complex is supposed to be one in which a hydroxide ion has become attached to the carbonyl carbon atom.[71] Consequently, although the unreacting molecule of ethyl *p*-dimethylaminobenzoate can resonate with structures like XVIII (along with other more important ones) no corresponding resonance is possible in the activated complex, for which only such Class B structures as XIX can be drawn (in addition to those with normal Kekulé structures of the ring). The resonance

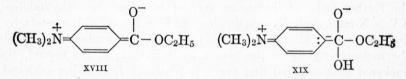

with structure XVIII therefore increases the activation energy and so lowers the rate of hydrolysis. As expected, the introduction of methyl groups in the two positions *ortho* to the dimethylamino group, as is shown in structure XX, increases the rate of hydrolysis to a marked degree by inhibiting the foregoing type of resonance. It is significant in this connection that in the absence of the dimethylamino group, as in

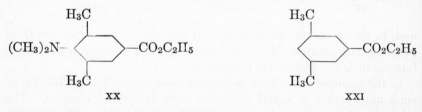

the ester XXI, the methyl groups have no such striking effect upon the rate of hydrolysis. We have here, therefore, an example in which an

[69] G. Baddeley, *Nature*, **144**, 444 (1939). Several further simple examples of the present type are given in this paper.

[70] F. H. Westheimer and R. P. Metcalf, *J. Am. Chem. Soc.*, **63**, 1339 (1941).

[71] See, for example, L. P. Hammett, pp. 354 ff. of reference 3.

effect that might be regarded as a special type of "steric hindrance" makes a reaction go faster.

**8·13 Molecular Rearrangements.**[72] The field of molecular rearrangements is nearly as broad as that of organic chemistry itself. Consequently, we shall make no attempt here to cover the whole subject, but we shall content ourselves instead with a brief discussion of a limited number of special problems in which the concept of resonance is particularly helpful.

A large number of rearrangements appear to take place by what is called the Whitmore mechanism.[73] Although the details necessarily vary to some extent from example to example, the essential features that are common to all the rearrangements of this class can be stated with reference to the type structure I. In this structure, B and C represent single atoms, whereas A may represent either an atom or (more frequently) a radical. The dots indicating electrons are written to show

quently) a radical. The dots indicating electrons are written to show that atom B has its full octet, but that C has only a sextet, of electrons in the valence shell; these electrons are usually, but not necessarily, shared with further atoms or groups which are not represented explicitly in the structure. Now, the essential feature of the Whitmore mechanism of rearrangements is that a structure of the general type I is produced in some way in an initial step of the reaction. The instability produced by the presence of only a sextet of electrons on the atom C is then partially relieved by the migration of A, *together with its pair of electrons*, to produce the structure II, in which the sextet is now upon the atom B. In the concluding step, the instability which still remains in the structure

$$\overset{\cdot\cdot}{B}—\overset{\cdot\cdot}{C}—A$$
$$\text{II}$$

II is relieved by an appropriate redistribution of the valence electrons, with or without the loss of an ion to, or the acquisition of an ion from, the solution. The various steps need not take place successively, since they could all occur simultaneously.

The principles of the above mechanism can be made clearer by a discussion of specific examples. When pinacol, III, is treated with sulfuric

[72] For a recent general survey of molecular rearrangements, see E. S. Wallis in H. Gilman, *Organic Chemistry*, John Wiley & Sons, New York, 1st ed., 1938, vol. I, Chapter 8; 2nd ed., 1943, vol. I, Chapter 12.

[73] F. C. Whitmore, *J. Am. Chem. Soc.*, **54**, 3274 (1932).

acid, it is transformed into pinacolone. The first step in the rearrangement is considered to be the removal, by the acid, of a hydroxyl group in the form of a hydroxide ion. The organic cation, IV, which is thereby formed, is then changed into V by the migration of a methyl group with its pair of electrons. In the concluding step, this latter ion loses a

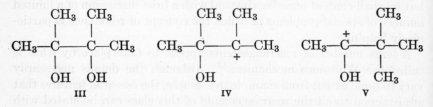

proton to the solution and becomes the final product, pinacolone, which is a resonance hybrid, receiving a small contribution from VI and probably a much larger one from the conventional structure VII. Similarly, in the Hofmann rearrangement of the acid amide, VIII, to an isocyanate by the action of bromine and sodium hydroxide, the

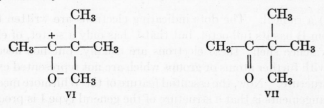

reaction is considered to proceed through the phases represented by structures IX–XIII. The first two of these structures (IX and X) correspond to stable substances which can be isolated. The last two (XII and XIII) are structures which contribute through resonance to the state of the isocyanate. (Structure XII, of course, is very unstable and so is very unimportant; it is mentioned here only because of its logical position in the present interpretation of the reaction.) The Lossen rearrangement of the hydroxamic acid, XIV, and the Curtius rearrange-

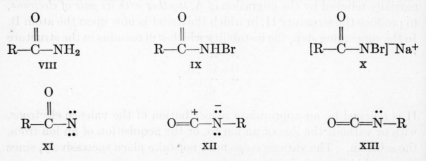

ment of the azide, XV, likewise lead to the isocyanate and probably proceed through essentially the same mechanism. These two sub-

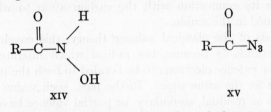

stances, by the loss of a molecule of water or of nitrogen, respectively, can in fact produce the same hypothetical intermediate, XI, as above, and then the remaining steps can proceed exactly as in the Hofmann rearrangement of the amide.

It would carry us too far afield to discuss at length the experimental evidence that can be brought forward in support of the mechanism described above,[72, 73] or to attempt to account for the driving forces that cause the rearrangements to proceed at all. The question which we shall consider here is that of the mechanism by which the migrating group A (of structure I) and its associated pair of electrons lose contact with the atom B and become joined instead to C (as in structure II). In the first place, attention should be called to the fact that A apparently does not break off from the rest of the molecule, in the form of either a radical or an ion, and then recombine again at a different position. The most conclusive experimental evidence pointing toward this conclusion is derived from a study of the Hofmann rearrangement of the amide XVI.[74] This substance can be obtained in an optically active form in

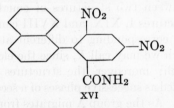

consequence of the restricted rotation about the bond between the benzene and naphthalene rings. If the amide which is subjected to the rearrangement is optically active, the resulting isocyanate is found also to be active and not appreciably racemized. This fact shows conclusively that the molecule cannot have broken up into two parts during the rearrangement, because, if it had done so, rotation about the bond in question would have been possible during the time that the two parts were separate, and so more or less racemization should have occurred.

[74] E. S. Wallis and W. W. Moyer, *J. Am. Chem. Soc.*, **55**, 2598 (1933).

It follows, therefore, that the radical, as it migrates, must already have become attached to the nitrogen atom, as in the isocyanate, before it entirely loses its connection with the carbon atom to which it was originally joined in the amide.

On the basis of the classical valence theory, this conclusion is not easily understandable because the radical which migrates does not have sufficient valence electrons to be bonded to both the nitrogen and carbon atoms at the same time. In the past, such vague and poorly defined terms as residual, secondary, or partial valence have been used for the description of situations of this kind. At the present time, however, the theory of resonance permits a more precise picture of the rearrangement to be drawn. If, for simplicity, we return to the structures I and II, we can visualize the transition between them in the following way. At the outset, the hypothetical intermediate which has been described hitherto by the structure I must actually receive also a negligibly small contribution from XVII. (As in Section 8·1, and for the same reason, we shall ignore here the distinction between formal and effective bonds.) Similarly, at the conclusion of the transition, the intermediate which has been described by the structure II must actually receive a negligibly small contribution from XVIII. At some intermediate time while the group A is in the process of migrating, the

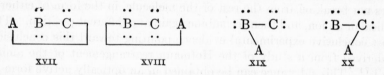

resonance occurs between two structures of equal stability like XIX and XX. Now, structures I, XIX, and XVIII can be regarded merely as successive phases, corresponding to different atomic positions, of a single structure, which we may call $R$, since the electrons are paired in the same way in each; moreover, the structures XVII, XX, and II can likewise be regarded as successive phases of a second single structure, which we may call $S$. As the group A migrates from the atom B to the atom C, the structure $R$, which was originally *the* structure of the system, becomes less important in a continuous manner and ultimately becomes negligible. Conversely, the structure $S$, which was originally negligible, achieves greater importance in a continuous manner and ultimately becomes *the* structure. At no time is the group A free from the remainder of the molecule. The similarity between the present situation and that discussed in Section 8·1 in connection with the reaction between a bromide ion and an alkyl bromide should be too obvious to require comment.

Not all rearrangements can occur by the Whitmore mechanism. That this statement is true is made particularly obvious by the fact that the migrating group does not always become attached ultimately to an atom adjacent to the one to which it was joined originally, but instead often goes farther to a more distant atom. An important additional type of rearrangement, which involves a so-called 1,3 shift instead of the 1,2 shift common to all the previous examples, is given by the allylic rearrangement, which can be illustrated by the reaction between phenylvinylcarbinol, XXI, and hydrogen bromide. The product is not the expected secondary bromide, XXII, but is the primary cinnamyl bromide, XXIII.[75] The most reasonable explanation

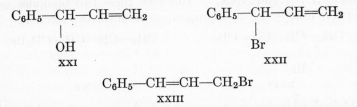

$$C_6H_5—CH—CH=CH_2$$
$$|$$
$$OH$$

XXI

$$C_6H_5—CH—CH=CH_2$$
$$|$$
$$Br$$

XXII

$$C_6H_5—CH=CH—CH_2Br$$

XXIII

of this rearrangement seems to be that the strong acid removes a hydroxide ion from the carbinol and leaves a positive organic ion which resonates between the structures XXIV and XXV. (The resonance between these structures of course stabilizes the ion in the usual manner

$$C_6H_5—\overset{+}{C}H—CH=CH_2$$

XXIV

$$C_6H_5—CH=CH—\overset{+}{C}H_2$$

XXV

$$C_6H_5—CH=CH—CH_2OH$$

XXVI

and so is presumably responsible in large part for the fact that the reaction proceeds by the present mechanism.) A bromide ion now comes up from the solution to complete the reaction; it could in principle approach the carbon atom which carries the positive charge in either of the two structures XXIV and XXV, to give either XXII or XXIII, respectively. We could hardly have predicted in advance that the reaction would actually follow only the second of these two conceivable courses, but we have at any rate come to an understanding of how the observed facts are *possible*. Moreover, we can now make the definite prediction on the basis of the above mechanism that cinnamyl alcohol, XXVI, must also give the same product, cinnamyl bromide, XXIII, as the phenylvinylcarbinol does under the same experimental conditions, because the same resonating organic cation is

[75] J. Meisenheimer and J. Link, *Ann.*, **479**, 211 (1930).

an intermediate in both reactions. There should therefore be no re-arrangement in this reaction. This prediction is in agreement with experiment.[75]

The situation is not always so clear-cut as in the preceding example. When either methylvinylcarbinol, XXVII, or crotyl alcohol, XXVIII, is treated with hydrogen bromide, the product is a mixture of the two

$$CH_3—CH—CH=CH_2 \qquad\qquad CH_3—CH=CH—CH_2OH$$
$$\qquad | $$
$$\qquad OH$$

XXVII                                                   XXVIII

bromides, XXIX and XXX.[76] However, these two bromides are not obtained in exactly the same proportions from the two alcohols. Thus,

$$CH_3—CH—CH=CH_2 \qquad\qquad CH_3—CH=CH—CH_2Br$$
$$\qquad | $$
$$\qquad Br$$

XXIX                                                   XXX

methylvinylcarbinol gives a somewhat higher proportion of its related bromide, XXIX, than does crotyl alcohol; and, conversely, crotyl alcohol gives a somewhat higher proportion of *its* related bromide, XXX, than does methylvinylcarbinol. This fact appears to be in conflict with the belief that both reactions proceed through an inter-mediate cation resonating between XXXI and XXXII (analogous to XXIV and XXV, respectively). However, Young and Lane have shown[76] that the data can be explained quantitatively if it is assumed

$$CH_3—\overset{+}{C}H—CH=CH_2 \qquad\qquad CH_3—CH=CH—\overset{+}{C}H_2$$

XXXI                                                   XXXII

that each reaction occurs by two independent mechanisms. On the one hand, most of the reaction proceeds by the mechanism already outlined, and gives identical products from the two alcohols; but, on the other hand, a small amount of reaction occurs simultaneously by a different mechanism in which a bromide ion directly displaces a hy-droxide ion in the un-ionized molecule, without any rearrangement. This second mechanism is presumably of the Walden inversion type described in Section 8·1.

$$CH_3—CH—CH=CH_2 \qquad\qquad CH_3—CH=CH—CH_2OC_2H_5$$
$$\qquad | $$
$$\qquad OC_2H_5$$

XXXIII                                                  XXXIV

[76] W. G. Young and J. F. Lane, *J. Am. Chem. Soc.*, **60**, 847 (1938).

Further evidence showing the existence of two mechanisms is provided by the preparation of the ethers XXXIII and XXXIV from the chlorides corresponding to XXIX and XXX.[77] If the chlorides are merely dissolved in alcohol, the same mixture of ethers is obtained from each. Apparently, therefore, the reaction proceeds exclusively through the common ion resonating between XXXI and XXXII. On the other hand, if the reactions are brought about by the action of sodium ethoxide in alcoholic solution, no rearrangements occur, and each chloride gives only the ether with analogous structure. Apparently here, therefore, the reaction proceeds exclusively by direct attack of an ethoxide ion upon the un-ionized chloride. The reason why this second mechanism is not apparent also in the reaction with alcohol alone is that then the concentration of ethoxide ion is so low that the reaction of the cation (resonating between XXXI and XXXII) with the solvent is much faster. Only if the ethoxide-ion concentration is greatly increased by the addition of sodium ethoxide can the relative importance of the two mechanisms be reversed.

[77] A. G. Catchpole, quoted by E. D. Hughes, *Trans. Faraday Soc.*, **37**, 603 (1941).

# APPENDIX

## INTERATOMIC DISTANCES IN ORGANIC MOLECULES[a]

| Formula | Name | Bond | Observed Lengths[c] | Exp. Meth.[d] | Reference[e] | Remarks |
|---------|------|------|---------------------|---------------|--------------|---------|
| C | Diamond | CC | $1.542 \pm 0.001$ | X | 11 | |
| C | Graphite | CC | 1.42 | X | 10 | See Section 4·4 |
| CBrN | Cyanogen bromide | CBr | $1.79 \pm 0.02$ | E | 8 | |
| | | CN | $1.13 \pm 0.04$ | E | 8 | |
| CBr$_4$ | Carbon tetrabromide | CBr | $1.91 \pm 0.02$ | E | 45 | |
| CCaO$_3$ | Calcite | CO | 1.313 | X | 24 | Planar ion with trigonal symmetry. |
| CClN | Cyanogen chloride | CCl | $1.67 \pm 0.02$ | E | 8 | |
| | | CN | $1.13 \pm 0.03$ | E | 8 | |
| CCl$_2$F$_2$ | Dichlorodifluoromethane | CCl | $1.74 \pm 0.03$ | E | 13 | |
| | | CF | $1.35 \pm 0.03$ | E | 13 | |
| CCl$_2$O | Phosgene | CCl | $1.68 \pm 0.02$ | E | 12 | Planar molecule. |
| | | CO | $1.28 \pm 0.02$ | E | 12 | |
| CCl$_2$S | Thiophosgene | CCl | $1.70 \pm 0.02$ | E | 12 | Planar molecule. |
| | | CS | 1.63 | E | 12 | |
| CCl$_3$F | Trichlorofluoromethane | CCl | $1.76 \pm 0.02$ | E | 13 | |
| | | CF | $1.40 \pm 0.04$ | E | 13 | |
| CCl$_4$ | Carbon tetrachloride | CCl | $1.755 \pm 0.005$ | E | 13 | |
| CF$_4$ | Carbon tetrafluoride | CF | $1.36 \pm 0.02$ | E | 13 | |
| CHBr$_3$ | Bromoform | CBr | (1.91) | | 45 | |
| CHClF$_2$ | Chlorodifluoromethane | CCl | $1.73 \pm 0.03$ | E | 13 | |
| | | CF | $1.36 \pm 0.03$ | E | 13 | |
| CHCl$_2$F | Dichlorofluoromethane | CCl | $1.73 \pm 0.04$ | E | 13 | |
| | | CF | $1.41 \pm 0.03$ | E | 13 | |
| CHCl$_3$ | Chloroform | CCl | $1.77 \pm 0.02$ | E | 13 | |
| CHI$_3$ | Iodoform | CI | $2.12 \pm 0.03$ | E | 12 | |
| CHN | Hydrogen cyanide | CH | 1.057 | S | 91 | |
| | | CN | 1.154 | S | 91 | |
| CHNO | Cyanic acid | CN | $1.19 \pm 0.03$ | E | 26 | |
| | | CO | $1.19 \pm 0.03$ | E | 26 | |
| CHNaO$_2$ | Sodium formate | CO | 1.27 | X | 97 | |
| CH$_2$Br$_2$ | Methylene bromide | CBr | $1.91 \pm 0.02$ | E | 12, 45 | |
| CH$_2$ClF | Chlorofluoromethane | CCl | $1.76 \pm 0.02$ | E | 13 | |
| | | CF | $1.40 \pm 0.03$ | E | 13 | |
| CH$_2$Cl$_2$ | Methylene chloride | CCl | $1.77 \pm 0.02$ | E | 13 | |
| CH$_2$F$_2$ | Methylene fluoride | CF | $1.36 \pm 0.02$ | E | 13 | |
| CH$_2$N$_2$ | Diazomethane | CN | $1.34 \pm 0.05$ | E | 12 | Linear molecule (except for hydrogen atoms). |
| | | NN | $1.13 \pm 0.04$ | E | 12 | |
| CH$_2$O | Formaldehyde | CH | $1.09 \pm 0.01$ | S, E | 88 | |
| | | CO | $1.21 \pm 0.01$ | E | 88 | |
| CH$_2$O$_2$ | Formic acid | See C$_2$H$_4$O$_4$ | | | | |
| CH$_3$Br | Methyl bromide | CBr | $1.91 \pm 0.06$ | E | 45 | |

## INTERATOMIC DISTANCES IN ORGANIC MOLECULES[a] (*Continued*)

| Substance[b] | | Observed | | Exp. | Refer- | Remarks |
|---|---|---|---|---|---|---|
| Formula | Name | Bond | Lengths[c] | Meth.[d] | ence[e] | |
| CH₃Cl | Methyl chloride | CCl | 1.77 ± 0.02 | E | 13 | |
| CH₃F | Methyl fluoride | CF | 1.39 | E | 81 | |
| | | | 1.396 | S | 21 | |
| CH₃Cl₂N | N,N-Dichloro-methylamine | NCl | 1.74 ± 0.02 | E | 89 | |
| CH₃NO₂ | Methyl nitrite | CO | 1.44 ± 0.02 | E | 78 | Planar (except for |
| [CH₃—O—N—O′] | | NO | 1.37 ± 0.02 | E | 78 | hydrogen |
| | | NO′ | 1.22 ± 0.02 | E | 78 | atoms). |
| CH₃NO₂ | Nitromethane | CN | 1.46 ± 0.02 | E | 12, 78 | |
| | | NO | 1.21 ± 0.02 | E | 12, 78 | |
| CH₃NO₃ | Methyl nitrate | CO | 1.43 ± 0.05 | E | 57, 78 | |
| [CH₃—O—NO′₂] | | NO | 1.36 ± 0.05 | E | 57, 78 | |
| | | NO′ | 1.26 ± 0.05 | E | 57, 78 | |
| CH₃N₃ | Methyl azide | CN | 1.47 ± 0.02 | E | 57 | Linear azide |
| [CH₃—N=N′=N″] | | NN′ | 1.24 ± 0.02 | E | 57 | group. |
| | | N′N″ | 1.10 ± 0.02 | E | 57 | |
| CH₄ | Methane | CH | 1.093 | S | 21 | |
| CH₄N₂O | Urea | CN | 1.37 | X | 96 | Planar (except for |
| | | CO | 1.25 | X | 96 | hydrogen atoms). See also CH₆N₂O₃. |
| CH₄N₂S | Thiourea | CN | 1.35 | X | 95 | Planar (except for |
| | | CS | 1.64 | X | 95 | hydrogen atoms). |
| CH₅NO | O-Methylhydrox-ylamine | CO | 1.44 ± 0.02 | E | 12 | |
| | | NO | 1.37 ± 0.02 | E | 12 | |
| CH₆N₂O₃ | Urea-hydrogen peroxide | CN | 1.34 ± 0.03 | X | 50 | Planar urea (ex- |
| | | CO | 1.24 ± 0.03 | X | 50 | cept for hydro- |
| [(NH₂)₂CO·H₂O′₂] | | O′O′ | 1.46 ± 0.03 | X | 50 | gen atoms). |
| CN₄O₈ | Tetranitromethane | CN | 1.47 ± 0.02 | E | 90 | |
| | | NO | 1.22 ± 0.02 | E | 90 | |
| CO | Carbon monoxide | CO | 1.129 | S | 27 | |
| COS | Carbon oxysulfide | CO | 1.16 ± 0.03 | E | 12 | |
| | | CS | 1.56 ± 0.04 | E | 12 | |
| CO₂ | Carbon dioxide | CO | 1.13 ± 0.04 | E | 12 | |
| | | | 1.159 | S | 21 | |
| CS₂ | Carbon disulfide | CS | 1.54 ± 0.03 | E | 12 | |
| C₂Br₂ | Dibromoacetylene | CC | 1.20 ± 0.03 | E | 12 | |
| | | CBr | 1.80 ± 0.03 | E | 12 | |
| C₂Cl₄ | Tetrachloroethy-lene | CC | (1.38) | E | 12 | |
| | | CCl | 1.73 ± 0.02 | E | 12 | |
| C₂HBr | Bromoacetylene | CBr | 1.80 ± 0.03 | E | 14 | |
| C₂HCl | Chloroacetylene | CCl | 1.68 ± 0.04 | E | 14 | |
| C₂HCl₃ | Trichloroethylene | CC | (1.38) | E | 12 | |
| | | CCl | 1.71 ± 0.03 | E | 12 | |
| C₂HCl₃O | Chloral | CC | 1.52 ± 0.02 | E | 20 | |
| | | CCl | 1.76 ± 0.02 | E | 20 | |
| | | CO | 1.15 ± 0.02 | E | 20 | |
| C₂H₂ | Acetylene | CC | 1.204 | S | 91 | |
| | | CH | 1.057 | S | 91 | |
| C₂H₂Br₂ | 1,2-Dibromoeth-ylene (*trans*) | CBr | 1.85 ± 0.04 | E | 39 | |
| C₂H₂Cl₂ | 1,2-Dichloroeth-ylene (*cis*) | CC | (1.38) | E | 12 | |
| | | CCl | 1.67 ± 0.03 | E | 12 | |
| C₂H₂Cl₂ | 1,2-Dichloroeth-ylene (*trans*) | CC | (1.38) | E | 12 | |
| | | CCl | 1.69 ± 0.02 | E | 12 | |
| C₂H₂Cl₂ | 1,1-Dichloroeth-ylene | CC | (1.38) | E | 12 | |
| | | CCl | 1.69 ± 0.02 | E | 12 | |

## INTERATOMIC DISTANCES IN ORGANIC MOLECULES[a] *(Continued)*

| Formula | Substance[b] Name | Bond | Observed Lengths[c] | Exp. Meth.[d] | Reference[e] | Remarks |
|---|---|---|---|---|---|---|
| $C_2H_2I_2$ | 1,2-Diiodoethylene (cis) | CI | 2.03 ± 0.04 | E | 39 | |
| $C_2H_2I_2$ | 1,2-Diiodoethylene (trans) | CI | 2.03 ± 0.04 | E | 39 | |
| $C_2H_2K_2O_5$ | Potassium oxalate monohydrate | CC | 1.60 | X | 33 | Planar ion. |
| | | CO | 1.14, 1.30 | X | 33 | |
| $C_2H_2O_2$ | Glyoxal | CC | 1.47 ± 0.02 | E | 51 | |
| | | CO | 1.20 ± 0.01 | E | 51 | |
| $C_2H_2O_4$ | α-Oxalic acid | CC | 1.57 | X | 33 | Planar. See also |
| HO'—C—C—O'H (with ‖O ‖O) | | CO | 1.22 | X | 33 | $C_2H_6O_6$. |
| | | CO' | 1.29 | X | 33 | |
| $C_2H_2O_4$ | β-Oxalic acid | CC | 1.59 | X | 33 | Planar. See also |
| HO'—C—C—O'H (with ‖O ‖O) | | CO | 1.20 | X | 33 | $C_2H_6O_6$. |
| | | CO' | 1.30 | X | 33 | |
| $C_2H_3Br$ | Vinyl bromide | CBr | 1.86 ± 0.04 | E | 39 | |
| $C_2H_3Cl$ | Vinyl chloride | CC | (1.38) | E | 12 | |
| | | CCl | 1.69 ± 0.02 | E | 12 | |
| $C_2H_3Cl_3$ | Methyl chloroform | CCl | 1.76 ± 0.02 | E | 7 | |
| $C_2H_3I$ | Vinyl iodide | CI | 2.03 ± 0.04 | E | 39 | |
| $C_2H_3N$ | Methyl cyanide | CC | 1.49 ± 0.03 | E | 63 | |
| | | CN | 1.16 ± 0.03 | E | 63 | |
| $C_2H_3N$ | Methyl isocyanide | CN | 1.44 ± 0.02 | E | 29 | Linear molecule |
| [$CH_3$—N≡C'] | | C'N | 1.18 ± 0.02 | E | 29 | (except for hydrogen atoms). |
| $C_2H_3NO$ | Methyl isocyanate | C'N | 1.19 ± 0.03 | E | 26 | |
| [$CH_3$—N≡C'≡O] | | C'O | 1.18 ± 0.03 | E | 26 | |
| $C_2H_4$ | Ethylene | CC | 1.34 ± 0.02 | E | 58 | |
| | | | 1.330 | S | 25 | |
| | | CH | 1.06 ± 0.03 | E | 58 | |
| | | | 1.087 | S | 25 | |
| $C_2H_4BrCl$ | 1-Bromo-2-chloroethane | CBr | 1.90 ± 0.02 | E | 9 | |
| | | CCl | 1.75 ± 0.02 | E | 9 | |
| $C_2H_4Br_2$ | Ethylene bromide | CBr | 1.91 ± 0.02 | E | 9 | |
| $C_2H_4Cl_2$ | Ethylene chloride | CCl | 1.76 ± 0.02 | E | 5 | |
| $C_2H_4N_4$ | Dimeric cyanamide | CN' | 1.22 ± 0.02 | X | 37 | Planar molecule. |
| | | CN' | 1.28 ± 0.02 | X | 37 | Linear cyani |
| [N≡C—N'≡C'(N''H_2)_2] | | C'N' | 1.36 ± 0.02 | X | 37 | mino group. |
| | | C'N'' | 1.34, | | | |
| | | | 1.37 ± 0.02 | X | 37 | |
| $C_2H_4O$ | Acetaldehyde | CC | 1.50 ± 0.02 | E | 87 | |
| | | CO | 1.22 ± 0.02 | E | 87 | |
| $C_2H_4O_4$ | Dimeric formic acid | CO | 1.29 ± 0.02 | E | 12, 98 | Planar molecule. |
| $C_2H_5Br$ | Ethyl bromide | CBr | 1.91 ± 0.02 | E | 7 | |
| $C_2H_5Cl$ | Ethyl chloride | CCl | 1.76 ± 0.02 | E | 7 | |
| $C_2H_5NO$ | Acetamide | CC | 1.51 ± 0.05 | X | 82 | |
| | | CN | 1.38 ± 0.05 | X | 82 | |
| | | CO | 1.28 ± 0.05 | X | 82 | |
| $C_2H_5NO_2$ | Glycine | CC | 1.52 ± 0.02 | X | 1 | |
| | | CN | 1.39 ± 0.02 | X | 1 | |
| | | CO | 1.25, | | | |
| | | | 1.27 ± 0.02 | X | 1 | |
| $C_2H_6$ | Ethane | CC | 1.55 ± 0.03 | E | 58 | |
| | | CH | 1.09 ± 0.03 | E | 58 | |
| $C_2H_6ClN$ | N-Chlorodimethylamine | CN | 1.47 ± 0.02 | E | 89 | |
| | | ClN | 1.77 ± 0.02 | E | 89 | |

## INTERATOMIC DISTANCES IN ORGANIC MOLECULES[a] (*Continued*)

| Substance[b] Formula | Name | Bond | Observed Bond Lengths[c] | Exp. Meth.[d] | Refer-ence[e] | Remarks |
|---|---|---|---|---|---|---|
| $C_2H_6Hg$ | Dimethyl mercury | CHg | $2.23 \pm 0.04$ | E | 30 | |
| $C_2H_6N_2$ | Azomethane | CN | $1.47 \pm 0.06$ | E | 12 | |
| | | NN | $1.24 \pm 0.05$ | E | 12 | |
| $C_2H_6O$ | Dimethyl ether | CO | $1.42 \pm 0.03$ | E | 12 | |
| $C_2H_6O_2S$ | Dimethyl sulfone | CS | $1.90 \pm 0.03$ | E | 48 | |
| | | SO | $1.44 \pm 0.03$ | E | 48 | |
| $C_2H_6O_6$ | Oxalic acid di-hydrate | CC | $1.44 \pm 0.04$ | X | 74 | Planar oxalic acid. |
| | | CO | $1.24 \pm 0.02$ | X | 74 | |
| $\begin{bmatrix} HO'-C-C-O'H \cdot 2H_2O'' \\ \parallel \quad \parallel \\ O \quad O \end{bmatrix}$ | | CO' | $1.30 \pm 0.02$ | X | 74 | |
| $C_2H_6S$ | Dimethyl sulfide | CS | $1.82 \pm 0.03$ | E | 12 | |
| $C_2H_6S_2$ | Dimethyl disulfide | CS | $1.78 \pm 0.03$ | E | 86 | |
| | | SS | $2.04 \pm 0.03$ | E | 86 | |
| $C_2H_{10}N_2O_5$ | Ammonium oxa-late mono-hydrate | CC | $1.581 \pm 0.01$ | X | 34 | 28° between planes of carboxyl groups. |
| | | CO | 1.23, | | | |
| | | | $1.25 \pm 0.02$ | X | 34 | |
| $C_2N_2$ | Cyanogen | CC | $1.37 \pm 0.02$ | E | 63 | |
| $C_3H_3Br$ | 3-Bromo-1-pro-pyne | C'C'' | $1.47 \pm 0.02$ | E | 60 | |
| | | C''Br | $1.95 \pm 0.02$ | E | 60 | |
| $[HC \equiv C'-C''H_2Br]$ | | | | | | |
| $C_3H_3Cl$ | 3-Chloro-1-pro-pyne | C'C'' | $1.48 \pm 0.02$ | E | 60 | |
| | | C''Cl | $1.82 \pm 0.02$ | E | 60 | |
| $[HC \equiv C'-C''H_2Cl]$ | | | | | | |
| $C_3H_3I$ | 3-Iodo-1-propyne | C'C'' | (1.47) | E | 60 | |
| $[HC \equiv C'-C''H_2I]$ | | C''I | $2.13 \pm 0.03$ | E | 60 | |
| $C_3H_3GdO_6$ | Gadolinium for-mate | CO | 1.27, 1.33 | X | 56 | |
| $C_3H_3N_3O_3$ | Cyanuric acid | CN | 1.36 | X | 94 | |
| | | CO | 1.28 | X | 94 | |
| $C_3H_4$ | Allene | CC | 1.330 | S | 25 | |
| | | | $1.34 \pm 0.02$ | E | 58 | |
| | | CH | 1.087 | S | 25 | |
| $C_3H_4$ | Methyl acetylene | CC' | $1.462 \pm 0.005$ | S | 35 | |
| $[CH_3-C' \equiv C''H]$ | | | $1.46 \pm 0.02$ | E | 63 | |
| | | C'C'' | $1.21 \pm 0.03$ | E | 63 | |
| $C_3H_6$ | Cyclopropane | CC | $1.53 \pm 0.03$ | E | 58 | |
| $C_3H_6Br_2$ | Propylene bro-mide | CBr | $1.92 \pm 0.02$ | E | 80 | |
| $C_3H_6N_6$ | Melamine | CN | 1.33, 1.34, | | | |
| $[C_3N_3(N'H_2)_3]$ | | | $1.35 \pm 0.02$ | X | 38 | |
| | | CN' | 1.35, | | | |
| | | | $1.36 \pm 0.02$ | X | 38 | |
| $C_3H_6O$ | Acetone | CC | $1.57 \pm 0.04$ | E | 12 | |
| $C_3H_6O_3$ | α-Trioxymethyl-ene (" Trioxane ") | CO | $1.42 \pm 0.03$ | X | 52 | Puckered six-membered ring. |
| $C_3H_6S_3$ | Trithioformalde-hyde | CS | $1.81 \pm 0.06$ | X | 53 | Puckered six-membered ring. |
| $C_3H_7Br$ | *i*-Propylbromide | CBr | $1.91 \pm 0.03$ | E | · 7 | |
| $C_3H_7Cl$ | *i*-Propylchloride | CCl | $1.75 \pm 0.03$ | E | 7 | |
| $C_3H_7NO_2$ | *d,l*-Alanine | CC | $1.54 \pm 0.03$ | X | 47 | |
| | | CN | $1.42 \pm 0.03$ | X | 47 | |
| | | CO | 1.23, | | | |
| | | | $1.25 \pm 0.02$ | X | 47 | |
| $C_3H_8$ | Propane | CC | $1.54 \pm 0.02$ | E | 58 | |
| $C_3H_9As$ | Trimethyl arsine | CAs | $1.98 \pm 0.02$ | E | 84 | |
| $C_3H_9B$ | Trimethyl boron | CB | $1.56 \pm 0.02$ | E | 46 | Planar molecule (except for hy-drogen atoms). |

## INTERATOMIC DISTANCES IN ORGANIC MOLECULES[a] (*Continued*)

| Substance[b] Formula | Name | Bond | Observed Lengths[c] | Exp. Meth.[d] | Refer- ence[e] | Remarks |
|---|---|---|---|---|---|---|
| $C_3H_9BO_3$ | Methyl borate | CO | 1.43 ± 0.03 | E | 2 | |
| | | BO | 1.38 ± 0.02 | E | 2 | |
| **$C_3H_9B_3O_3$** | **Trimethyl tribo-** | CB | 1.57 ± 0.03 | E | 2 | Planar molecule |
| | rine trioxane | BO | 1.38 ± 0.02 | E | 2 | (except for hy- |
| | | | | | | drogen atoms). |
| $C_3H_9In$ | Trimethyl indium | CIn | 2.16 ± 0.04 | E | 61 | |
| $C_3H_9N$ | Trimethylamine | CN | 1.47 ± 0.02 | E | 12 | |
| $C_3H_9NO$ | Trimethylamine | CN | 1.54 ± 0.03 | E | 48 | |
| | oxide | NO | 1.36 ± 0.03 | E | 48 | |
| $C_3H_9P$ | Trimethyl phos- | CP | 1.87 ± 0.02 | E | 84 | |
| | phine | | | | | |
| $C_3N_{12}$ | Cyanuric triazide | CN | 1.31, 1.38 | X | 42 | Planar molecule. |
| $[C_3N_3(N'{=}N''{=}N''')_3]$ | | CN' | 1.38 | X | 42 | Linear azide |
| | | N''N'' | 1.26 | X | 42 | group. |
| | | N''N''' | 1.11 | X | 42 | |
| $C_3O_2$ | Carbon suboxide | CC | 1.29 ± 0.03 | E | 12 | Linear molecule. |
| | | CO | 1.20 ± 0.02 | E | 12 | |
| $C_4H_2$ | Diacetylene | CC' | 1.19 ± 0.02 | E | 63 | |
| $[HC{\equiv}C'{-}C'{\equiv}CH]$ | | C'C' | 1.36 ± 0.03 | E | 63 | |
| $C_4H_4N_2$ | Pyrazine | CC | (1.39) | E | 79 | |
| | | CN | 1.35 ± 0.02 | E | 79 | |
| **$C_4H_4O$** | Furan | CC | 1.46 ± 0.03 | E | 4, 79 | |
| $\begin{bmatrix} C'H{=}CH{-}CH{=}C'H \\ \underline{\qquad O \qquad} \end{bmatrix}$ | | CC' | (1.35) | E | 4, 79 | |
| | | C'O | 1.40 ± 0.02 | E | 4, 79 | |
| $C_4H_4O_2$ | Dioxadiene | CC | 1.35 ± 0.03 | E | 4 | |
| | | CO | 1.41 ± 0.03 | E | 4 | |
| **$C_4H_4S$** | Thiophene | CC | (1.44) | E | 79 | |
| $\begin{bmatrix} C'H{=}CH{-}CH{=}C'H \\ \underline{\qquad S \qquad} \end{bmatrix}$ | | CC' | (1.35) | E | 79 | |
| | | C'S | 1.74 ± 0.03 | E | 79 | |
| **$C_4H_5N$** | Pyrrole | CC | (1.44) | E | 79 | |
| $\begin{bmatrix} C'H{=}CH{-}CH{=}C'H \\ \underline{\qquad NH \qquad} \end{bmatrix}$ | | CC' | (1.35) | E | 79 | |
| | | C'N | 1.42 ± 0.02 | E | 79 | |
| **$C_4H_6$** | Dimethylacetylene | CC' | 1.47 ± 0.02 | E | 63 | |
| $[CH_3{-}C'{\equiv}C'{-}CH_3]$ | | | | | | |
| **$C_4H_6$** | 1,3-Butadiene | CC' | 1.35 ± 0.02 | E | 79 | |
| $[CH_2{=}C'H{-}C'H{=}CH_2]$ | | C'C' | 1.46 ± 0.03 | E | 79 | |
| **$C_4H_6N_2O_2$** | Diketopiperazine | CC' | 1.47 ± 0.03 | X | 17 | |
| | | CN | 1.33 ± 0.03 | X | 17 | |
| | | C'N | 1.41 ± 0.03 | X | 17 | |
| | | CO | 1.25 ± 0.03 | X | 17 | |
| **$C_4H_6O$** | 2,5-Dihydrofuran | C'C | 1.54 ± 0.03 | E | 4 | |
| $\begin{bmatrix} C'H_2{-}CH{=}CH{-}C'H_2 \\ \underline{\qquad O \qquad} \end{bmatrix}$ | | C'O | 1.43 ± 0.03 | E | 4 | |
| **$C_4H_6O_2$** | Diacetyl | CC' | 1.54 ± 0.02 | E | 51 | |
| $[CH_3{-}C'O{-}C'O{\rightarrow}CH_3]$ | | C'C' | 1.47 ± 0.02 | E | 51 | |
| | | C'O | 1.20 ± 0.02 | E | 51 | |
| **$C_4H_6O_4$** | Succinic acid | CC | 1.51, 1.52 | X | 92 | |
| | | CO | 1.31 | X | 92 | |
| | | CO' | 1.28 | X | 92 | |
| **$C_4H_7Cl$** | *i*-Crotyl chloride | CCl | 1.72 ± 0.02 | E | 7 | |

## INTERATOMIC DISTANCES IN ORGANIC MOLECULES[a] *(Continued)*

| Substance[b] | | Observed | | Exp. | Refer- | Remarks |
|---|---|---|---|---|---|---|
| Formula | Name | Bond | Lengths[c] | Meth.[d] | ence[e] | |
| $C_4H_8$ | 2-Butene *(cis)* | CC' | 1.54 ± 0.02 | E | 12 | |
| [$CH_3$—C'H=C''H—$CH_3$] | | | | | | |
| $C_4H_8$ | 2-Butene *(trans)* | CC' | 1.53 ± 0.02 | E | 12 | |
| [$CH_3$—C'H=C''H—$CH_3$] | | | | | | |
| $C_4H_8$ | *i*-Butene | CC' | 1.54 ± 0.02 | E | 58 | |
| [$(CH_3)_2$C'=C''$H_2$] | | | | | | |
| $C_4H_8O$ | Tetrahydrofuran | CC | 1.54 ± 0.02 | E | 4 | |
| | | CO | 1.43 ± 0.03 | E | 4 | |
| $C_4H_8O$ | 2-Butene oxide | CC | 1.53 ± 0.02 | E | 12 | |
| | *(cis)* | CO | 1.42 ± 0.02 | E | 12 | |
| $C_4H_8O$ | 2-Butene oxide | CC | 1.54 ± 0.02 | E | 12 | |
| | *(trans)* | CO | 1.43 ± 0.02 | E | 12 | |
| $C_4H_8O_2$ | Dioxane | CO | 1.46 ± 0.04 | E | 12 | |
| $C_4H_9Br$ | *t*-Butyl bromide | CBr | 1.92 ± 0.03 | E | 6 | |
| $C_4H$ Cl | *t*-Butyl chloride | CCl | 1.78 ± 0.03 | E | 6 | |
| $C_4H_{10}$ | *i*-Butane | CC | 1.54 ± 0.02 | E | 6, 58 | |
| $C_4H_{12}Ge$ | Tetramethyl germanium | CGe | 1.98 ± 0.03 | E | 12 | Tetrahedral germanium. |
| $C_4H_{12}Pb$ | Tetramethyl lead | CPb | 2.30 ± 0.05 | E | 12 | Tetrahedral lead. |
| $C_4H_{12}Si$ | Tetramethyl silicon | CSi | 1.93 ± 0.03 | E | 12 | Tetrahedral silicon. |
| $C_4H_{12}Sn$ | Tetramethyl tin | CSn | 2.18 ± 0.03 | E | 12 | Tetrahedral tin. |
| $C_5H_5N$ | Pyridine | CC | (1.39) | E | 79 | |
| | | CN | 1.37 ± 0.03 | E | 79 | |
| $C_5H_6$ | Cyclopentadiene | CC' | (1.53) | E | 79 | |
| [C'H=C''H—C''H=C'H | | C'C'' | (1.35) | E | 79 | |
| └———$CH_2$———┘] | | C''C'' | 1.46 ± 0.04 | E | 79 | |
| $C_5H_6$ | 1-Pentene-3-yne | CC' | (1.47) | E | 85 | |
| [$CH_3$—C'≡C''—C'''H=C^{IV}$H_2$] | | C'C'' | (1.20) | E | 85 | |
| | | C''C''' | (1.42) | E | 85 | |
| | | C'''C^{IV} | (1.35) | E | 85 | |
| $C_5H_8$ | Methylene cyclo- | CC | 1.56 ± 0.03 | E | 3 | |
| | butane | CC' | 1.34 ± 0.02 | E | 3 | |
| [$H_2$C—C=C'$H_2$ | | | | | | |
| │       │ | | | | | | |
| $H_2$C—$CH_2$] | | | | | | |
| $C_5H_{10}$ | Cyclopentane | CC | 1.52 ± 0.03 | E | 58 | |
| $C_5H_{12}$ | Neopentane | CC | 1.54 ± 0.02 | E | 58 | |
| $C_5H_{12}O_4$ | Pentaerythritol | CC | 1.50 ± 0.03 | X | 49 | |
| | | CO | 1.46 ± 0.03 | X | 49 | |
| $C_6Cl_6$ | Hexachloroben- | CC | (1.41) | E | 15 | |
| | zene | CCl | 1.70 ± 0.03 | E | 15 | |
| $C_6H_2Cl_4$ | 1,2,4,5-Tetra- | CC | (1.40) | E | 15 | |
| | chlorobenzene | CCl | 1.72 ± 0.04 | E | 15 | |
| $C_6H_2IN_3O_6$ | Picryl iodide | CC | 1.39 | X | 40 | Nitro group N'$O_2$ |
| | $NO_2$ | CI | 2.10 | X | 40 | lies in plane of |
| | | CN | 1.45 | X | 40 | benzene ring; |
| $O_2N'$——I | | CN' | 1.35 | X | 40 | groups $NO_2$ nearly perpen- |
| | $NO_2$ | | | | | dicular to ring. |
| $C_6H_3Br_3$ | 1,3,5-Tribromo- | CC | 1.39 ± 0.02 | E | 43 | |
| | benzene | CBr | 1.84 ± 0.02 | E | 43 | |
| $C_6H_3Cl_3$ | 1,3,5-Trichloro- | CC | (1.41) | E | 15 | |
| | benzene | CCl | 1.69 ± 0.03 | E | 15 | |
| $C_6H_3I_3$ | 1,3,5-Triiodo- | CC | (1.41) | E | 12 | |
| | benzene | CI | 2.05 ± 0.03 | E | 12 | |

## INTERATOMIC DISTANCES IN ORGANIC MOLECULES[a] (*Continued*)

| Substance[b] Formula | Name | Bond | Observed Lengths[c] | Exp. Meth.[d] | Refer- ence[e] | Remarks |
|---|---|---|---|---|---|---|
| $C_6H_3N_3O_6$ | 1,3,5-Trinitro-benzene | CC | 1.4 | X | 66 | Planar molecule. |
| | | CN | 1.4 | X | 66 | In addition com- |
| | | NO | $1.2_3$ | X | 66 | pound with |
| | | | | | | *p*-iodoaniline. |
| $C_6H_4Br_2$ | *p*-Dibromobenzene | CC | (1.41) | E | 12 | |
| | | CBr | 1.88 ± 0.02 | E | 12 | |
| $C_6H_4Cl_2$ | *m*-Dichloroben-zene | CC | (1.40) | E | 15 | |
| | | CCl | 1.69 ± 0.03 | E | 15 | |
| $C_6H_4Cl_2$ | *p*-Dichloroben-zene | CC | (1.40) | E | 15 | |
| | | CCl | 1.69 ± 0.03 | E | 15 | |
| $C_6H_4Cl_2$ | *o*-Dichloroben-zene | CC | (1.40) | E | 15 | |
| | | CCl | 1.71 ± 0.03 | E | 15 | |
| $C_6H_4F_2$ | *o*-Difluoroben-zene | CF | 1.35 ± 0.03 | E | 55 | |
| $C_6H_4I_2$ | *o*-Diiodobenzene | CC | (1.42) | E | 12 | |
| | | CI | 2.00 ± 0.10 | E | 12 | |
| $C_6H_4I_2$ | *m*-Diiodobenzene | CC | (1.42) | E | 12 | |
| | | CI | 2.00 ± 0.10 | E | 12 | |
| $C_6H_4I_2$ | *p*-Diiodobenzene | CC | (1.42) | E | 12 | |
| | | CI | 2.02 ± 0.03 | E | 12 | |
| $C_6H_4O_2$ | *p*-Benzoquinone | CC' | 1.50 | X | 71 | Planar molecule. |
| | | CC | 1.32 | X | 71 | |
| | | C'O | 1.14 | X | 71 | |
| $C_6H_5Cl$ | Chlorobenzene | CC | 1.39 ± 0.02 | E | 15 | |
| | | CCl | 1.69 ± 0.03 | E | 15 | |
| $C_6H_5F$ | Fluorobenzene | CF | 1.34 ± 0.04 | E | 55 | |
| $C_6H_6$ | Benzene | CC | 1.39 ± 0.02 | E | 79 | |
| | | CH | 1.08 ± 0.04 | E | 79 | |
| $C_6H_6$ | Dimethyldiacety-lene | CC' | 1.47 ± 0.02 | E | 63 | |
| | | C'C'' | 1.20 ± 0.02 | E | 63 | |
| $[CH_3{-}C'{\equiv}C''{-}C''{\equiv}C'{-}CH_3]$ | | C''C'' | 1.38 ± 0.03 | E | 63 | |
| $C_6H_6Br_6$ | Benzene hexabro-mide | CBr | 1.94 | X | 23 | |
| $C_6H_6IN$ | *p*-Iodoaniline | CC | 1.4 | X | 66 | In addition com- |
| | | CN | $1.4_3$ | X | 66 | pound with |
| | | CI | 2.1 | X | 66 | 1,3,5-trinitro- |
| | | | | | | benzene. |
| $C_6H_6N_9Na_3O_3$ | Trisodium tricyan-melamine tri-hydrate | CN | 1.34, 1.35 | X | 36 | Planar ion. |
| | | CN' | 1.40 | X | 36 | |
| | | C'N' | 1.32 | X | 36 | |
| $\left[[C_3N_3(N'{=}C'{=}N'')_3]{\equiv}3Na^+\right]$ $\cdot 3H_2O$ | | C'N'' | 1.21 | X | 36 | |
| $C_6H_6O_2$ | *α*-Resorcinol | CC | 1.39 ± 0.01 | X | 72 | |
| | | CO | 1.36 | X | 72 | |
| $C_6H_6O_2$ | *β*-Resorcinol | CC | 1.39 | X | 77 | |
| | | CO | 1.36, 1.37 | X | 77 | |
| $C_6H_{12}$ | Tetramethyl-ethylene | CC' | 1.54 ± 0.02 | E | 58 | |
| $[(CH_3)_2C'{=}C'(CH_3)_2]$ | | | | | | |
| $C_6H_{12}$ | Cyclohexane | CC | 1.53 ± 0.03 | E | 58 | |
| $C_6H_{12}N_4$ | Hexamethylene-tetramine | CN | 1.47 ± 0.02 | E | 32 | |
| | | | 1.42 | X | 96 | |
| $C_6H_{12}O_3$ | Paraldehyde | CC | 1.54 ± 0.02 | E | 12 | Puckered six- |
| | | CO | 1.43 ± 0.02 | E | 12 | membered ring. |

## INTERATOMIC DISTANCES IN ORGANIC MOLECULES[a] (*Continued*)

| Substance[b] Formula | Name | Observed Bond | Lengths[c] | Exp. Meth.[d] | Refer-ence[e] | Remarks |
|---|---|---|---|---|---|---|
| $C_6H_{18}Al_2$ | Aluminum methyl | CAl | $2.05 \pm 0.05$ | E | 19 | "Ethane-like" |
| | | AlAl | $2.02 \pm 0.06$ | E | 19 | structure. |
| $C_6H_{18}Pb$ | Di-lead-hexa-methyl | CPb | $2.25 \pm 0.06$ | E | 83 | "Ethane-like" |
| | | PbPb | $2.88 \pm 0.03$ | E | 83 | structure. |
| $C_8H_8Br_2$ | 4,5-Dibromo-*o*-xylene | CC | $1.40 \pm 0.02$ | E | 43 | |
| $[C_6H_2Br_2(C'H_3)_2]$ | | CBr | $1.88 \pm 0.02$ | E | 43 | |
| $C_8H_{10}$ | *p*-Xylene | CC | $1.40 \pm 0.01$ | E | 12 | |
| $[C_6H_4(C'H_3)_2]$ | | CC' | $1.50 \pm 0.01$ | E | 12 | |
| $C_8H_{16}O_4$ | Metaldehyde | CC | $1.54 \pm 0.03$ | X | 59 | Puckered eight- |
| | | CO | $1.43 \pm 0.03$ | X | 59 | membered ring. |
| $C_8H_{18}$ | Hexamethyl-ethane | CC' | $1.54 \pm 0.02$ | E | 3 | |
| $[C'_2(CH_3)_6]$ | | C'C' | $1.58 \pm 0.03$ | E | 3 | |
| $C_9H_8Br_2$ | 5,6-Dibromohy-drindene | CC | $1.42 \pm 0.02$ | E | 43 | |
| $[Br_2C_6H_2(C'H_2)_3]$ | | CBr | $1.84 \pm 0.02$ | E | 43 | |
| $C_9H_{12}$ | Mesitylene | CC | $(1.39)$ | E | 58 | |
| $[(C_6H_3(C'H_3)_3]$ | | CC' | $1.54 \pm 0.01$ | E | 58 | |
| $C_{10}H_8$ | Naphthalene | CC | $1.41$ | X | 69 | Planar molecule. |
| $C_{10}H_{10}Br_2$ | 6,7-Dibromo-1,2,-3,4-tetrahydro-naphthalene | CC | $1.42 \pm 0.02$ | E | 43 | |
| $[Br_2C_6H_2(C'H_2)_4]$ | | CBr | $1.86 \pm 0.02$ | E | 43 | |
| $C_{10}H_{14}$ | Durene | CC | $1.41$ | X | 68 | |
| $[C_6H_2(C'H_3)_4]$ | | CC' | $1.47$ | X | 68 | |
| $C_{12}H_8I_2O$ | *p,p'*-Diiododi-phenyl ether | CC | $1.42$ | E | 12 | |
| | | CI | $2.00$ | E | 12 | |
| | | CO | $1.42$ | E | 12 | |
| $C_{12}H_9IN_4O_6$ | 1,3,5-Trinitroben-zene-*p*-iodoani-line addition compound | See $C_6H_3N_3O_6$ and $C_6H_6IN$ | | | | |
| $C_{12}H_{10}$ | Biphenyl | CC | $1.42$ | X | 22 | Planar molecule. |
| $[C_6H_5—C'_6H_5]$ | | C'C' | $1.42$ | X | 22 | |
| | | CC' | $1.48$ | X | 22 | |
| $C_{12}H_{10}N_2$ | Azobenzene (*cis*) | CC | $1.39 \pm 0.03$ | X | 31 | Non-planar mole- |
| | | CN | $1.46 \pm 0.03$ | X | 31 | cule. |
| | | NN | $1.23 \pm 0.03$ | X | 31 | |
| $C_{12}H_{10}N_2$ | Azobenzene (*trans*) | CC | $1.39$ | X | 44 | Planar molecule. |
| | | CN | $1.40 \pm 0.03$ | X | 44 | |
| | | NN | $1.23 \pm 0.05$ | X | 44 | |
| $C_{12}H_{10}N_2$ | Azobenzene (*trans*) | CC | $1.39$ | X | 44 | Phenyl groups in |
| | | CN | $1.43 \pm 0.03$ | X | 44 | parallel planes. |
| | | NN | $1.23 \pm 0.05$ | X | 44 | |
| $C_{12}H_{18}$ | Hexamethylben-zene | CC | $1.39$ | X | 16 | |
| | | | $(1.39)$ | E | 58 | |
| $[C_6(C'H_3)_6]$ | | CC' | $1.53$ | X | 16 | |
| | | | $1.54 \pm 0.01$ | E | 58 | |
| $C_{12}H_{18}Be_4O_{13}$ | Basic beryllium acetate | CC | $1.54 \pm 0.05$ | X | 62 | Tetrahedral |
| | | CO | $1.29 \pm 0.05$ | X | 62 | beryllium. |
| | | BeO | $1.65 \pm 0.05$ | X | 62 | |
| $C_{13}H_{20}O_8$ | Pentaerythritol tetraacetate | CC' | $1.52 \pm 0.03$ | X | 28 | |
| $\left[ C(C'H_2—O—C''—C'''H_3)_4 \right]$ | | C''C''' | $1.52 \pm 0.03$ | X | 28 | |
| | | C'O | $1.41 \pm 0.03$ | X | 28 | |
| $\left\| O' \right.$ | | C''O | $1.41 \pm 0.03$ | X | 28 | |
| | | C''O' | $1.33 \pm 0.03$ | X | 28 | |

# INTERATOMIC DISTANCES IN ORGANIC MOLECULES[a] *(Continued)*

| Substance[b] Formula | Name | Observed Bond Lengths[c] | | | Exp. Meth.[d] | Refer- ence[e] | Remarks |
|---|---|---|---|---|---|---|---|
| $C_{14}H_{10}$ | Anthracene | CC | 1.41 | | X | 67 | Planar molecule. |
| $C_{14}H_{10}$ | Diphenylacetylene | CC | (1.39) | | X | 76 | Planar molecule. |
| $[C_6H_5\!-\!C'\!\equiv\!C'\!-\!C_6H_5]$ | | CC′ | 1.40 | ± 0.02 | X | 76 | |
| | | C′C′ | 1.19 | ± 0.02 | X | 76 | |
| $C_{14}H_{12}$ | Stilbene (*trans*) | CC | 1.39 | | X | 75 | Planar molecule. |
| $[C_6H_5\!-\!C'H\!=\!C'H\!-\!C_6H_5]$ | | CC′ | 1.44 | | X | 75 | |
| | | C′C′ | 1.33 | | X | 75 | |
| $C_{14}H_{12}$ | Stilbene (*trans*) | CC | 1.39 | | X | 75 | Phenyl groups in |
| $[C_6H_5\!-\!C'H\!=\!C'H\!-\!C_6H_5]$ | | CC′ | 1.45 | | X | 75 | parallel planes. |
| | | C′C′ | 1.35 | | X | 75 | |
| $C_{14}H_{14}$ | Dibenzyl | CC | 1.41 | | X | 70 | Phenyl groups in |
| $[C_6H_5\!-\!C'H_2\!-\!C'H_2\!-\!C_6H_5]$ | | CC′ | 1.47 | | X | 70 | parallel planes. |
| | | C′C′ | 1.59 | | X | 70 | |
| $C_{16}H_{10}$ | Diphenyldiacety- | CC | 1.39 | ± 0.03 | X | 93 | Planar molecule. |
| | lene | CC′ | 1.44 | ± 0.03 | X | 93 | |
| $[C_6H_5\!-\!C'\!\equiv\!C''\!-\!C''\!\equiv\!C'\!-\!C_6H_5]$ | | C′C″ | 1.18 | ± 0.03 | X | 93 | |
| | | C″C″ | 1.39 | ± 0.03 | X | 93 | |
| $C_{18}H_{12}$ | Chrysene | CC | 1.41 | | X | 41 | Planar molecule. |
| $C_{18}H_{14}$ | *p*-Terphenyl | CC | 1.42 | | X | 64 | Planar molecule. |
| $[C_6H_5\!-\!C'_6H_4\!-\!C_6H_5]$ | | C′C′ | 1.42 | | X | 64 | |
| | | CC′ | 1.48 | | X | 64 | |
| $C_{24}H_{18}$ | *p*-Quaterphenyl | CC | 1.42 | | X | 65 | Planar molecule. |
| $[C_6H_5\!-\!C'_6H_4\!-\!C_6H_4\!-\!C'_6H_5]$ | | C′C′ | 1.42 | | X | 65 | |
| | | CC′ | 1.48 | | X | 65 | |
| $C_{24}H_{20}AsI$ | Tetraphenylar- | CC | 1.39 | | X | 54 | Tetrahedral |
| | sonium iodide | CAs | 1.95 | | X | 54 | arsenic. |
| $C_{32}H_{18}N_8$ | Phthalocyanine | CC | (1.39) | | X | 73 | Planar molecule. |
| | | CC′ | 1.49 | ± 0.03 | X | 73 | |
| | | C′N | 1.33, | | | | |
| | | | 1.34 | ± 0.03 | X | 73 | |

| | | | | | | | |
|---|---|---|---|---|---|---|---|
| $H_2O$ | Water | HO | 0.9580 | | S | 21 | |
| $H_2S$ | Hydrogen sulfide | HS | 1.35 | | S | 18 | |
| $H_3N$ | Ammonia | HN | 1.014 | | S | 21 | |
| $NNaO_3$ | Sodium nitrate | NO | 1.210 | | X | 24 | Planar ion with trigonal symmetry. |

[a] Although some omissions must inevitably occur, the effort has been made to have this list of organic compounds complete up to about June, 1943. A few simple inorganic compounds also are included for purposes of comparison.

[b] The various substances are listed in the order employed in the formula indexes of *Chemical Abstracts*. For most of the substances, the molecular formulas and names are sufficient identification; for certain others, however, the structures must be indicated in somewhat greater detail, in order that the identity of the bonds referred to in the subsequent columns may be made unambiguous. For simplicity, only a single structure is given for each substance, even though resonance among several structures may be important.

[c] In angstrom units. The probable errors listed are as estimated by the original authors. Bond

lengths, which have been assumed to be equal to the sum of the appropriate atomic radii, are ordinarily not listed. Assumed lengths of bonds between hydrogen and any other element are not listed, whether equal to the sum of the atomic radii or not. Other assumed bond lengths are placed in parentheses. Bond lengths separated by commas represent different values assigned by the original authors to different, but apparently equivalent, bonds in the molecules in question.

[d] The meanings of the symbols in this column are: $E$, electron diffraction by the gaseous substance $S$, spectroscopic method; and $X$, x-ray diffraction by the crystalline substance. See Section 4·3.

[e] The references to the original literature are:

1. G. Albrecht and R. B. Corey, *J. Am. Chem. Soc.*, **61**, 1087 (1939).
2. S. H. Bauer and J. Y. Beach, *J. Am. Chem. Soc.*, **63**, 1394 (1941).
3. S. H. Bauer and J. Y. Beach, *J. Am. Chem. Soc.*, **64**, 1142 (1942).
4. J. Y. Beach, *J. Chem. Phys.*, **9**, 54 (1941).
5. J. Y. Beach and K. J. Palmer, *J. Chem. Phys.*, **6**, 639 (1938).
6. J. Y. Beach and D. P. Stevenson, *J. Am. Chem. Soc.*, **60**, 475 (1938).
7. J. Y. Beach and D. P. Stevenson, *J. Am. Chem. Soc.*, **61**, 2643 (1939).
8. J. Y. Beach and A. Turkevitch, *J. Am. Chem. Soc.*, **61**, 299 (1939).
9. J. Y. Beach and A. Turkevitch, *J. Am. Chem. Soc.*, **61**, 303 (1939).
10. J. D. Bernal, *Proc. Roy. Soc.* (*London*), **A106**, 749 (1924).
11. W. H. Bragg and W. L. Bragg, *Proc. Roy. Soc.* (*London*), **A89**, 277 (1913). W. Ehrenberg, *Z. Krist.*, **63**, 320 (1926).
12. L. O. Brockway, *Rev. Modern Phys.*, **8**, 231 (1936).
13. L. O. Brockway, *J. Phys. Chem.*, **41**, 747 (1937).
14. L. O. Brockway and I. E. Coop, *Trans. Faraday Soc.*, **34**, 1429 (1938).
15. L. O. Brockway and K. J. Palmer, *J. Am. Chem. Soc.*, **59**, 2181 (1937).
16. L. O. Brockway and J. M. Robertson, *J. Chem. Soc.*, 1324 (1939).
17. R. B. Corey, *J. Am. Chem. Soc.*, **60**, 1598 (1938).
18. P. C. Cross, *Phys. Rev.*, **46**, 536 (1934).
19. N. R. Davidson, J. A. C. Hugill, H. A. Skinner, and L. E. Sutton, *Trans. Faraday Soc.*, **36**, 1212 (1940).
20. C. Degard, *Bull. soc. roy. sci. Liége*, **7**, 36 (1938). *C.A.*, **33**, 467 (1939).
21. D. M. Dennison, *Rev. Modern Phys.*, **12**, 175 (1940).
22. J. Dhar, *Indian J. Phys.*, **7**, 43 (1932). *C.A.*, **26**, 4517 (1932).
23. R. G. Dickinson and C. Bilicke, *J. Am. Chem. Soc.*, **50**, 764 (1928).
24. N. Elliott, *J. Am. Chem. Soc.*, **59**, 1380 (1937).
25. E. H. Eyster, *J. Chem. Phys.*, **6**, 580 (1938).
26. E. H. Eyster, R. H. Gillette, and L. O. Brockway, *J. Am. Chem. Soc.*, **62**, 3236 (1940).
27. L. Gerö, G. Herzberg, and R. Schmid, *Phys. Rev.*, **52**, 467 (1937).
28. T. H. Goodwin and R. Hardy, *Proc. Roy. Soc.* (*London*), **A164**, 369 (1938).
29. W. Gordy and L. Pauling, *J. Am. Chem. Soc.*, **64**, 2952 (1942).
30. A. H. Gregg, G. C. Hampson, G. I. Jenkins, P. L. F. Jones, and L. E. Sutton, *Trans. Faraday Soc.*, **33**, 852 (1937).
31. G. C. Hampson and J. M. Robertson, *J. Chem. Soc.*, 409 (1941).
32. G. C. Hampson and A. J. Stosick, *J. Am. Chem. Soc.*, **60**, 1814 (1938).
33. S. B. Hendricks, *Z. Krist.*, **91**, 48 (1935). Further data for several alkali metal oxalates are also given in this paper.
34. S. B. Hendricks and M. E. Jefferson, *J. Chem. Phys.*, **4**, 102 (1936).
35. G. Herzberg, F. Patat, and H. Verleger, *J. Phys. Chem.*, **41**, 123 (1937).
36. J. L. Hoard, *J. Am. Chem. Soc.*, **60**, 1194 (1938).
37. E. W. Hughes, *J. Am. Chem. Soc.*, **62**, 1258 (1940).
38. E. W. Hughes, *J. Am. Chem. Soc.*, **63**, 1737 (1941).
39. J. A. C. Hugill, I. E. Coop, and L. E. Sutton, *Trans. Faraday Soc.*, **34**, 1518 (1938).
40. G. Huse and H. M. Powell, *J. Chem. Soc.*, 1398 (1940).
41. J. Iball, *Proc. Roy. Soc.* (*London*), **A146**, 140 (1934).
42. I. E. Knaggs, *Proc. Roy. Soc.* (*London*), **A150**, 576 (1935).
43. A. Kossiakoff and H. D. Springall, *J. Am. Chem. Soc.*, **63**, 2223 (1941).
44. J. J. de Lange, J. M. Robertson, and I. Woodward, *Proc. Roy. Soc.* (*London*), **A171**, 398 (1939).
45. H. A. Lévy and L. O. Brockway, *J. Am. Chem. Soc.*, **59**, 1662 (1937).
46. H. A. Lévy and L. O. Brockway, *J. Am. Chem. Soc.*, **59**, 2085 (1937).
47. H. A. Lévy and R. B. Corey, *J. Am. Chem. Soc.*, **63**, 2095 (1941).
48. M. W. Lister and L. E. Sutton, *Trans. Faraday Soc.*, **35**, 495 (1939).
49. F. J. Llewellyn, E. G. Cox, and T. H. Goodwin, *J. Chem. Soc.*, 883 (1937).
50. C. Lu, E. W. Hughes, and P. A. Giguère, *J. Am. Chem. Soc.*, **63**, 1507 (1941).
51. J. E. LuValle and V. Schomaker, *J. Am. Chem. Soc.*, **61**, 3520 (1939).

52. N. F. Moerman, *Rec. trav. chim.*, **56**, 161 (1937).
53. N. F. Moerman and E. H. Wiebenga, *Z. Krist.*, **97**, 323 (1937).
54. R. C. L. Mooney, *J. Am. Chem. Soc.*, **62**, 2955 (1940).
55. H. Oosaka, *Bull. Chem. Soc. Japan*, **15**, 31 (1940).
56. A. Pabst, *J. Chem. Phys.*, **11**, 145 (1943).
57. L. Pauling and L. O. Brockway, *J. Am. Chem. Soc.*, **59**, 13 (1937).
58. L. Pauling and L. O. Brockway, *J. Am. Chem. Soc.*, **59**, 1223 (1937).
59. L. Pauling and D. C. Carpenter, *J. Am. Chem. Soc.*, **58**, 1274 (1936).
60. L. Pauling, W. Gordy, and J. H. Saylor, *J. Am. Chem. Soc.*, **64**, 1753 (1942).
61. L. Pauling and A. W. Laubengayer, *J. Am. Chem. Soc.*, **63**, 480 (1941).
62. L. Pauling and J. Sherman, *Proc. Natl. Acad. Sci.*, **20**, 340 (1934).
63. L. Pauling, H. D. Springall, and K. J. Palmer, *J. Am. Chem. Soc.*, **61**, 927 (1939).
64. L. W. Pickett, *Proc. Roy. Soc. (London)*, **A142**, 333 (1933).
65. L. W. Pickett, *J. Am. Chem. Soc.*, **58**, 2299 (1936).
66. H. M. Powell, G. Huse, and P. W. Cooke, *J. Chem. Soc.*, 153 (1943).
67. J. M. Robertson, *Proc. Roy. Soc. (London)*, **A140**, 79 (1933).
68. J. M. Robertson, *Proc. Roy. Soc. (London)*, **A142**, 659 (1933).
69. J. M. Robertson, *Proc. Roy. Soc. (London)*, **A142**, 674 (1933).
70. J. M. Robertson, *Proc. Roy. Soc. (London)*, **A150**, 348 (1935).
71. J. M. Robertson, *Proc. Roy. Soc. (London)*, **A150**, 106 (1935).
72. J. M. Robertson, *Proc. Roy. Soc. (London)*, **A157**, 79 (1936).
73. J. M. Robertson, *J. Chem. Soc.*, 1195 (1936).
74. J. M. Robertson and I. Woodward, *J. Chem. Soc.*, 1817 (1936).
75. J. M. Robertson and I. Woodward, *Proc. Roy. Soc. (London)*, **A162**, 568 (1937).
76. J. M. Robertson and I. Woodward, *Proc. Roy. Soc. (London)*, **A164**, 436 (1938).
77. J. M. Robertson and A. R. Ubbelohde, *Proc. Roy. Soc. (London)*, **A167**, 122 (1938).
78. F. Rogowski, *Ber.*, **75**, 244 (1942); *C.A.*, **37**, 3646 (1943).
79. V. Schomaker and L. Pauling, *J. Am. Chem. Soc.*, **61**, 1769 (1939).
80. V. Schomaker and D. P. Stevenson, *J. Am. Chem. Soc.*, **62**, 2423 (1940).
81. V. Schomaker and D. P. Stevenson, *J. Am. Chem. Soc.*, **63**, 37 (1941).
82. F. Senti and D. Harker, *J. Am. Chem. Soc.*, **62**, 2008 (1940).
83. H. A. Skinner and L. E. Sutton, *Trans. Faraday Soc.*, **36**, 1209 (1940).
84. H. D. Springall and L. O. Brockway, *J. Am. Chem. Soc.*, **60**, 996 (1938).
85. R. Spurr and V. Schomaker, *J. Am. Chem. Soc.*, **64**, 2693 (1942).
86. D. P. Stevenson and J. Y. Beach, *J. Am. Chem. Soc.*, **60**, 2872 (1938).
87. D. P. Stevenson, H. D. Burnham, and V. Schomaker, *J. Am. Chem. Soc.*, **61**, 2922 (1939).
88. D. P. Stevenson, J. E. LuValle, and V. Schomaker, *J. Am. Chem. Soc.*, **61**, 2508 (1939).
89. D. P. Stevenson and V. Schomaker, *J. Am. Chem. Soc.*, **62**, 1913 (1940).
90. A. J. Stosick, *J. Am. Chem. Soc.*, **61**, 1127 (1939).
91. H. Verleger, *Physik. Z.*, **38**, 83 (1937).
92. H. J. Verweel and C. H. MacGillavry, *Nature*, **142**, 161 (1938).
93. E. H. Wiebenga, *Z. Krist.*, **102**, 193 (1940).
94. E. H. Wiebenga and N. F. Moerman, *Z. Krist.*, **99**, 217 (1938).
95. R. W. G. Wyckoff and R. B. Corey, *Z. Krist.*, **81**, 386 (1932).
96. R. W. G. Wyckoff and R. B. Corey, *Z. Krist.*, **89**, 462 (1934).
97. W. H. Zachariasen, *J. Am. Chem. Soc.*, **62**, 1011 (1940).
98. For recent, more precise data regarding formic acid (and some further simple carboxylic acids) see J. Karle and L. O. Brockway, *J. Am. Chem. Soc.*, **66**, 574 (1944).

# SUBJECT INDEX